Electronic Signals and Systems

Television, Stereo, Satellite TV, and Automotive

Electronic Signals and Systems

Television, Stereo, Satellite TV, and Automotive

Stan Prentiss

TAB BOOKS

Blue Ridge Summit, PA

Notices

C-QUAM®	Motorola
Crossfire®	Channel Master
Mini-State®	TDP Electronics (Tandy Corp.)
Mityvac®	Neward Enterprises
Pinnacle®	Winegard
Quantum®	Channel Master
Superwinch®	Superwinch
Touch Hold®	Fluke
Ultra-Hi Crossfire®	Channel Master

FIRST EDITION
FIRST PRINTING

© 1991 by **TAB Books**.
TAB Books is a division of McGraw-Hill, Inc.

Library of Congress Cataloging-in-Publication Data

Prentiss, Stan.
    Electronic signals and systems : television, stereo, satellite TV and automotive / by Stan Prentiss.
      p.   cm.
    Includes index.
    ISBN 0-8306-8557-X   ISBN 0-8306-3557-2 (pbk.)
    1. Signal theory (Telecommunication) 2. System analysis.
  I. Title.
  TK5102.5.P666 1991
  621.382′23—dc20   91-6535
                             CIP

TAB Books offers software for sale. For information and a catalog, please contact TAB Software Department, Blue Ridge Summit, PA 17294-0850.

Acquisitions Editor: Roland S. Phelps
Production: Katherine G. Brown
Book Design: Jaclyn J. Boone
Cover Design: Lori E. Schlosser

Contents

Acknowledgments

WE WOULD VERY MUCH LIKE TO EXPRESS OUR GRATITUDE TO ALL those who have been of great support and assistance in making this publication possible. It has been no problem conducting the research for much of the text, but the operational aspects and descriptions of various types of equipment has been most helpful. Therefore, many, many thanks are due to the following.

John Emmert, Chuck Smearley, and Paul M. Preuss of Ford Motor Company; Bill Malloy of Superwinch; Duffy Paul and Ken Sinnick of Channel Master; David Breville of Wiltron; Lisa Rizzio of Casio; Tak Tsang of John Fluke Mfg. Co.; Frank Gregorio of Interplex Electronics; Bob Milewski of Sprague Electric; Alan Kafton of Hewlett-Packard; Bill Benedict, Lynn Hurd, and Bob Oblack of Tektronix; Mike Balsom, Steve Koogler, and Michael Brubaker of R.L. Drake; Dennis Schwab of California Amplifier; Jerry Von Behren and Hans Rabong of Winegard; Bob Tyler of Maxtec International; Hal Hawthorne, Jim Yannick, and Jim Kuykendall of TOP Electronics; John Taylor, Bob Sawyer, Don Chilson, and Ed Polcen of Zenith Electronics; Jim Schwab, Marshall Leighton, and Debbie Addison of Majestic Industries; Bill Towers of Jerrold/Cometic; Jacob Aronovich of Hameg; Dale and Terrie Sherrill of Comm/Scope; Seicor Corp.; Gerry Blachley; National A.D.L; Gary Kanipe of Prodelin; and Ben Herr of SBX.

Introduction

INTERPRETING MODERN ELECTRONIC SIGNALS IS CONSIDERABLY MORE thorough and expansive than simply illustrating waveforms from selective sources and describing them. We need to go back to their origins, the equipment, and detailed theories of operation as well as the information they produce. In this way, not only are the results understandable, but you also receive considerable insight into both commercial and consumer electronics not normally contained in a single volume.

As a refresher, this book begins with basic electronics and a short description of bipolars, FETs, digital logic, and integrated circuits (ICs). Then an intensive chapter on test equipment follows, including spectrum analyzers, digital storage oscilloscopes (DSOs), logic analyzers, high-end multimeters, and frequency counters. The book then discusses coaxial cable and fiberoptics analysis, stereo modulation and demodulation in both AM and FM, vectors, and a full video investigation at both RF and baseband.

No television explanation is complete, however, without a broad-spectrum study of today's major television antennas, especially in view of the imminence of high-definition television (HDTV), due out in approximately 1995 or 1996. Nor would any electronic-signal study be complete without a knowledgeable study of satellite earth terminals, including all the new developments in both C and Ku bands, low-noise block-down converters and a 1.2-meter reflector that should see considerable service in cities for both Ku band video, voice, and data traffic. Only first-class equipment is used and described, along with spectral displays of transponder waveforms.

In chapter 7, special attention is given to monophonic and stereophonic audio, including Bessel functions and tables, harmonic distortion, and stereo separation—all illustrated with spectrum-analyzed waveforms. C-QUAM AM stereo transmission and reception receives special attention because many more amplitude-modulated broadcasters are now offering that service, and automobile radios are now available at relatively reasonable prices with both FM and AM stereo.

You will also find careful descriptions of both multiple and satellite master antenna systems with new item offerings and special calculations for a small and expandable MATV as well as suggestions for SMAT and MATV combinations, including warnings and special electronic conversion charts. Usually, satellite systems must be initially designed rather than simply converted.

For those interested in automotive electronics, conventional distributors, EGR valves in emission systems, fuel injection, turbos and superchargers, the final chapter is for you. Finally, for those who would like to understand the latest in analog color television systems, the newest offering in this field is described in detail. Its name, like its performance, is Majestic.

1

Basic electronics and solid state

IT MIGHT BE DIFFICULT TO TEACH, BUT IT'S SOMETIMES FUN TO LOOK back on and decide what's appropriate in today's consumer/business hustle that might help those in entry levels or the current hour of need. It isn't the complex equations of the great Einstein that affect the majority, but the simple fundamentals of everyday usage that are important to most people in the electronics industry. Fortunately or otherwise, there is no escaping fundamental mathematics, even though usage might extend no further than arithmetic, algebra, plane geometry, trigonometry, logic, and logarithms. If these concepts are mastered and intelligently applied, further advances into higher mathematics should be more progressive than excessive, although applied calculus and differential equations certainly aren't appropriate luncheon conversation for apprentice wiremen.

On the other hand, if you really want to learn algebra, do expose yourself to integral, differential calculus and analytic geometry.

What seems beneficial here would be a general (but applied) review of math basics along with working examples of how they can aid in solving everyday problems that often arise in both ordinary and exasperating situations, some of which can be rather embarrassing. Therefore, let's begin with electronics' Adam and Eve and work up at least to the Roaring '20s.

Ohm's law

Named in honor of German physicist Georg Simon Ohm (1787 – 1854), this is a unit of electrical resistance in any conductor registering 1 ampere of current over a potential difference of 1 volt. It is represented by the simple equation:

$$R(resistance) = E(volts)/I(current)$$

From this equality, it follows that:

$$E = IR$$
$$I = E/R$$

This law is used in dc inductance and resistance measurements or anywhere these three entities might appear. There are also instances where individual measurements are possible without connecting the other two, for example the resistance between a metal pole and earth, voltage in an open-ended (nonterminated) circuit, or measuring short-circuited current to ground (common). But if these individual elements are linked by a common circuit, then all three apply to the original equation. Ohm's law is really the basic equation for all electronics.

However, there's a great deal more to electronics than simple series circuits. In addition, you have parallel and series combinations, input and output characteristics, frequency effects, and the actions of coils, transformers, capacitors, and derived or generated power. Then, in analog (signal processing) configurations, consider charge times of inductors and capacitors, timing delays, stage and circuit gains, coupling peculiarities, frequency-reactive impedances, and phase shifts. Add to that the 1s and 0s of logic that have also entered into the situation, producing gates, flip-flops, inverters, wired ORs, ANDs, NANDS and the like. But don't be too concerned, because I will at least touch on most, if not all, of these subjects as the text continues (not in exhaustive depth, but with gentle memory nudges that should awaken or restore a few electronic gleams to some of the more impressionable RAMS and retinas still around).

Elements in series and parallel

In series, values of inductors and resistors (not capacitors) add arithmetically. But in parallel, the values divide. You must work with the various values and equations to produce an answer. For two resistors in parallel:

$$\frac{R_1 \times R_2}{R_1 + R_2} = R_{total}$$

But when there are several resistors in parallel:

$$1/R_{total} = 1/R_1 + 1/R_2 + 1/R_3 + ... + 1/R_n$$

Or, because conductance is the reciprocal of resistance,

$$G_{total} = G_1 + G_2 + G_3 + G_n$$

which goes back to simple addition. Add *series* resistors or inductors mixed in with others in parallel, as before. Conversely, capacitor values add in parallel and divide in series, which is the opposite of resistance and inductance.

Do not, however, confuse dc resistance with resistance induced by alternating ac current. Alternating current across any resistor in terms of peak-to-peak or peak voltage must have its value divided by 2.828 or 1.414, respectively, to derive the rms heating effect equivalent to that of a dc voltage. Inductors or capacitors produce complex reactances, depending on the applied frequencies. Remember that at low frequencies, capacitive reactance is maximum, while at high frequencies, inductive reactance becomes greatest except in large iron-core chokes and transformers specifically designed to couple or smooth power line ac.

Relatively simple equations exist to solve noncomplex reactions by scalar quantities describing only magnitudes or more involved conditions where both magnitudes and directions apply and are real, working numbers. As an example, with a 10 μF capacitance and a 20 mH inductance as opposing elements in a series circuit:

$$X_C = 1/(\pi f C)$$

$$X_L = 2\pi f L$$

with π, as always, equal to 3.1416. Let's say the frequency is 15 kHz (see Fig. 1-1):

$$X_C = 1/6.2832 \times 15 \times 10^3 \times 10 \times 10^{-6}$$

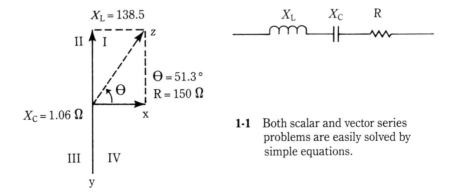

1-1 Both scalar and vector series problems are easily solved by simple equations.

$$= 1/942 \times 10^{-3}$$

$$= 1.06\ \Omega$$

$$X_L = 6.2832 \times 20 \times 10^{-3} \times 15 \times 10^{3}$$
$$= 188.5\ \Omega$$

Inductance is therefore the major reactance. Now add a circuit resistance of 150 ohms for vector inclusion to find impedance, current, and the various voltages that flow in the circuit, knowing that the net reactance of the circuit is an inductive 188.5 – 1.06, or 187.44 ohms:

$$\tan^{-1} \theta = X_{circuit}/R$$

$$= 187.44/150$$

$$= 51.3^{\circ}$$

$$Z = X/\sin \theta$$

$$= 187.44/\sin 51.3^{\circ}$$

$$= 187.44/0.78$$

$$= 240.3$$

$$I = E/Z$$

$$= selected\ voltage/240.3$$

Consequently, current times the resistance and the two reactances would provide the voltages across the three components. Current lags voltage and voltage leads current. Observe how reactive inductance takes over even at what really only amounts to a little more than the scanning rate of any National Systems Television Committee (NTSC) TV receiver. Furthermore, no longer is this a simple reactive circuit, but it has become a vector quantity because direction has also been added. To find the natural resonance of an LC circuit:

$$f = 1/(2\pi \sqrt{LC}\,)$$

with L in henrys and C in farads.

If you wanted to dispense with a component or two in the previous circuit, replace with a 187.44-ohm inductive reactance and a 150-ohm resistor unless you need a dc block, for example to protect a sensitive IC or other discrete (stand-alone) semiconductor.

Some of these examples could easily be solved with a scientific computer, but most people don't have such a luxury (besides, for me, it wouldn't be half the fun). The roman numerals in Fig. 1-1, by the way, represent the four quadrants where y (vertical) and x (horizontal) signs change for positive and negative angles (or quantities).

Alternating-current circuits consisting of pure reactances actually consume no power because the received power returns to the source upon component discharge. But when you add a resistance, part of the power returns to the source while some is dissipated by the resistance. Therefore, the simple power equations for dc and ac rms power are as follows:

$$P = E \times I$$
$$= I^2 \times R$$
$$= E^2/R$$

expressed in terms of watts, which applies directly to the circuit just described after selecting an operating voltage and determining its current. At resonance, maximum current flows in a series circuit, while parallel RLC circuits always offer a high current impedance. Then, if you know the power dissipation for a coil or inductance, its effective resistance can be found by the equality:

$$R_{\text{coil}} = P/I^2$$

provided its core is air (those with metal cores have additional dissipations due to eddy currents, hysteresis, etc.). In transformers, there's also mutual inductance, couplings, flux lines, and several other factors that complicate the assessment.

Like inductors, capacitors also charge and discharge, are convenient couplers, filters, time constants (with resistances), and also block dc. Capacitors usually have two plates and two connecting leads, so

$$C = 0.2244 \times KA/D$$

where A is the area of each plate in square inches, D is the spacing between plates, and K becomes a constant, depending on the dielectric (insulator) used. Expressed another way, when a charge of 1 volt per second produces 1 ampere of current, a capacitor develops a capacitance of 1 farad. Therefore,

$$C = tI/E$$

The degree of charge is usually expressed in coulombs where 1 farad of capacitance and 1 volt of potential difference across it produces 1 coulomb. This can now be expressed simply as

$$Q = CE$$

which is the charge quantity in coulombs, with 1 coulomb equivalent to the charge quantity of 6.28×10^{18} electrons.

Elements (components) in parallel can also have their various circuit operations outlined by vectors in a method called *geometric circuit design*, but this requires considerable explanation and can become somewhat confusing when there are many components. The best attack for parallel circuits, therefore, is to reduce their separate values to those of an equivalent series circuit and then proceed as before, which involves phase angles and the *j* operator. The *j* operator simply changes signs as it moves in 90 degree steps through the four quadrants, beginning with quadrant I. You can also call the *x* (horizontal) and *y* (vertical) terms coordinates, and all are measured from center origin, or the point where the *x* and *y* axes intersect.

Quadrants	I	II	III	IV
x axis	+	−	−	+
y axis	+	+	−	−

All *x* values to the right of origin (O) are positive and *y* values above the origin are also positive, so all other values are negative. Consequently, various numbers among the four quadrants require the *x* and *y* sign values, respectively, shown in Fig. 1-2.

As you have already learned, the reference vector in series circuits is current because it's the same throughout the circuit. But in parallel circuits, currents divide, so in that case, the applied voltage is the reference vector. See Fig. 1-3.

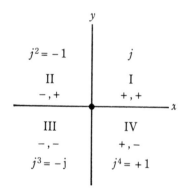

1-2 Operator *j* works in all four quadrants with changing *x-y* signs rotating counterclockwise in 90-degree intervals.

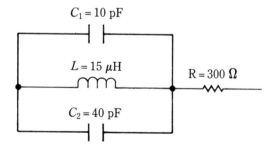

1-3 For easy calculation, a parallel circuit should be reduced to a series circuit. This one is a pure vector with series resistor added.

Reactances

Using ω for $2\pi f$, find reactances for the two capacitances and the inductor as in the previous example, combine them into a single reactance with rectangular coordinates, and then add the resistance for further translation into polar coordinates. The frequency is 5 MHz, and the voltage is 10 V.

At 5 MHz, ω becomes $6.2832 \times 5 \times 10^6 = 31.42 \times 10^6$. Capacitors in parallel, of course, add arithmetically; therefore, 10 and 40 pF appear as 50×10^{-12}.

$$X_C = 1/\omega C$$
$$= 1/31.62 \times 10^6 \times 50 \times 10^{-12}$$
$$= 1/1581 \times 10^{-6}$$
$$= 0.6325 \times 10^2$$
$$= 63.25 \text{ ohms}$$

$$X_L = \omega L$$
$$= 31.42 \times 10^6 \times 15 \times 10^{-6}$$
$$= 471.3 \text{ ohms}$$

Consequently,

$$E/X_C = 10/63.25 = 158 \text{ mA}$$
$$E/X_L = 10/471.3 = 21.2 \text{ mA}$$

So total current flow through the three reactances becomes

$$I_C^* = O + j158 \text{ mA}$$
$$I_L = O - j21.2 \text{ mA}$$

However, since we're dealing in current, not voltage, and current in a capacitor leads by 90 degrees and lags voltage in an inductor by 90 degrees. Therefore, current in the inductor is negative, and the two reactive components being out of phase by 90 degrees. For the two reactances,

I_T then becomes $j158 - j21.2$, or $+ j136.8$

Now add in the series 300-ohm resistance, which becomes 10V/300 ohms or a current of 33 mA, and the final I_{total} (with series resistor added) then amounts to

$$I_T = 33R + j136.8 \text{ in mA}$$

and rectangular coordinates. Ordinarily, theta (θ) remains at 90 degrees because series current through a resistor does not change phase. But here, this resistor becomes part of a network and there are changes.

In polar coordinates, 33R + j136.8 mA translates to a new tangent θ, which is now X/R.

$$X/R = 136.8/33 = 4.145$$

$$\tan^{-1} \theta = 76.44 \text{ °}$$

Therefore,

$$R/\cos \theta = 33/\cos 76.44$$

$$= 33.0/0.234$$

$$= 141 \text{ mA}$$

Phase is now 76.44 degrees instead of 90 degrees, and the current amounts to 141 milliamperes. Impedance in this circuit becomes:

$$Z = E/I$$

$$= 10/.141$$

$$= 70.92 \text{ ohms}$$

Semiconductors

The temptation among many authors is to throw in a shot of physics and fields at this point, but this section deals with ordinary semiconductors to enhance analog familiarity. I deliberately say "analog" because digital switches, gates, and flip-flops can also be thought of as saturated amplifiers with help from specialized transistors and fast diodes. Most usually think of a square wave's origin as that of a sine wave, even though today's logic is primarily clock driven and originates from hard transistor conduction near ground to power supply limits at base or gate-drive cutoff. Since voltage is high at transistor cutoff, this is called a level that is designated as a "high" or a "1." When conducting, the level is known as a "low," or "0." For some, this concept is sometimes hard to grasp, but it is absolutely essential. The common characteristics between logic and analog circuits are the rise, fall, and settling times, in addition to analog slew rates. Therefore, some study of both analog and digital is essential because they're both used almost everywhere in electronics.

There are three main types of transistor semiconductors in current use, aside from gallium arsenide (GaAs), high-electron-mobility transistor (HEMT) technology, power MOSFETS, and the like. These three are ordinary three-terminal bipolars, field-effect (FET) transistors, and silicon-controlled rectifiers (SCRs), the latter being also in the thyristor category. Pulse and rectifier diodes are simple two-terminal devices with cathodes, anodes, and noncritical biasing. As long as there's current flow, you know they're operating since approximately 0.7 V of appropriate bias overcomes the cathode/anode barrier and places them in conduction. They do, however, represent the p-n junctions from which all transistors are formed and, for that reason, are very important.

Bipolars

Regular transistors and simple field-effect transistors (FETs) are three-element semiconductors (Fig. 1-4) with emitter/source, base/gate, and collector/drain terminals, respectively. Arrow symbols, however, are reversed: an arrow on a transistor's emitter terminal if pointed toward its base means a p type, and FET arrows in the same direction indicate an n type. In bipolars, the arrow always indicates current flow direction, while FET arrows all point directly to their gates, which control single-channel current flow (*conduction*). MOSFETS (metal-oxide semiconductor field-effect transistors) often have two gates instead of one; the second gate acts as a bias gate for extra conduction regulation or automatic gain control (AGC).

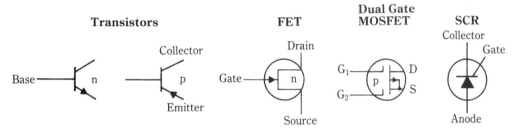

1-4 Bipolars, FETs, and SCRs (silicon-controlled rectifiers) are prevalent in many consumer products.

Bipolar transistors, so called because they contain both negative-electron and positive-hole charge carriers, are manufactured as nonlinear, active semiconductors that must be biased accurately to operate over the more linear portions of their characteristic curves. Although thought of as three-terminal devices, they are usually analyzed as four-terminal units, with a common reference for inputs and outputs (which suggests the *h*-parameter mathematical approach and matrix derivations).

Ordinarily considered in one of three prime configurations, both bipolars and FETs are usually shown in common-base/gate, common-collector/drain, or common-emitter/source positions with R_L loads as indicated in Fig. 1-5. Common-base units have voltage-gain low-input and high-output impedances; the common emitter has power ($I \times E$) output with medium input impedance; and the common collector offers high-input and low-output impedances with voltage gain of less than unity but with plenty of current. In the common-emitter configuration, transistors and FETs might also have transistor current sources as well as in the R_L loads listed. But this occurs more in integrated circuits rather than simple, discrete devices. Direct-current biasing always takes place either in the base or emitter circuits, while the collector, if not grounded, handles signal inversion in the common-emitter configuration and noninversion in common base. Output impedance of the common collector is normally determined by the value of its emitter resistor. A quick gain estimate of

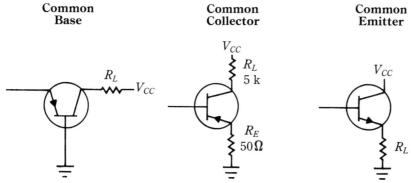

1-5 The three prime configurations for bipolars and FETs, except in the latter the base becomes the gate, the collector is the drain, and the emitter is the source.

single stages with emitter and collector resistors amounts to simple division of the emitter value into that of the collector. For example, the gain is

$$R_L/R_e = 5000/50$$

$$= 100$$

Analog problems can become sticky when attempting to evaluate device leakage, gain, and in-circuit applications. Here, transistor curve tracers and manufacturer specifications are absolutely required for all parameters if replacement or substitution becomes necessary. Guessing games never outwit the original designer's considered calculations.

In our repertory the television video output amplifier pictured in Fig. 1-6 is of indeterminate age and origin and has enough peculiar characteristics to model nicely for many of its brethren who don't react with precision either. Hence, I partially adjusted this curve tracer for reasonable results so that the collector voltage, from the right edge of the graticule, would measure some 6 volts, and collector current, measured vertically, would be indicated at approximately 4.5 mA. Each step in the curve tracer display amounts to 10 microamperes (μA). So if the straight reference line at the

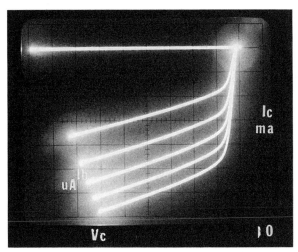

1-6 B&K-Precision 501A curve tracer produces very acceptable transistor response on a Hameg HM 604 oscilloscope readout.

top was moved another division, the center step would rest on the fifth graticule, at a point of 5 mA. For static beta, then,

$$\text{dc current gain} = 5 \text{ mA}/0.030 \text{ mA} = 167$$

But ac current gain is a *change* in I_c/I_b or $\Delta(I_c/I_b)$, so the I_c change is 1.6 mA compared with 8 μA, which then is

$$\text{ac current gain} = \Delta(1.6 \text{ mA}/8 \text{ } \mu\text{A}) = 200$$

This value might be a little above that of a $3,000 curve tracer, but at least you know that dc and ac beta gains are in the ballpark, and your transistor's operation is certainly reasonable.

You might also notice that the indicated baseline is absolutely straight, indicating no leakage, and there is neither abrupt nor gradual bending of the curve ends (usually due to overdrive). Actually, this is a rather sloppy curve for a transistor (it really looks more like a FET than a bipolar). In this example, pnp's exhibit downward curves, while npn's are exactly the reverse. There are a number of other things you can do with curve tracers, but for now this initial example serves as a sample of what's to come.

FETs, MOSFETs, and BIFETs

All three of these FET categories and their offspring are very much alive in the electronics industry, and with good reason. Many require very little current, exhibit high input impedance, are becoming progressively faster, and manufacturers have now discovered how to deposit analog and digital functions directly on the same IC monolithic chip (BI FET) without undue adverse interaction among or between the two. Although not yet as fast as some current-hogging bipolars, FETS are becoming more and more useful in military, commercial, and consumer electronics as new processes are developed.

The junction field-effect transistor (JFET) depends on majority carrier flow for conduction and is considered unipolar because it contains only a single current carrier. Conduction occurs because of a transverse field initiated by a voltage-controlled electrode, usually the gate.

The insulated-gate FET (IGFET), originally developed from a thin-film transistor and then applied to silicon, is made of metal oxide that is physically separated from its metal control electrode. It can operate via either forward or reverse bias. These MOSFETs actually have two operating modes: *enhancement* and *depletion.* The former conducts with the gate forward biased, and the latter must have a gate bias to turn it off before it stops conducting, which is called *pinchoff* because such a bias reduces or eliminates current flow through its single channel.

Originally, MOSFETs were easily destroyed by rough handling and electro-static charges, but gate-protective diodes added between the gate and source have improved this condition considerably so that ordinary handling does them little or no harm. However, such transistors should be stored and transported in conductive foam, and unused inputs should be connected to V_{dd} or V_{ss}, the drain and source operating voltages, respectively (see Fig. 1-7). This figure also shows a complementary MOS configuration where the p-channel device is the active load for the n-channel and vice versa as the two conduct alternately to produce an output waveform that's full wave and symmetrical.

Single FETs find the greatest consumer uses in FM and TV RF amplifiers and sometimes current sources (generators). Complementary MOS are superb as switches that are very temperature stable, require little power, and then dissipate power only when active. Therefore, MOSFETS actually use virtually no power in either of their stable states.

In Fig. 1-7, when the p-channel MOSFET turns on with no gate input, the only current flow is I_{dss} in the picoampere range. With positive input, the p device turns off and the n channel conducts, but at only picoamperes of current because there is no active load. It is only between these steady states that the complementary MOSFET draws current. Switching operations are functions of the attached load and its impedance.

MOSFETs are also very good analog switches when operated singly or in multiple setups. They are now moving into use as power amplifiers because they possess fast switching speeds, simple drive arrangements, and no secondary breakdown failure modes, with operation, and good gain and response over considerable temperature shifts.

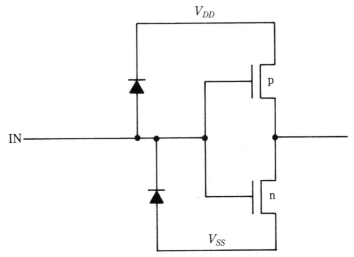

1-7 Complementary MOS transistors with diode gate protection.

FETs are called square-law devices because their drain current is proportional to the square of the gate voltage to pinchoff voltage ratio. Therefore,

$$I_D = I_{DSS} \left(1 - \frac{V_{GS}}{V_{GS\,(off)}} \right)^2$$

Some of the latest applications for FETs are gallium arsenide FETs (GaAs FETs) that operate at millimeter wavelengths, MESFETs (metal semiconductor GaAs FETs) which are depletion-mode FETs with diode-type gates much like a junction FET, and similarly fabricated HEMTs so named since they are high-electron mobility transistors with gate lengths in the 0.5 μm range. The latter have very low noise figures and are currently used in both C- and Ku-band block down-converter satellite receiving systems. Finally, as device geometries, reliability, and manufacturing processing have all contributed, CMOS is now assuming its rightful place in important digital signal processing, challenging bipolar technology in aspects such as ease of fabrication and exhibiting considerable advantages in the speed/power parameters that are necessary in large scale integration (LSI).

An important thyristor

Thyristors are a specific class of semiconductor switches with bistable characteristics that operate by regenerative feedback. Thyristors include the silicon-controlled rectifier (SCR), bidirectional triodes (TRIACs), dual-electrode avalanche diodes (DIACs), etc.

The most important of these is the SCR because semiconductors are typically current carriers, switches, and amplifiers that are ordinarily turned on and off by some signal device that either requires gating, amplification, or both. An SCR looks like a pair of bipolar transistors tied from collector to base (see Fig. 1-8), that is, in feedback. These are pnpn devices with single anodes, cathodes, and gates. When the loop gain of an SCR is less than unity, it remains in the high-impedance OFF state and does not conduct. But when its p gate is forward biased and loop gain moves toward unity, one transistor drives the other into saturation so that all are forward biased and anode current becomes that of the input circuit, effectively flowing through a single p-n junction. Total current then becomes that of the two sets of semiconductor junctions in addition to any leakage.

The SCR remains in conduction until turned off, but not by its gate. Once the gate has triggered thyristor conduction, it has no further control, and the only way the device returns to its high-impedance blocking state is through anode current reduction below what's called *holding current*, which is less than that of its conduction region. Therefore, simple gating has no effect on SCRs while sufficient anode current continues to flow.

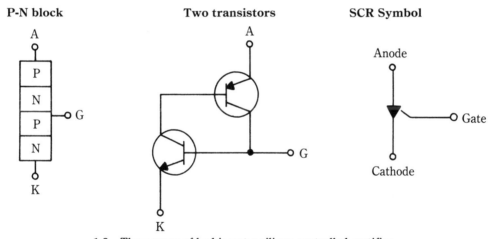

P-N block   **Two transistors**   **SCR Symbol**

1-8   Three ways of looking at a silicon-controlled rectifier.

But when that flow is interrupted, the SCR reverts to its high-impedance state and awaits another gate excitation. These thyristors have been found to be very useful in switch-mode power supplies and throughout electronics, especially popular consumer products.

Having examined bipolar and CMOS switching the same treatment for digital logic might also be helpful. The next section looks at some of the basic principles of logic.

Digital logic

Popular because of the emergence of all sorts of communications, computers, audio, and video displays and effects, digital logic—thought to be the brainchild of Dublin University's George Boole more than 130 years ago—has come a long way since the publication of *Investigation of the Laws of Thought.*

The basis for logic is the proposition that statements or conditions are either true (1) or not true (0). In practice, letter symbols, say A (for true) and $\overline{A}$ (for false) denote these conditions. The bar over $\overline{A}$ denotes "false," or "not." Logic functions can be executed in four simple statements: AND, NAND, OR, and NOR. It's how you use them singly and in complex combinations that counts. In addition, many families of hardware logic have evolved:

RTL (resistor-transistor logic)

RCTL (resistor-capacitor-transistor logic)

DCTL (diode-transistor-coupled logic)

DTL (diode-transistor logic)

CML (current-mode logic)

TTL or T^2L (transistor-transistor logic)

ECL (emitter-coupled logic)

. . . to name a few, not to mention all the simple and complex integrated circuits, including the multitude of memories, microprocessors, multipliers, and inverters.

Today, programmable logic devices (PLDs) even permit *primitives* such as ANDs, ORs, inverters and flip-flops on schematics to be used as direct inputs. I won't lead you down that thorny path, but will illustrate a few of these primitives and their truth tables to provide you with a foundation for understanding more complex operations such as those used by ultra-fast computers. Today, there's enough complex logic to perform virtually any desired function. Just hook it up correctly.

Simple gates and truth tables

Let's return to the basics so you can understand some of the beginnings of this enormous surge in digital electronics. To begin with AND and OR gates, the AND, OR, NAND, and NOR operations are shown combined in a single shorthand truth table (Fig. 1-9). The left column has the symbols A and B and the possible combinations these two inputs could have to the four different types of gates. For instance, if A is O and B is 1, read right to find that an AND output would be 0, the output of an OR gate would be 1, a NAND would be 1, and a NOR would be 0. AND gates require two simi-

Truth table

A B	AND	OR	NAND	NOR
0 0	0	0	1	1
0 1	0	1	1	0
1 0	0	1	1	0
1 1	1	1	0	0

1-9   Truth table for basic gate logic and their respective schematic symbols.

Symbols

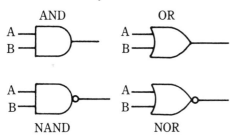

AND   OR

NAND   NOR

lar inputs to change state, OR gates require only one positive input for a positive output, and NAND and NORs are the exact opposite of AND and ORs.

An important equation to know is De Morgan's equivalency theorem where $\overline{A} + \overline{B} = \overline{A \cdot B}$. This reads "A not or B not equals (or is equivalent to) A and B not." Similarly, $\overline{A + B} = \overline{A} \cdot \overline{B}$.

There is also the language of double negation where

$$\overline{\overline{A}} = A$$

$$\overline{\overline{AB}} = A + B$$

$$\overline{\overline{A + B}} = AB$$

For an example of practical use JK flip-flops which were developed to reject changes from 1s to 0s except when both inputs are high (Fig. 1-10). Other primitives also exist such as wired ANDs, implied ORs, exclusive ORs, etc.

Other concepts include Karnaugh maps, Boolean manipulations, and other logic operations, but basic familiarities are all I really want to cover here. As a reference, however, Table 1-1 provides equivalents for several number systems. The reason for these various bases is that decimal digits aren't unique following digit 9. Thereafter, when using different bases, logic operations might be compressed or expanded to fit the need, depending on available hardware and purpose. Also, binary numbers are often

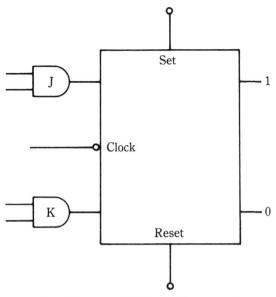

1-10 The highly useful J-K flip-flop only changes state with two positive inputs.

Table 1-1. Number system equivalents

Decimal	Binary	Octal	Hexadecimal
0	0000	0	0
1	0001	1	1
2	0010	2	2
3	0011	3	3
4	0100	4	4
5	0101	5	5
6	0110	6	6
7	0111	7	7
8	1000	10	8
9	1001	11	9
10	1010	12	A
11	1011	13	B
12	1100	14	C
13	1101	15	D
14	1110	16	E
15	1111	17	F

rather long; group them into sets of four to convert to hexadecimal ("hex") or into sets of three for octal. For instance:

$$1110\ 1101\ 1100 = E\ D\ C\ \text{in hex}$$
$$= 7\ 6\ 5\ 4\ \text{in octal}$$

In decimal, 1110 1101 1100 amounts to a cumulative 3804. Therefore, binary symbols applied to different bases reduces the number count considerably, which simplifies manipulation. Twenty or thirty 1s and 0s in binary could produce a prodigious number that would be very difficult to handle without a power-of-two converter or computer.

Integrated circuits

Integrated circuits (ICs) are the highly complex outgrowth of the various individual transistors that are monolithically or thick/thin-film formed in very small packages. They can be either analog, digital or with the latest technology, combined analog and digital. Where a few transistors, resistors, and back-biased diodes produced varactors or capacitors in the past, literally thousands of these same components can now occupy a single PC board or monolithic substrate. ICs have produced a multiplicity of functions in tiny spaces, improving electronics and offering great reliability and flexibility to a host of commercial, military, and consumer designs. The recent emergence of digital television is a unique example of what ICs can do for video and much-improved sound, and these advances are only the forerunners of high-definition television and many other great advances on the horizon.

For starters, let's break these two categories into individual sectors and then try and recombine the two towards chapter's end. This should aid discussing the merits of each in succession and then looking at their tricky combination later. It's interesting how switching digital logic is kept separate from interfering with standard signal processing. Called *radiation*, this is no more than the 1s and 0s of medium or rapid-speed logic delivering crosstalk into ordinary signals formed and amplified by transistors out of saturation and operating on a fairly linear curve.

Synchronous detection

Synchronous detection refers to full-wave video detection following TV tuner and video intermediate frequency amplifiers. Previously, a single half-wave germanium diode offered the prime detection means via nonlinear currents developed into voltage across either R or RL components that in themselves, produced problems that were all too evident in chroma and luminance reproductions that followed. In consequence, full-wave synchronous detection of video allowed and even prompted the development of "seagull" (straight gut) video IFs that no longer require sweepgenerator and marker alignments today. Of course, surface-wave acoustical filters (SAWs) also help because they allow only a single channel bandpass to reach the IFs while sharply curtailing extraneous and undesirable frequencies. Therefore, complexity has actually simplified an old process that can now be executed, in many instances, with a simple multiburst signal. Later, I explain how positively reliable this advanced method has become. The process consumes approximately 30 seconds compared to hours of sometimes unrequited toil, especially when automatic gain control (AGC) was improperly applied or there was an actual defect in the IFs. Now, a channel 3 or 4 carrier modulated with multiburst up to 4.2 MHz actually matches IFs to the tuner and tunes the synchronous detector, all at the same time. To see how the full-wave detector works, recall the early 1970s and Motorola's MC1330A (Fig. 1-11). In an eight-pin plastic package, this detector contains 24 transistors, a few diode-type capacitors, numerous resistors, and three diodes. IF inputs come in via pin 7. Outputs for video develop across the collector and emitter of transistor Q23. Transistor Q24 is for automatic fine tuning (AFT).

Accurately described as a fully-balanced multiplier detector, the 45.75 MHz oscillator portion of the circuit consists of differential switching amplifiers Q12 and Q13, a tuned "tank" circuit between pins 3 and 7, and diodes D1 and D2, which are phase limiters inserted to prevent excess differential gain. IF inputs pass through pin 7 and buffer Q7 to lower differential amplifier Q8 and dc-biased counterpart Q17 that, in turn, supply IF information to switches Q9/Q10 and Q15/Q16 above. Buffered by Q11 and Q14, these cross-coupled quad detectors then synchronously switch at the 45.75 MHz oscillator rate as IF information reaches all four emitters, detecting video in synchronism with the IF carrier.

Near the IF input at pin 7, Q6 supplies bias for Q7 and Q18, while transistors Q2 through Q5 are current sources. Q4 is also part of the Q4/

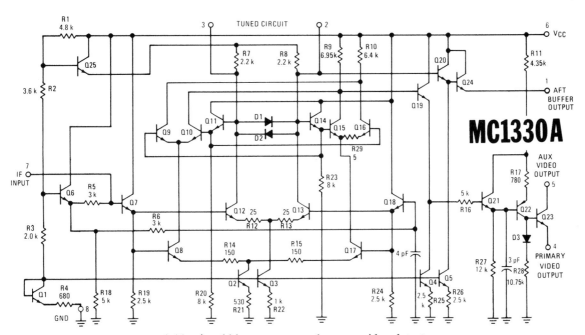

1-11 An old but proven synchronous video detector. Motorola, Inc.

Q19 intermediate amplifier that supplies the final outputs Q21/Q23. Also note an additional signal takeoff in the collector of Q13. This is part of the 45 MHz oscillator that provides automatic fine tuning through Darlington pair Q20 and Q24, responding probably to the differential phase action of oscillator transistors Q12 and Q13. Note also that detector outputs are developed across load R9.

Now you should begin to see why a video IF integrated circuit has a "seagull"-wide passband and probably no tuned circuits. This, then, becomes a natural for most frequencies from the low Hz to 5 MHz for easy detection. Intercarrier 4.5 MHz audio is not illustrated here because there is no apparent beat difference between sound and video carriers. Realize, too, that the MC1330 is a very early synchronous detector, and changes have developed in the 19 or so years since it was first marketed. Audio could, however, be contained in a composite output and demodulated later by some type of FM detector, which is the next topic.

FM detection

In television and audio, frequency-modulated sound was initially demodulated by discriminators, then ratio detectors, quadrature detectors, etc. The *discriminator* normally consists of a transformer and two parallel diodes that conducted with frequency changes at the input, rectifying these patterns and producing currents (then voltages) at the output, whose amplitude varied accordingly.

The *ratio detector* exhibited series rather than parallel diodes, retaining the transformer input, but its output depended on the ratio of currents through the diodes and not the difference between them. This circuit was developed to offset the discriminator's affinity for amplitude as well as frequency variations at its input, thereby nullifying any required AM limiter preceding the discriminator.

Often referred to in vacuum-tube language as a *gated-beam detector*, the *quadrature detector* offers both limiting and FM detection. The input is bias limited with the usual tuned resonant tank circuit that passes electrons in phase quadrature to the tube plate or transistor collector. Phase relationships between input and the quadrature circuit depend on input frequency. Collector or plate current only flows when the two circuits are "open" and is in the form of widening or narrowing pulses, depending on incoming frequencies. An RC network converts these pulse charges into audio voltage.

A fourth method of audio demodulation is *peak detection*. The one that has served RCA television for so many years with considerable distinction is the CA3065 TV sound system. Once again, it's a late 1960s circuit, but the design is significant and widely used in industry. The CA3065 is a 16-pin monolithic amplifier, detector, driver, and electronic attenuator circuit with its own regulated power supply and very few external components except a tank circuit and several coupling and shunt capacitors, primarily filters (Fig. 1-12).

The initial portion, beginning at pin 2, is a series of three noninverting differential amplifiers, a clamp circuit, and three level shifters followed by a pair of buffers and the audio detector itself. Primary input is through pin 2, with intercarrier flowing from base through each of the three emitters into Q13, Q16, and Q21 level shifters. Diode D7 is a clamp with Q17 remaining in conduction in the presence of excess output from the emitter of Q16. Q20 is a constant-current generator for differential amplifier Q18/Q19. Capacitors C1 and C2 are shapers and filters before the signal enters the tank circuit across IC pins 9 and 10. Buffered by Q22 and Q27, audio information is now peak detected by transistors Q23 and Q16 with capacitors C3 and C4. The detected output continues on to the emitters of differential amplifier Q7/Q8 above, which is tied directly through its collector to the collector of Q10. Transistors Q28 and Q29 are constant-current sources for Q24/Q25 and Q9/Q10.

IC pins 6 and 7 connect to a filtered dc volume control and a 0.01 μF deemphasis capacitor, while pins 8 and 14 support a coupling capacitor

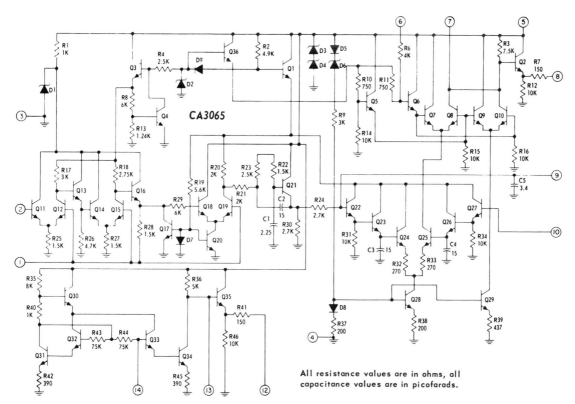

1-12 Another ancient but excellent example of innovative engineering and good audio FM detection.

from the electronic attenuator output to the input of the audio driver. The attenuator receives dc bias for transistors Q5 and Q6 from Q36 (top left) in the power supply, which has been regulated by zener diode D2. Q6, in turn, maintains a relatively constant bias on Q6 and Q10, while Q5 supplies the bases of Q8 and Q9. Since Q7 through Q10 are effectively in parallel and each heavily biased, the two collector-coupled outputs can operate at good sensitivities, but current through Q10 only develops a set output across R3 and into Q2 and resistive dividers R7 and R12.

Further regulated clamping now appears in the audio driver receiving sound through IC pin 14. Here transistors Q30 through Q32 act as base and collector supplies for buffer-driver Q33. Larger inputs via pin 14 into the base of Q33 cause Q32 to conduct harder, which turns on Q31 even more, lowering the bias on the base of Q30. This in turn subsequently lessens conduction at the emitter of Q30 as well as the collector of Q33, reducing inputs to inverter Q34 and emitter-follower output Q35. This is a good lesson in analog IC operations and a worthwhile model for some concentrated study.

Regulated power from the Q11/Q12 and Q14/Q15 differential amplifiers is somewhat similar in that Q3 has its base somewhat loosely regulated by zener D2. However, it compensates for this when unusual amounts of current flow out of its emitter, developing additional bias voltage across R8 and R13. This turns on Q4, reducing base input into Q3 and therefore Q3's current output.

The importance of these two video-audio detector ICs cannot be overemphasized because of their relationships to integrated circuits of today. Just as in real life, you must have adequate foundations on which to build, and these ICs are excellent sources. (Later in this book, most of the text discussion is limited to block diagrams because of the huge number of deposited components on both monolithic and film microcircuits.)

IC logic

Following the 1970s, requirements for faster and more low-powered logic devices increased, along with that of new and improved IC uses. Today we have *advanced low-power Schottky* (ALS), *advanced Schottky* (AS/F), *advanced CMOS* (AC/ACT), and *bipolar CMOS* (BCT), which are all lumped into a single classification called *standard logic*. In the meantime, 5-volt TTL has come into use along with advanced CMOS, which can operate successfully with this TTL logic at 3.3 volts, resulting in a good I/O match and lowering both dynamic and quiescent (idle) power consumption at low and intermediate frequencies, with dynamic power drain a function of the switching frequency. And by converting ALS to ACMOS, power savings can amount to 50 to 95 percent subject to repetition rates. However, with careful attention to shunt or series resistor terminations, sloppy waveforms and ringing can often be conveniently avoided. In TTL logic, a ferrite bead often works successfully without the usual resistive voltage drop.

Now that I've brought you up to date in the world of logic, let's continue with a BIMOS example (promised earlier) in an application by Sprague Semiconductor Group (Sprague Electric Co.). The UNC-4808A is a dual in-line, 18-pin, plastic-encapsulated IC that operates from -20 degrees C to $+85$ degrees C at a V_{DD} logic supply voltage range of from 4.5 V to 18 V, delivering an output of 50 V with continuous current to 600 mA (max) at 25 degrees C. It is an eight-bit, latched driver capable of operating peripheral power loads such as lamps, relays, solenoids, LEDs, printer heads, heaters, and stepper motors. Each array consists of a three-bit to eight-line decoder, eight type-D latches, eight open-collector output drives, and MOS control for chip select, clear, and output enable. All eight power loads can be turned on and off independently.

Figure 1-13 illustrates the IC's pinout diagram with inputs/outputs, chip select, output enable, clear, etc. The lower part of the figure shows a

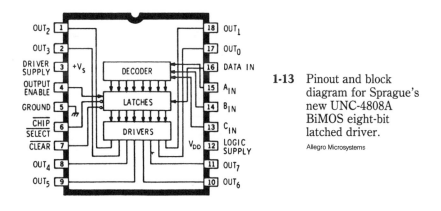

1-13 Pinout and block diagram for Sprague's new UNC-4808A BiMOS eight-bit latched driver.

Allegro Microsystems

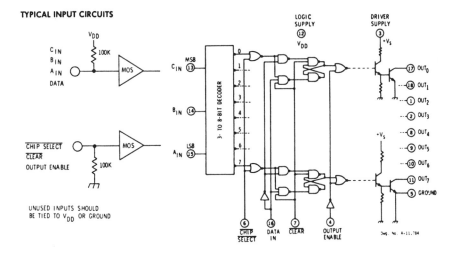

I/O WAVEFORMS

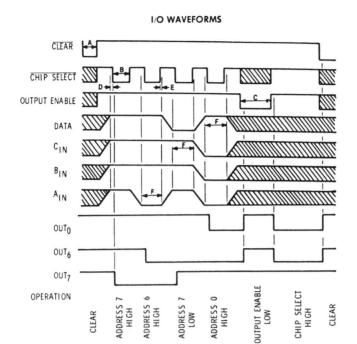

1-14 I/O waveforms and truth table for the UNC-4808A. Allegro Microsystems

TRUTH TABLE

CHIP SELECT	CLEAR	DATA	C_{IN}	B_{IN}	A_{IN}	OUTPUT ENABLE	OUT_7	OUT_6	OUT_5	OUT_4	OUT_3	OUT_2	OUT_1	OUT_0	
X	L	X	X	X	X	X	H	H	H	H	H	H	H	H	Clear
H	H	X	X	X	X	H	R	R	R	R	R	R	R	R	Memory
L	H	D	L	L	L	H	R	R	R	R	R	R	R	$\bar{D}$	Address Latch 0
L	H	D	L	L	H	H	R	R	R	R	R	R	$\bar{D}$	R	Address Latch 1
L	H	D	L	H	L	H	R	R	R	R	R	$\bar{D}$	R	R	Address Latch 2
L	H	D	L	H	H	H	R	R	R	R	$\bar{D}$	R	R	R	Address Latch 3
L	H	D	H	L	L	H	R	R	R	$\bar{D}$	R	R	R	R	Address Latch 4
L	H	D	H	L	H	H	R	R	$\bar{D}$	R	R	R	R	R	Address Latch 5
L	H	D	H	H	L	H	R	$\bar{D}$	R	R	R	R	R	R	Address Latch 6
L	H	D	H	H	H	H	$\bar{D}$	R	R	R	R	R	R	R	Address Latch 7
X	X	X	X	X	X	L	H	H	H	H	H	H	H	H	Blanking
X	X	X	X	X	X	H	R	R	R	R	R	R	R	R	

L = Low Logic Level
H = High Logic Level
D = Data (High or Low)
X = Irrelevant
R = Previous State

functional block diagram. Figure 1-14 illustrates the truth table as well as I/O waveforms, which show the various states of operation. Data and inputs A_{IN}, B_{IN}, and C_{IN} are allowed to have somewhat sloppy rise and fall transition times by design. Driver outputs, however, are sharply defined as are the clear and chip select pulses. A three-bit binary address selects one of the eight latches, with C_{IN} as the most significant bit and A_{IN} as the least significant.

This is a good illustration of why and how BIMOS can be gainfully used in a fairly uncomplicated logic arrangement, but with great effectiveness. A more complex design might not provide such comprehensive data.

This chapter on solid state and basic electronics should set the stage for many more circuit and waveform explanations in later chapters to provide you with a well-rounded exposure to many of the electronic disciplines existing today.

2

The power and glory
of test equipment

AS DIGITAL BIT RATES BECOME FASTER, SATELLITE ANALOG TRANSMIS-
sion bandwidths become wider, high-definition television nears its entry
aboard terrestrial broadcasts, and recorders and players of all descriptions
proliferate, the need for testing these disciplines and devices becomes
even more critical, demanding greater ingenuity from developers and
manufacturers than we've ever known before. The days of simple multimeters and low-frequency oscilloscopes are long gone since software programming, high-megahertz (MHz) logic, gigahertz (GHz) Clarke Belt
satellite transmissions, and microwave communications on earth fill the
atmosphere and beyond with every imaginable signal for the world's vast
network of national and international exchange.

What was once Marconi's wireless and Edison's light bulb have now
circled our planet with intelligent discourse and controlled illumination,
allowing all nations the privilege of talking to one another and radiating
their vast, gleaming cities. These developments did not appear in the
recent past months or even decades; they took time, energy, education,
perseverance, and just plain hard work. "Rome," it's often said, "wasn't
built in a day," nor did the communications explosion suddenly appear
overnight. It's been in the planning and design stages for years. We're only
recently discovering that so much of it is now possible and have only esti-
mates of what the future actually holds.

Such symbols, reality, and futurities are what this chapter is all about.
Perhaps we can add a few means and ways to improve and possibly solve
some of the troublesome problems that often come our way. And since we
already have most of the instrumentation for attacking these difficulties,
well-considered applications for using test equipment from a variety of

sources include not only my contributions but also those from prime distributors and manufacturers throughout the U.S. and elsewhere. Application notes from abroad, unfortunately, are often either non-English or poorly written and usually dedicated to narrow uses of a single piece of equipment. I prefer a rounded explanation and general utility for maximum benefit to everyone to feature the best and inform the most, rather than become overly selective.

However, there are limits to generic types of instrumentation that can be operated and described, therefore we will limit test gear to those units readily available and generally less costly than $10,000. Sometimes this presents a challenge in obtaining certain results, but a little innovation usually permits quality and quantity, too. Let's begin with spectrum analyzers, analog and logic oscilloscopes, and one of the new super analog and digital multimeters to cover most of the ordinary applications with conventional instruments.

The spectrum analyzer

From dc to multigigahertz, there is no instrument that is more useful or necessary. The spectrum analyzer can measure amplitudes in both logarithms and linear voltages, accurately peak-detect video and audio bandpasses, rate carrier-to-noise information, and determine digital readouts to four or more places (thus, a frequency counter) and sensitivities from -80 dB (or less) to $+20$ dB. Some instruments have a power meter reading in dBm, AM and FM detection, video and audio reproduction, and TV line and field sweep triggering. An analyzer can conduct noise and spurious signal analysis, phase checks, electromagnetic interference and filter examinations, two-way radio carrier checks, satellite antenna characterizations (gains and sidelobes), vibration measurements, RF displays for radio, TV, and satellite uplinks and downlinks, plus any and all frequency-versus-amplitude examinations within various instrument ranges.

A spectrum analyzer operates in the frequency domain, while an oscilloscope tracks the time domain. Together, they can produce visual displays of virtually anything within design parameters, i.e., provided their electronics and cathode-ray-tube accelerating voltages are designed correctly. A cheap spectrum analyzer, for instance, isn't worth consideration because its ranges are limited and accuracies are forever subject to question. An inexpensive oscilloscope, on the other hand, might operate reasonably well within given ranges but is severely limited in bandpass and vertical deflection factors, as well as accuracy.

As in any instrumentation, the asking (or selling) prices are usually indicative of degree of utility (general or specific). Since oscilloscopes are considerably less complex, they are usually less expensive and produce different results.

Analyzer attributes

There are three general types of spectrum analyzers: *real time, fast Fourier transform* (FFT), and swept-tuned. The three prime parameters are resolution bandwidth, dynamic range, and frequency accuracy over both short and extended periods. Instrument frequency characteristics are often categorized into the following groups: less than 100 kHz, from 100 kHz to 5 MHz, from 10 kHz to 1.8 GHz, and from there to 22 GHz and above, with waveguide extenders to 200 GHz or better—a vast coverage that's not duplicated by any ordinary equipment commonly available today. And as microwave and satellite communications continue to expand, analyzer measurements become even more necessary in every respect. Frequency ranges are developed by local oscillators, mixers, and various amplifiers and converters. Frequency accuracy is often as precise as 10^{-5} or 10^{-7}, an almost unheard of figure only a few years ago, and most units are almost as accurate as some expensive frequency counters. Resolution is achieved via IF bandwidths and shape factors due to special filters and controlled amplification.

The swept display is normally automatically adjusted by the analyzer but can be manually set between milliseconds and microseconds. The spans per division and resolution are usually coupled so that they remain in calibration throughout the various measurement ranges. Linear and logarithmic ranges that accept input signals, however, are always manually set, with considerable care taken not to exceed the input dB ratings or overload the first mixer with above normal dc voltage. The older analyzers tolerated no dc input at all, while the newer ones often permit as much as 100 V without harmful overload. Alternating current inputs are limited to 20 to 30 dBm (or the equivalent in dBV). The better spectrum analyzers also permit dual input impedances of 50 and 75 ohms as well as special measurements as low as 1 dB/division (the common value is 10 dB/div).

Remember: Unless you want to spend hundreds and possibly even thousands of dollars, don't introduce more input voltages than the equipment can handle. In this respect, analyzers are exceptionally touchy.

The newest wrinkle involves microcomputer and microprocessor controls for the entire analyzer operated from the front panel. Features including attenuation, video filters, marker indications, graticule lighting, storage, sweep speeds, frequency range, bandwidth resolution, sensitivities, AM/FM detectors, and other displays are all subject to exacting microcomputer commands and responses. Here, practice makes perfect because operating one of these more complex units isn't learned in a day, or even a week, to develop its full potential. Amplitude accuracies on the better units are usually between 0.5 and 1.0 dB, depending on scales and design. On inexpensive display units—not spectrum analyzers—you're lucky to come within 3 dB (half power in dBm) on limited vertical deflections and sensitivities, plus uncalibrated sweeps: *beware*! To proceed from generalities to specifics, consider the three major categories of analyzers:

Real time analyzers   These analyzers have been a somewhat neglected category until recently when Tektronix began delivering a state-of-the-art unit with 1,024 digitally controlled filters and a maximum bandwidth span of 10 MHz. Exceptional for signal-to-noise measurements and flat responses, the unit is 100 times faster than fast Fourier transform instruments and can accommodate signals into the GHz with special downconverters which are available. As you probably guessed, these RTA equipments are usually lower frequency instruments that have both special filters and a basic superheterodyne radio. They are especially useful in detecting transients and periodic/random voltages.

Fast Fourier transform   These units analyze waveshapes by resolving complex parts into frequency components and computing the results via Fourier transforms. Today, microcomputers and microprocessors have sufficient speed and power to operate in the hertz and megahertz ranges to synthesize complex waveshapes on the basis of sine waves that are harmonically related and integer multiples of their fundamentals. Here, the highest frequency determines the minimum sampling rate, which is always equal to or less than the Nyquist frequency (one-half of the sampling frequency). This automatically restricts the range of such analyzers, but it also makes them particularly suited to low-frequency, highly accurate analyses of analog waveshapes.

Swept-tuned analyzers   These analyzers are the popular types offered by virtually every general-purpose analyzer manufacturer. Their various instrument frequency spans begin at dc and extend to hundreds of GHz (with waveguide extenders). For general utility, they are unequalled and often very cost effective.

The frequency coverage for medium-priced swept-tuned instruments is often between 10 kHz and 1.8 GHz, while others might range from 10 kHz to 22 GHz without waveguide extenders, if you're willing to pay the toll. Many current units are microprocessor controlled and have synthesized tuning, providing remarkable accuracy. Amplitude ranges go from around − 130 dBm to + 30 or + 50 dBm. Finally, the frequency plus resolution abilities are almost amazing compared to equipment of only a few years ago (see Fig. 2-1). Swept-tuned instruments are actually frequency-selective, peak-reading voltmeters calibrated to display an accurate voltage via a crt. They can resolve all frequencies of a complex signal in a very wide dynamic range. They can also be used in the zero-span mode to deliver time-domain measurements much like an oscilloscope because their time bases are often calibrated in milliseconds or microseconds.

Today's desktop technical computers can also be connected to some analyzers to control their operations and supply customized routines for additional features. As you might have surmised, such analyzers are useful from low audio to video frequencies, satellite emissions and receptions, and even further into high microwaves. As demonstrated throughout this book, their applications are almost unlimited.

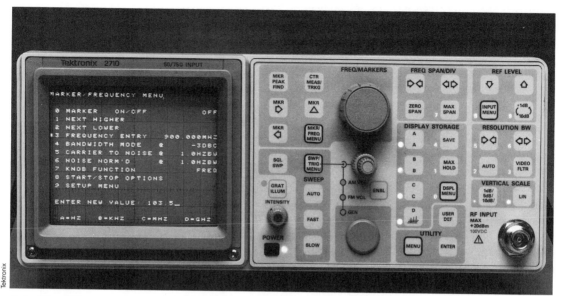

2-1 The Tektronix 2710 is an excellent microprocessor-controlled spectrum analyzer with dual-input impedances, menus, and on-screen readouts. It's portable and has a frequency range between 10 kHz and 1.8 GHz. Excellent for video and satellite measurements, it is relatively inexpensive (less than $10,000).

In selecting an analyzer, however, you must know both the applications and limitations and consider future tasks that might ultimately require measurements. If all these can be accommodated by a single instrument, then it might be worth investing a bit more money for better or more versatile equipment. YIG oscillators, A/D converters, and digital controls are permitting considerable versatility in even moderately priced ($8,500 to $10,000) testers, whose ranges and accuracies are often sufficient for the majority of modest frequency and fault examinations. When choosing, always examine dynamic range, resolution, accuracy, stability, sensitivity, functional and programmability, plus good specifications on internal noise and distortion. Understand that in a swept-tuned analyzer, its resolution depends on the passbands of its IF filters. Therefore, selective bandwidths from Hz to kHz are always important, although not mandatory in limited measurements. Narrow filters produce maximum resolution. You might also like to know that a *real time analyzer* shows all frequency components it measures simultaneously, while a *swept frequency analyzer* exhibits readouts in sequence as its filters or local-oscillator outputs are swept.

Oscilloscopes

Oscilloscopes claim the time domain measurement spectrum and have passbands from dc to low GHz, but their amplitude displays are always in millivolts and volts rather than decibels. There are some crossovers, however, that are worthwhile and are illustrated later during various applications. For the moment, just remember that the inverse of time is frequency, so that an oscilloscope, too, can become a gross analog counter, just as a spectrum analyzer can exhibit time domain measurements in its zero-span mode. Logarithms and linear measurements, however, don't match, so vertical displays remain separated unless you want to mathematically convert one to the other. Use the following equation:

$$\text{oscilloscope dBs} = 20 \log \text{volts}$$

For instance, 10 volts becomes 20 dB because the log of 10 is 1. This is a pure ratio, however, and has no ready reference such as dBm because dBm is a power measurement relative to millivolts, but dBV does refer to volts. This concept is useful when an analyzer isn't handy in a relatively gross measurement. Nonetheless, in terms of dBW (watts), there is a connection, and the equation is then:

$$\text{oscilloscope dBW} = 10 \log \text{power}$$

To convert from watts to milliwatts, just add $+30$ to the number of watts, and you have dBm, or 10^{-3}W.

These are all gains, while losses in voltage/current and power are processed as negative ratios. If you have a loss of 10 dB (-10 dB), then

$$-10 \text{ dB} = 20 \log (X \text{ ratio})$$
$$X = -10/20$$
$$= -0.5 \, X \log^{-1} (\text{antilog})$$
$$= -3.16$$

In terms of power, this would then become $-10/10 = -1$ X $\log^{-1} = -0.100$. This is not at all difficult once you understand that a minus sign always precedes the power or voltage/current ratio followed by the antilog of the decimal for your answer. (This is a "minor" detail many books usually neglect; I believe it's important for a well-rounded explanation.)

Oscilloscope types

The two prime types of oscilloscopes are analog and digital. There are others, such as *sampling* and *storage*, but the former types are now the most popular and serve the prime markets for individual or combined instruments. At the moment, both analog and digital scopes are often marketed separately, due to cost. But as experience and engineering innovation improve, most of the better, medium-range equipments will be combined, making them exceedingly useful in virtually all types of measurements.

The signal-processing analog scope still has the greatest range and general versatility, but the newer digital storage oscilloscopes (DSOs) are becoming more popular every day due to the mass of logic consumer and commercial equipments now on the market. One drawback to the storage portion relates to the number of megasamples it can process in a second. Normally, the more megasamples per second (MS/s), the greater the details appear in the digitized waveform. (This sampling rate is also called the *digitizing rate* because it results from operations of A/D converters.) For instance, a popular 50 MHz analog oscilloscope offers 20 MS/s and a digital capacity of 10 MHz, one-fifth that of its analog companion. Naturally, the faster this digitizing takes place, the more expensive the DSO. Bandwidths will increase, however, as competition and engineering learning curves progress until 60 to 100 MS/s or better are commonplace. Costs, hopefully, will be around $2,000 to $3,500.

Analog oscilloscopes Since analog scopes have now acquired considerable accuracies and expanded time bases in place of miserable recurrent sweeps, their values and utilities are manifold. An analog scope is a voltmeter, an ammeter (with special probes), produces time measurements, differential and composite waveform combinations, ac and dc individual values, a gross frequency counter, a gated rainbow (generated) vectorscope, and can check the charge and discharge rates of capacitors and the voltage drop across resistors for in-circuit values using Ohm's law. What's more, the better instruments even have sweep and signal waveform outputs that are useful in driving other circuits or electronic counters. Also, cursors (markers) have been added to the more expensive instruments so that accurate times and time intervals can be either evaluated by eye or digitally read out. In short, the analogs can do everything the digitals can except store and display a still image. Also, there are ancillary processing units that can even add a low-frequency digital capability to most or all analog scopes.

In many scope service categories, however, some units have top-end vertical deflection of only 5 V/div. This means that 5×8 divisions produce only 40 V, and even with a $10\times$ low-capacitance probe, the range is but 400 V maximum. Frankly, this isn't enough, and I hesitate to endorse any oscilloscope that doesn't possess at least 10 V/div. A $10\times$ probe would then produce a maximum deflection of 800 volts, which is sufficient for most servicing operations unless working with an old vacuum tube TV receiver whose vertical output measures some 1,500 volts. But under such unlikely circumstances, a sledge hammer might be more appropriate than an oscilloscope that, because of age, multiple infirmities, and the probability of replacing all paper and some electrolytic capacitors, a number of $1/2$ W resistors, and all tubes, would be an extremely expensive and time-consuming undertaking for very poor audio and video compared to today's better color receivers. The advent of semiconductors did, indeed, make a massive reliability and signal-processing difference, from three service calls per year to possibly one call in three or more years.

Regardless, 20 V/div. (Fig. 2-2) and a time base calibrated in seconds and nanoseconds is preferred for any oscilloscope that still serves the analog domain. Such front-end amplifiers and frequency dividers or multipliers do cost more to design, but you never know when high voltages and tight, high-frequency parameters need attention. Fortunately (or otherwise), digital designs are usually contained within a swing of 24 V or less, so smaller deflection factors for 1s and 0s are adequate. Very fast time bases, however, are needed for glitch and spurious response analysis, accompanied by excellent square-wave amplifier characteristics. Always try before you buy and don't overlook the probes that should come with it. Look for miniature ×1 (10 k resistance) and ×10 low-capacitance combinations with both capacitor and inductor adjustments for both low- and high-frequency compensation. You'll also want removable claw tips plus needlepoints to punch through epoxy coatings or land on narrow, crowded IC leads.

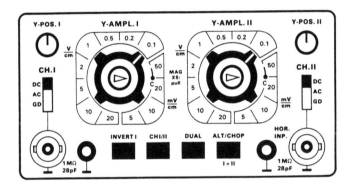

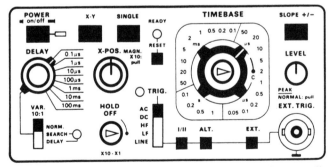

2-2   The West German Hameg HM604 has a modern amplifier and time base controls with pseudo delay, dual-input inversion, special TV triggering, and vertical deflection from 5 mV to 20 V per division. Hameg, Inc.

Digital storage oscilloscopes Digital scopes are very different in certain respects from their analog compatriots due to the amount of logic necessary for stop motion, storage, and motionless display (Fig. 2-3).

To produce a 10 MS/s display, the digitizer sampling must motor along at 100 MHz, which is at a pretty good clip. Such sampling, according to Tektronix, can be either *real time* or *equivalent time*. In the former, samples are collected in sequence from a single waveform, usually 6 to 10 samples per cycle. But in equivalent time operation, repetitive waveshapes can be fully sampled during ensuring sweeps so that a full image can be developed. This latter method is said to allow digital and analog bandwidths to become approximately equal, matching the two frequency ranges. To determine a DSO's sampling rate, divide the number of displayed points per division by the sweep/div. If, for instance, there were 150 points/div. at a sweep of 10 μs/div., the sampling rate would be $150/10 \times 10^{-6} = 15$ MS/s.

Should peak detection be available, digital sampling will take place at the instrument's maximum rate, notwithstanding any time base setting. And max/min values are retained in memory so that the original waveshape can be reconstructed in addition to any errors such as glitches. Without peak detection, many such aberrations would be lost between samples. An exotic application of this principle is identified as the envelope or peak accumulation mode, which displays max/min values for some individual time that will identify pulse jitter, occasional noise generation, and amplitude or time drifts.

The most commonly used DSO method is real-time sampling where sample rates and bandwidths are ratio constant, and sample rates are some four times the bandwidth. In choosing a DSO for your application, choose between a one-shot, nonrepetitive capture instrument and one that will "see" various transients if they repeat at designated intervals. It could save you considerable money. The way to tell is to try a measurement first with an analog scope. If a transient or glitch is visible, then your DSO

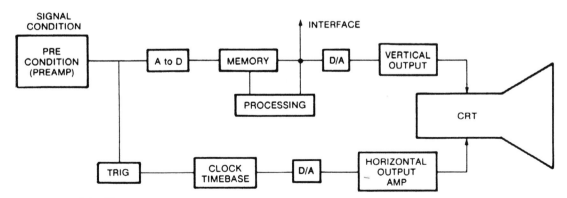

2-3 Very simplified block diagram of a digital storage oscilloscope (DSO). Tektronix

should be designed for equivalent time; otherwise, a real-time instrument will be required.

In working with DSOs, there are some terms with which you should become familiar:

- *Aliasing* commences when analog frequencies exceed the instrument's Nyquist range.
- *Aperture width* is the DSO's waveform sampling time.
- *Averaging* takes place once for a complete waveform but doesn't affect the DSO's output if repetitive; however, it can if time varying, probably influencing both noise content and signal variations.
- *Coding* means A/D conversion of signal levels into digital words.
- *Dynamic range* refers to large and small signal input ratios.
- *Interpolation* describes approximations of extra data information between waveform samples.
- *Quantizing* produces A/D step levels of analog inputs, and quantizing errors equal $\pm 1/2$ of the quantizing level.
- *Scroll mode* signifies reproduction of a number of repetitive events that can be scrolled up or down.
- *Resolution* in DSOs is a binary power of 2.
- *Roll modes* allow the signal to scroll through its length in real time. New signals in roll begin at the right side of the display.

In the future, the better analog oscilloscopes will possess digital functions including cursors (markers). Prices should regress somewhat as technology advances. If your present analog equipment does the job, watch the DSO market as requirements and manufacturing advances progress. Some 40 to 60 megasamples could be soon forthcoming at more attractive prices, along with 100 MHz analog scope bandwidths. If you only have modest frequency needs, one of the current 60 MHz analog/20 ms digitals might do the job nicely at a very reasonable outlay. Regardless, study all DSO specifications and get the best for the least, along with a major national manufacturer's reputation as operating insurance.

Logic and signature analyzers

Logic and signature analyzers are a very broad category of test instrument with all sorts of product offerings and, in many instances, substantial prices, depending on channel access, instrument sophistication, and overall functions. If, as one engineer describes such analyzers, they are "smart multichannel digital recorders" with multidata display modes that include waveform timing, digital word states, and microprocessor op disassembly codes, then your pocketbook had better contain a genuine silver/gold lining with some depth. Should the instrument have adjustable zoom for edge details, time differentials, and line combinations on data bus, then you might want to study alchemy in precious metals.

For those who have need, there are also op-code prefetch cycles, automatic data recognition and recording, and highly developed triggering that allows data retrieval about the trigger point as well as selective stop-start sampling with an internal or external clock. Timing examinations are often asychronous, while microprocessors or state instrument checks operate synchronously; that is, in time with the equipment under test.

All this suggests a secure knowledge of what you want to test, with a little room left over for futurity. Microprocessors, for instance, continue to run faster, as do many types of messaged logic, especially ECL bipolar and some of the FETs. Thirty or 40 MHz today might be more than 50 to 100 MHz tomorrow. Prices can range between $2500 to $150,000, depending on speed, channels, memory, special triggering abilities, and crt readouts. Invaluable in both design and troubleshooting, these logic instruments soon pay for themselves in test simulations, fault locations, and design rule verifications. With complex logic, you really can't do without one!

Timing considerations

A good rule of thumb states that clock speed or resolution of a logic analyzer (Fig. 2-4), needs to be 5 to 10X that of the system being investigated. If not, many spurs and glitches will certainly be missed—some sorely— and the entire troubleshooting process will inevitably fail. You must also recognize the value of data storage, both during each clock pulse or logic transition (change) in addition to well-designed latching circuits for those special low-nanosecond spikes that often appear in the faster microprocessors. This latter feature is especially important among the slower and less costly analyzers because they don't have the resolution of their blue-blooded brethren. Some manufacturers are suggesting at least a 5 ns glitch-capture circuit that does not interfere with existing width, depth, or resolution. You should also know that analyzers that rely on traditional timing require considerable memory, while those with transitional timing store information only with up/down changes. Where data is largely redundant, you can see how transitional storage could contain much more effective intelligence in a considerably condensed memory and, therefore, greater recording length. There might be instances, however, when slower-moving data could have special meaning and more than a few important glitches, so traditional storage and special triggering could become quite necessary.

In units that have glitch-capture latches and separate glitch memories, beware that your instrument's memory isn't cut in half because glitch storage can amount to 50 percent. There are some analyzers that use tradi-

2-4   A 32-channel logic analyzer with 100 MHz timing on all channels and two 400 megasample digital channels with 25 MHz state speed.

tional timing during glitch capture, and others use outright transitional timing where the glitch memory directly affects overall resolution by a considerable percent.

High resolution is best for serious glitch hunts in addition to presenting the truest readout with maximum logic information. Any analyzer or probe that loads the circuit under test can hide even larger glitches, and impedances between tester and testee must always be observed and considered when making anything other than low-impedance bipolar measurements. Some logic inputs and even outputs are very sensitive when shunted by low-value loads. This is especially true when checking circuits or subsystems with an ancillary tester supplying information to an ordinary oscilloscope. In one such instance, I had to use oscilloscope probes to record accurate data. Otherwise, most inputs to the checker were wiped out.

When push comes to shove in troubleshooting, there's no substitute for a good analyzer. Do you have a 16- or 32-channel system or subsystem that isn't behaving? Just hook up the probes and get busy. Look at data patterns before, during, or after the various trigger points, work the suspected glitch area, and roll or scroll until the problem becomes apparent. Thereafter, store the problem and read it out for careful study.

Signature analysis

Hailed as the "perfect" troubleshooter for all sorts of logic systems in the early 1980s, signature analysis (Fig. 2-5) doesn't receive quite the same accolades today, but it could make a substantial comeback as more digital consumer equipment reaches the market. This is because its special cumulative logic trains will permit examining various electrical branches, nodes, and subsystems with a single measurement. All that's needed are start and stop points and a clock reference. Thereafter, your equipment produces a simple readout on an illustrative seven-segment display that can indicate good, bad, or indifferent operation for components, even a collection or associated integrated circuits. Right now there's no significant activity toward consumer applications from relevant manufacturers, but with new ICs and microprocessors entering the market in droves, perhaps something will soon crop up. The automobile industry uses a means of subsystem readouts with indicative numbers; why shouldn't games and digital TV? It seems to me a signature analyzer would be more useful and economical than a cheap digital storage oscilloscope.

For example, a signature analysis can consist of the alphanumerics of 0, 9, 4, C, F, P, and U, a total of seven for display. With certain data compression, serial bit streams of any length are read out as in hexadecimal notation, which, as many of you know, replaces four binary digits with one alphanumeric symbol. Often as many as six letters of the alphabet are used and are considered also as numbers; usually U through Z. Character sets, therefore, can begin with digits 0 through 9, plus those taken from the alphabet. Addition and multiplication are typical for this method of computation, although subtraction is also possible.

Basics of signature analysis are free-running and software-implemented operations in these microprocessor-driven products. During free run, the processor cycles continuously across its field, limited by start/stop

2-5   A new 5006A programmable signature analyzer currently on the market.

commands derived from test circuits stored in software energized ROMs. These also write specific data for the data bus testing outputs.

Older signature analyzers often used a 6800 microprocessor, several switches, buffers, an address bus, one RAM and several ROMs, plus only a few outboard components and a display, making them rather simple devices indeed. All this doesn't sound like too much of an investment in electronics and, therefore, forthcoming requirements could see some resurrection of these instruments. ROMs and RAMs are also checkable if feedback paths are disabled. Hopefully, some major manufacturer will pick up the challenge and make these testers even more useful and flexible.

Network and vector analyzers

Network and vector analyzers are two of the latest developments in the realm of smart or "intelligent" instruments now appearing on the market (Fig. 2-6). Both are microwave-technology devices that can operate on their own without constant operator supervision. The first measures frequency, gain, input loss, and return loss; the second often has narrow-band detectors for accurate phase and noise measurements, principally among intermediate frequency amplifiers (IFs). Often this equipment is guided by internal controllers, microprocessors, and floppy disks. Programming is often executed in BASIC, which is compatible with a major interface bus system or subsystem connector; and some network analyzers offer dual-trace inputs so that various parameters of the unit under test may be recorded and directly compared. Others even exhibit sweep oscillators or synthesis for this type of measurement over extended ranges, while a few are actually modular, allowing various function and frequency plug-ins for measurement flexibility.

Microprocessors in these and other smart instruments not only control many programmed functions, but also aid in operator programming, startup memory, and menu definitions and instructions. You need a cathode-ray tube to view these "help" aid and necessary on-screen displays for operator or factory programming. Internal, self-calibration routines are also part of the characteristics of many of the more sophisticated instruments, especially spectrum analyzers.

What are they?

Network and vector analyzers are linear analyzers, usually high frequency, that examine and even characterize linear networks in the frequency domain, often by creating models that can predict transfer functions and impedances, as well as measure signal magnitudes and phase in units with sweep functions. This constitutes a complete analysis of signal and network functions as opposed to scalar analyzers (magnitudes) and vector analyzers, which respond to both magnitude and phase. More complex network analyzers even have the ability to transform measurements from

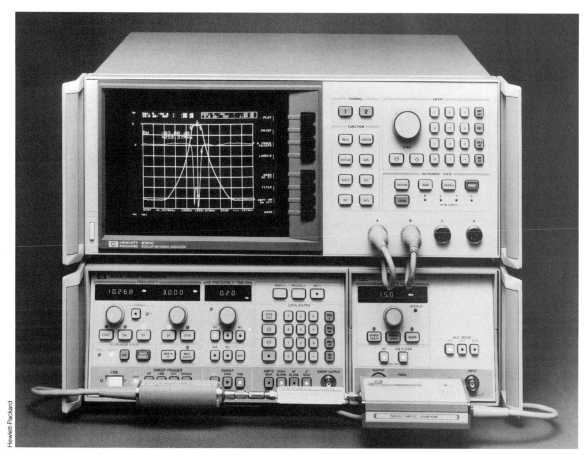

2-6 Above, an extremely useful (but pricey) HP 8757 scalar network analyzer that measures transmission and reflection parameters of microwave components to 100 GHz; below, the HP 8350 sweep oscillator for generating test signals.

the frequency domain to the time domain ($t = 1/f$ and $f = 1/t$). Active and passive networks are included.

Network analyzer measurements are made with sine waves. These then circulate within the unit under test so that the analyzer can detect such signals as they separate, develop various ratios of voltages and currents, and thereby record transfer and impedance parameters as they occur. A sweep oscillator can aid in exercising the circuit or system being tested. Detection can be full-frequency broadband or narrowband IF information down-converted from RF. Broadbanding is said to reduce analyzer costs due to no IF section, but it is subject to both noise and harmonics. Conversely, vector analyzers are usually narrowbanded for phase and improved noise detection. The better analyzers have both a reference channel (zero phase) and one or more test channels, according to Hewlett-Packard. S parameters for transistors, two-port linear networks, group delays, and passband reflection coefficients are all part of these analyzer operations.

Popular instruments by HP include the 8757A scalar analyzer for insertion loss or gain, return loss, power, and SWR (standing wave ratio). There is even a combined network and spectrum analyzer, Model 4195A, for frequencies between 10 Hz and 500 MHz. It has color graphics and direct copy displays. The high end of the line features the HP 8757S, which is completely automatic and has a range of from 10 MHz to 100 GHz.

The foregoing types of specialized analyzers were included for your overall edification rather than suggested use in anything but design work and highly sophisticated products. Most are fairly expensive and dedicated to analog rather than digital functions where specific parameters require precise examinations and predictions. Some of these principles could appear in other instruments any time, so I felt a suitable description of their activities was in order.

Signal and sweep generators

More and more low- and high-frequency signal generators have sweep functions that are very important in characterizing tuned IF and RF circuits, especially for observing their bandpasses and shaped responses. And all sorts of low-, medium- and high-frequency instruments are now appearing that offer surprising flexibility and range to tackle virtually any routine or difficult problem. Not necessarily limited to sine-wave outputs, such signal/sweepers could be pulse or function generators that operate satisfactorily even at MHz.

In communications and laboratories, such instruments are extremely valuable because they are often microwave generators with AM and FM modulation built in. Primarily sine-wave cw or modulated devices, their outputs are very clean (high spectral purity), they have selectable stop and start points, output attenuators, and dynamic ranges of over 100 dB, and are usually microprocessor controlled for very high accuracy and flat sweep characteristics (Fig. 2-7).

Once exclusively YIG cavity tuned, many of the signal generator parts of the sweepers, and the plain signal sources, are excited by *frequency synthesizers*, of which there are two categories: *direct* and *indirect*. The direct-type of synthesizers mix, multiply, and filter their references, while the indirect group has voltage-controlled oscillators, phase-locked loops, and dc correction voltages. Although synthesis often adds undesirable blips and spurs, sophisticated filtering (sometimes with YIG tuning) can remove most of them and drop harmonics and spurs as low as −60 dBc. There are also synthesized sweepers in combination with synthesized signal generators for a very neat, useful, and highly effective package.

Today, most signal generators are of the indirect synthesizer type

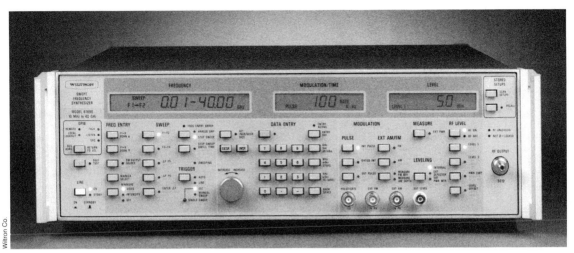

2-7   A new and highly useful microwave synthesized generator covering the range from 10 MHz to 40 GHz.

where a phase detector operates with a voltage-controlled oscillator (VCO), producing sum and difference frequencies. Sums and references are low-pass filtered, but any difference frequency corrects the VCO and places the system in complete phase lock. In direct systems, a reference frequency is established via a harmonic generator that delivers outputs at some harmonic of that reference and is then filtered. Selecting the appropriate harmonic establishes a particular frequency output. Shielding, because of the many harmonics and extensive filtering, are prime problems with this approach, along with switch-path isolation and slow frequency changes. This is why indirect synthesis has become so popular.

In upper frequencies, with YIG drives, frequency synthesizers can operate successfully from the low MHz to as much as 18 GHz with a considerable range of control. Often such extended spectrums do not use a single synthesizer due to cost but divide coverage into 10 to 16 GHz bites, with frequency resolutions in single-megahertz steps and settling time in milliseconds. Well-designed units have low single-sideband phase noise, suppressed harmonics, and very low nonharmonic spurs. Ordinary internal reference sources ensure frequency accuracy of 10 parts per million.

When designing wideband synthesizers, pay close attention to loop gain and loop filter time constants, often over damping coefficients and special frequency considerations. One engineer has demonstrated that loop gain K approximates loop bandwidth if the loop time filter constant provides critical damping.

Mathematically, these might be tough concepts to assimilate, but they forcefully indicate present-day progress in synthesizer design and offer considerable insight into what will follow in another several years.

Phase-locked loops

The basis for any of these synthesizer systems is a phase-locked loop
(PLL) circuit consisting of a phase comparator, low-pass filter, dc amplifier
and a voltage-controlled oscillator (VCO), as illustrated in Fig. 2-8. Basically, these are feedback systems that synchronize the frequency and
phase of an oscillator with that of the received signal. The comparator

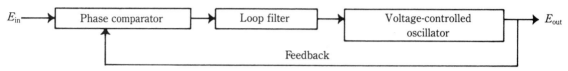

2-8 Basic PLL feedback system with comparator, low-pass filter, and VCO.

detects the difference between input and feedback information and delivers an error output proportional to any phase difference. With low-pass filtering, high frequency or noise is ignored and the VCO corrects only for
average frequencies as it responds to varying dc levels. Now that discrete
semiconductors have been supplanted by single-chip PLLs, their use
extends from many types of test equipment to AM/FM demodulators, data
modems, speed control systems, voltmeters, and even spectrum analyzers.
They can be either analog or digital, depending on what phase comparator
is used.

In examining or choosing such subsystems, you must be aware of the
center frequency, VCO output, the pull-in, pull-out, holding ranges, and
lock-in characteristics. A divide-by-n counter is often found between the
VCO and phase comparator so that the VCO oscillates at n times the input
frequency. Any associated crystal reference should also have an equivalent
divide-by-n counter for frequency comparison and stability. These are
often found in electronic television tuners. Math calculations for PLLs
usually involve Bode plots, open-loop transfer functions, and Laplace
transforms—none of which are either simple or nonacademically attractive. Computer modeling can often ease these burdens if you can scare up
a model and execute a specific program. As one engineer describes the
PLL, it's a "circuit that locks the frequency of one oscillator . . . to another
oscillator," the output voltage being the difference between a master oscillator and the slave VCO via a phase detector, amplifier, and filter.

Continuing with the excruciating details would add virtually nothing
to your general working knowledge. You might be interested to know,
however, that PLLs are now included in satellite tuning systems (Fig. 2-9)
with digital dividers altering voltage-tuned oscillator frequencies to those
of their references. Ratio changes deliver output frequency changes while
being locked to some crystal-controlled divided-down lower frequency ref-

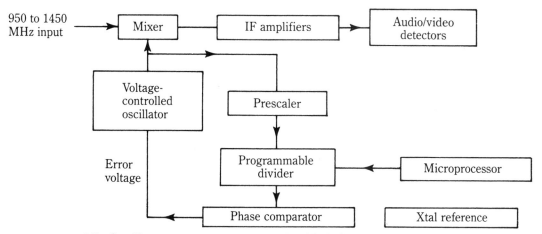

2-9 Satellite second converter PLL tuning block downconverter systems.

erence. Here, UHF prescalers are common as are surface-wave acoustical (SAW) filters for bandwidth reduction and undesirable external frequency suppression.

The sweeper

In the past, a 60 Hz sweep 15 MHz wide with dubious linearity was almost a major triumph. Today, gigahertz sweeps, programmable from start to finish, along with markers, superb linearity, and electronically leveled outputs are more the rule than the exception. You'd like to sweep a block down-converter's output between 950 and 1450 MHz? Be my guest. If the frequency characteristics of your generator/sweeper approaches 2 GHz, you're absolutely in business, including variable sweep rates and electronically attenuated outputs that range in the low dBms up to +10 or + 20 dBm.

These exceptional sweep instruments have oscillators whose frequencies vary rapidly and continuously over a given band. Heretofore, their modulation abilities have been restricted to kHz, but today several MHz in FM modulation is often possible due to advances in frequency synthesis. There are also digital as well as analog sweepers available today. The latter are CW frequencies that can be stepped through their various bands at some digitally specified rate. And there are even linear/log sweeps available in the better equipment. According to Hewlett-Packard, they're useful for scalar/vector analysis, frequency translation and noise figure measurements, passband validation, inductor tuning, and many other applications that are always required when working with bandpass and critically tuned circuits. Dual-tone sweeps are another in the series of uses where the difference frequency of two oscillators are phase locked to a stable source. Then add modulation in the form of AM, FM, and sometimes PM to these sweeps, and a great deal of information about the device under test becomes available. In such instruments, linearity, time base accuracy, frequency bands, readout accuracy, markers, and frequency range are all important parameters. Unfortunately, the good ones operating in the GHz range are rather expensive, and cheap ones don't really exist. Continuous-wave signals are also useful from these instruments in satellite antenna measurements, system and circuit gains, and frequency checks. Wideband modulation abilities, however, only appear in the most recent instruments, especially FM deviation. Otherwise, YIG units just handle intermediate kilohertz, which is great for audio but catastrophic for video and satellite examination.

Although there is a waveform analyzer category, these units occupy the *n*th degree of sophistication at very high prices and are essentially nailed-down laboratory instruments that only large corporations and the government can really afford. Therefore, this concludes my discussion of crt display instruments used for more-or-less everyday utilities. More could be said, but what's been described already should furnish adequate background for most measurements.

Nonetheless, phase, frequency, amplitude, and time domain information evaluations are already possible, while only the basics of ohms, current and remnants of ac/dc sectors have not yet been covered. A broad understanding of many of the aforesaid principles and applications is essential for progressive engineers and technicians in electronic design and repair. Today's huge diversity of electronic products probably needs a healthy mixture of both a working knowledge of analog as well as digital disciplines. Unfortunately, it seems that many colleges' electrical engineering programs skim over analog but emphasize digital. Experienced, quality RF engineers are treasured like precious metals. In engineering, marketing, or the arts, there's always demand with small supply.

Meters

Meters is a category that most electronics people profess to "know," but few actually do. Long past is the era of the vacuum-tube voltmeter or the 1,000-ohm/volt multimeter that would load virtually anything but an iron bar. A handful of resistors, a cramped multiscale dial, a coil, a metal indicator, and possibly a fuse won't cut it today. Back then, a 1-milliampere meter movement needs 1 mA for full-scale deflection, $1/10^{-3}$, or 1,000 ohms/volt. Now shunt a 10 kΩ resistor with this 1 kΩ sensitivity and you'll actually only measure current flowing through 900 ohms, or 0.9 V. Advance this sensitivity to 10,000 ohms/volt, and the shunt load is obviously a great deal less, but it still reduces the voltage readout to one-half. This is why additional ranges with higher resistances were developed, so that readings could be taken on part of the scale rather than full scale.

Even 100,000 ohms/volt wasn't entirely satisfactory because slow meter movements and expensive divider resistors increased costs considerably. As vacuum tube technology surrendered to solid state, very small voltages, tiny currents, and all sorts of resistances appeared that completed obsolescence of both primitive multimeters as well as VTVMs.

This mandated the introduction of multimeters with input impedances of as much as 10 to 16 megohms, liquid crystal readouts, and even ac bar graphs for overall direct and alternating flow applications. That's precisely where we are today. However, instead of $59 VOMs, prices for these new and highly sophisticated units can exceed $300 or more, depending on the specialization. Good-quality ac radio-frequency (RF) meters that include frequency ranges that extend into the MHz and readouts in current, rms volts, and decibels are often expensive, with prices exceeding $1,000 for each unit. Input impedances are usually 10 megohms, and millivolt/microvolt ranges are not uncommon.

Once again, though, rather than dwell on greater or lesser esoterics, let's describe one of the better multimeters readily available on the open market by a leading manufacturer at relatively reasonable cost. Few, if any, multimeters equal the Fluke 87 for versatility and utility.

Fluke's model 87 true rms multimeter

The Fluke model 87 is shown in Fig. 2-10. Its ranges include: ac, from 100 microvolts to 1,000 volts; dc (two ranges), from 10 microvolts to 1,000 volts; ohms, from 10 milliohms to 40 megohms; conductivity from 0.001 to 40 nanosiemens; capacitance, from 0.01 nanofarad to 5 microfarads; dc current, from 0.1 microampere to 20 amperes; and ac current, from 0.1 microampere to 400 milliamperes, in two ranges. But these values don't even begin to tell the story. You'll discover a great deal more.

The Fluke 87 has a beeper to warn if the leads are plugged into the improper input terminals for the function being measured if you're careless. You'll also find a Touch Hold key that holds the highest reading registered if you're busy or in tricky territory with the probes. Then, the MIN MAX recording mode remembers high-low values, even over a period of 24 hours, and displays them on the LCD readout. Changes from previous values also triggers the beeper.

The 87 is a 4,000-count instrument powered with a 9 V battery. It has a sturdy case sealed against both dirt and moisture and a second "rubberized" enclosure with a stand further protects the meter from shocks and drops. A 4.5-digit LCD display increases resolution 10 times over prior 3.5-digit units, while frequencies between 0.5 Hz and 200 kHz can be measured with 0.01 Hz resolution. Any single reading also can be stored for future reference and its difference compared with another at a later time. For dark areas, there's a display backlight. In short, the Fluke 87 combines the operation of a very accurate digital readout with that of a high-resolution analog bar graph display that updates 40 times per second and

2-10 Photo of the self-calibrating deluxe multimeter showing readout and controls.

John Fluke Mfg.

consists of 32 segments plus polarity indicators. Figure 2-11 shows the block diagram. Digital updates are 3 to 4 times per second. Once the measurement mode is selected autoranging provides the best resolution.

In the MIN MAX condition, voltage changes of 100 ms or longer are displayed, and peak MIN MAX charges of 1 ms or longer are also recorded. The meter is reasonably tolerant of noise and will usually accept up to several volts of ac transients unless indicated by analog oscillations or rotating readout numbers. Fluke says if this occurs, a range change of MIN MAX recording might resolve the condition. Capacitors should always be discharged before measurement because a known current is injected by the 87, and then capacitance is calculated on the basis of charge up to 1.2 volts. Short test leads or a fixture are required in low nanofarads or less. Diode tests are little more than shunt readings across the cathode-anode junction at approximately 1 mA. No reading, or the same reading in both directions, indicates an obvious open or short.

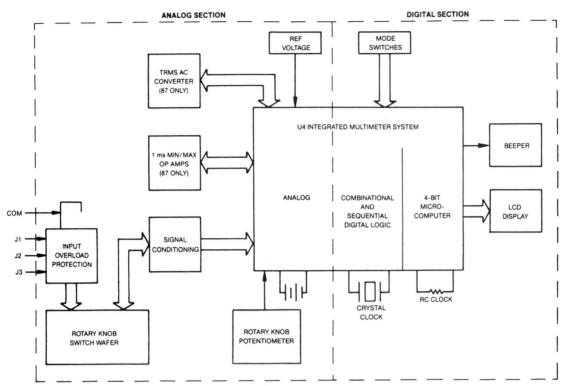

2-11 Block diagram of the Fluke 87 multimeter, illustrating both analog and digital sections. John Fluke Mfg.

Frequency counters

If you think digital/analog voltmeters are tough, counters are a sure bag of worms. If you pay for a good one, you won't regret being stuck with an off-impedance, low-frequency, inaccurate, shaky-gate cheapie. This does not mean you have to raid the Philadelphia mint for sufficient coin, but you're certainly going to collect what you pay for.

Many counters now operate from dc to many gigahertz, with others somewhere in between. My own antiquated Data-Precision unit ranges to 250 MHz, which is barely enough for video/RF measurements and no-where nearly suitable for satellite and microwave tallies. But I make do, sometimes with a 10:1 oscilloscope probe for some critical applications where impedance loads upset readings or supply additional signal amplifi-cation. Where there are no known relative numbers, you'd better have a good oscilloscope or spectrum analyzer handy to establish a good initial frequency. Should this measurement be waveforms other than sine waves, your counter has to be capable of "reading" these voltages too. Counters can propogate many strange dots and digits if they're mismatched with some circuit or system output. Futhermore, they do need calibration fairly often, and the standard should really be traceable to some standard frequency. Therefore, the concern is not with simple millivolts or occasional microvolts, but low-value parts per million that require not only excellent calibration but super stability to retain that calibration. And a counter that ranges from milliseconds to gigahertz with, say, 12-digit resolution, does, indeed, require very special electronics and superior design.

Fortunately, digital logic, advanced solid state, and engineering ingenuity have and are producing highly useful instruments today that answer most requirements for under $1,000. Then there are other, even less expensive devices that are almost equally useful if carefully calibrated at least monthly or even bimonthly. In selecting a counter for your applications, consider the ultra and intermediate requirements and their comparative costs. Sometimes, unless your needs are precise and especially long range, you might save considerable money by selecting useful equipment that can adequately serve the purpose for relatively little cash outlay. But do read and understand all specifications!

How counters work

Conventionally, counters measure frequency by passing unknown information through a main gate that opens and closes in a timed sequence (Fig. 2-12). Such timing is via a crystal oscillator and a time-base divider, often a fraction or multiple or a single second. Such pulses are stored in a decimal counter, displayed, and then updated as new intelligence arrives. Direct counting through 1 GHz is always possible today, but economy dictates dividing or prescaling these frequencies down so that standard ICs can handle and then remultiply (if there's such a word) by some factor that will

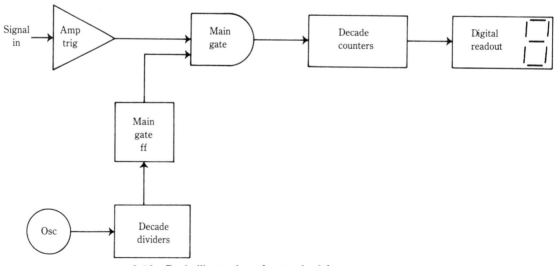

2-12 Basic illustration of a standard frequency counter.

exhibit the correct counter readout. However, both measuring time or digit resolution will suffer. Unfortunately, direct gating and accompanying readouts require exceedingly high stability with expensive oscillators that increase prices dramatically and often require more than occasional calibration. Frequencies above 1 GHz are more complex conversions involving transfer oscillators and heterodyne radio-type converters.

Counters might also measure period and time intervals both one-shot and repetitive (Figs. 2-13 and 2-14). But often, potentiometers are required to set signal levels for best counter accuracy up to 100 MHz, with pin diodes and possibly certain AGC (automatic gain control) circuits thereafter. Opening and closing gate operations are required for interval measurements so that the main gate can be precisely controlled for accurate counting. As this counting occurs, be sure the waveform source is not contaminated with undue noise or modulation. Many counters are not too smart and you have to adjust for levels, gating times, and even input impedances for accurate results. Also keep in mind that any counter's crystal timing oscillator is always affected by temperature, aging, and incoming

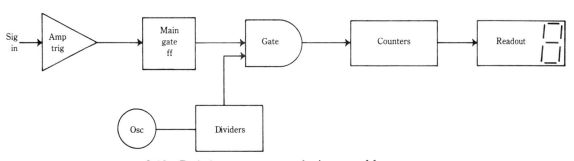

2-13 Period measurements, the inverse of frequency.

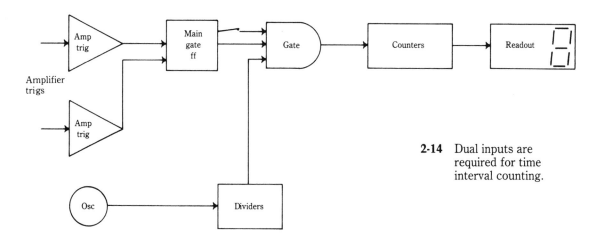

2-14 Dual inputs are required for time interval counting.

power (line) voltage. You might also like to know that 1 ppm (parts per million) equals 10^{-6}; 10 ppm equals 10^{-5}; 100 ppm becomes 10^{-4}, etc. This equality also says that 10^{-9} is the equivalent of 0.001 ppm, and this is highly desirable accuracy, indeed.

Should the input signal be smaller or larger than the counter can absorb, most of the better oscilloscopes have video outputs that supply adequate signal for reasonable operation. When you realize that ultimate counting accuracy not only depends on the time base but also ± 1 count, time base error, trigger error, and trigger level set, it's not difficult to understand that accurate counting of anything but a very clean input signal with rigidly calibrated equipment is a necessity rather than a luxury.

For those who dote on mathematical symbols, pulse counting requires counter input sensitivity of

$$S = 2\sqrt{2}...$$

The trigger-level control moves so that such pulses occupy as much of the full amplifier input range as possible. Known as the *dynamic range*, this is the linear range of the input. Up to 100 MHz, an input impedance of 1 megohm will suffice, but above that, the counter must reduce its impedance to 50 ohms with very low shunt capacity for almost any accurate measurement.

Ordinary frequencies are measured by the number of cycles (n) divided by the time period (t), or

$$\text{frequency} = n/t$$

The decade dividers are controlled by a gate time switch that allows the oscillator input to be varied in decade steps. Time, as the inverse of frequency, is

$$\text{time} = n/f$$

An industry search

In scouring the industry for a suitable, up-to-date electronic counter at a reasonable price, many of the big names were and are offering intriguing units with considerable versatility but at prices exceeding $1,000. There are even counters now available that are combined with power meters for microwave measurements—absolute engineering gems. Most people, however, don't have such resources immediately available, nor do they necessarily work with microwaves up to 30 GHz. Therefore, I suggest a counter with considerable range, reasonable reliability, and company backing that would ensure responsibility if and when there were electronic or mechanical problems: the West German HM8021-3 1 GHz counter meets reasonable expectations in both range, functions, and selling price (Fig. 2-15).

2-15 An inexpensive oc-to-1 GHz counter with seven-digit resolution. Ovenized crystal oscillator's stability is 0.5 ppm over the temperature range.

The HM8021-3 is a relatively recent market offering with a sensitivity of 20 millivolts, a frequency range from dc to 1 GHz, and a pair of BNC receptors that split the frequency range at recommended impedances, with input noise specified at 100 microvolts. This permits low-frequency signals from dc to 150 MHz to be received at an impedance of 1 MHz, and those between 100 MHz and 1,000 MHz to enter the instrument at an impedance of 50 ohms. Maximum input voltages range between 5 and 8 volts except from 0 to 440 Hz, where dc plus ac peaks can be accepted up to 250 V.

Best of all, the "ovenized" time base is rated at an accuracy of 5 × 10^{-7}, which is 5 parts per million (ppm) over the entire operating range, including frequency, periods, and time intervals, plus a totalized count, display hold, and full-range offset for special problems. A variable trigger control or built-in autotrigger permits accurate measurements of complex and noisy waveforms, accompanied by an eight-digit, seven-segment bright readout with both sign and exponent. Power needs are 7 VA (volt-amperes), and the weight amounts to 1.3 lbs. The microprocessor-controlled counter features reciprocal counting, resolving seven digits during 1-second measuring times on all frequencies. Self-test and calibration electronics are built in.

Further explanation on counters would involve all sorts of characteristics appropriate for a few but not required by the majority. Therefore, if you want additional functions, it's best to order catalogs from Hewlett-Packard, Tektronix, EIP Microwave, and others who make specialty, top-of-the-line instruments.

A 1 GHz range, however, should see you through most counting requirements that don't involve things like microwaves, radar, and special satellite signals. Furthermore, dual inputs of the HM8021-3 offer an interesting advantage among lower-cost units.

3
Cable versus fiberoptics

STRANGELY ENOUGH, SELECTION OF CABLE OR FIBEROPTICS AS A transmission medium isn't always a difficult choice. Each has advantages and disadvantages, and the latest technology might not be required in many circumstances, especially where there are minor rather than major applications and cost becomes a prime consideration. But in terms of bandwidth and multi-channel availability per mile, the trade-off might largely favor fiber, particularly if it can be strapped to existing cableways, resulting in minimum installation fees and few right-of-way constraints.

For the consumer, cable remains the prime CATV, satellite earth station, telephone, and power conveyance medium, that is until the telephone companies gain Federal Communications Commission approval to introduce fiber into local switchers and from there into homes. That day is certain to come because of the overwhelming need for all sorts of data, video, and business communications. The world population continues to become larger, and those who can usually meet the challenge thrive. But that's not all. Minimum insertion loss, very high propagation efficiencies, tiny size, enormous reliability, virtually miles of cable without amplification, and resistance to outside interference and no signal radiation present offers more than a few attractive options for fiberoptics. It's no coincidence that New York/Washington/Chicago fiber links are already in place and intercontinental cables between the U.S., Europe, and Asia are either being laid or are now securely resting many miles beneath the ocean surface.

Conversely, analog signals are easily transmitted over regular CATV cable without laser carriers and unique detectors, there's no special fiber-to-copper connector matching, home drops (feeders) are readily attached, and local installers are usually totally familiar with the rote process of running miles of coax along phone poles, boosted by an occasional amplifier.

Will HDTV make a difference? Only if a CATV system is either so channel-crowded or ineffective that additional bandwidth and new components have to be added. Otherwise, many existing CATV installations in prime locations will only require front-end modifications: new, broadband decoders atop TV receivers to process this new technology. At the moment, since no single system has received the blessing of the Federal Communications Commission, we can't be positive about anything other than that one or two channels will probably be required to handle the increased passbands or simulcasts, such as one NTSC and the augmented or pure HDTV transmission, simulcasting being the more probable. Unfortunately, we simply don't know right now and won't until some Federal decision is handed down in the second quarter of 1993. Then another couple of years will have to elapse before production receivers reach the market. Meanwhile, we can work with the best of satellite and terrestrial NTSC transmissions, which are superb anyway when viewed from the K-2 G.E.-Americom satellite with its 54 MHz broadband transponders. Even with 27 MHz consumer-type satellite receivers and a video/audio monitor, the sights and sounds of good, live pickups are virtually spectacular.

This is probably as good a break point as any to begin fiberoptic and cable descriptions that expand into somewhat more detail than those that preceded. Since cable is no strange concept to most people, let's tackle fiberoptics first and then cover cable later.

Fiberoptic cable

In our library of record, a stream of poured water guided light in the 1850s, and that was 140 years ago. Between 1930 and 1950, glass filaments in bundles were manufactured, suggesting fiber transmission possibilities. And by 1970, single-mode fibers could be made. Multimode fibers came along shortly, and by 1981, multimode fibers (MMF) appeared in links that extended over 18 miles. Today, fiberoptic cable is in place over thousands of miles, and almost all of its potential has yet to be realized, much less applied.

Considerable optimism began to flow in the mid-1970s with a prediction that 1990 would establish a market of over $1.5 billion. At chapter's end, you should have a good estimate of whether this goal has been reached or even surpassed. One would expect the latter, considering the multiple uses that seem available.

In the beginning

When scientists began seriously working with fiberoptic cable, the combination of fiberoptics and optoelectronics evolved, offering the possibility of explosively expanding national and international data and digital transmission. In it they recognized and developed a light-transmittable source, single or bundles of optical fibers, and a light detector for the receiver. In the beginning, this was usually a light-emitting diode (LED) coupled to drive a circuit at its input and an fiberoptic cable at its output. On the other end, the detector might consist of a silicon phototransistor, avalanche photodiodes, or silicon pin diodes, with the latter becoming the more popular of the three.

At first, LEDs were simply added to a flat or oval portion of glass for radiated throughput. That was all right for simple applications, but the power loss could amount to as much as 20 dB, so improvements were necessary in this department, and they have been made, but it wasn't easy.

To couple any transmission device efficiently, optical fibers have cores with high index refractions and are "cladded" with an additional layer of material to isolate such fibers and reject crosstalk. Signals are carried by the core and are reflected from the core-cladded tunnel as they travel along. The best cable efficiently results from maximum ratio of core to cladding areas, other characteristics taken into consideration. Because of these deflections/reflections, however, pure analog transmissions aren't feasible over distances yet, but engineers aren't in total despair.

You might think that glass derived from silicon/sand would be one of the most inexpensive materials; certainly a great deal less expensive than copper conductors and their multiwrap shielding, but that's not so. Because low loss is a paramount requirement of fiberoptic cable, such glass must be highly purified, subject to flawless finish, be uniform, and have maximum strength to avoid either absorbing or scattering the radiated light. Poor fiberoptic cable manufacture will result in loss attenuation (measured in dB/km) at a specific light frequency, in addition to poor couplings or positioning within bundles of cables. Today's classifications include high-, medium-, and low-loss fiberoptic cable with related pricing. And when multicable requirements dictate the bundling of several or many fibers together, a "packing fraction" becomes the ratio between core areas and air spaces, whether these fibers are multimode (more than one transmission), or single mode (one transmission), usually determined by the diameter of the core. In any event, the core *index* (inside) must always be greater than the cladding *index* (outside) and allow transmissions based on specific angles of light. Those larger than normal will simply be attenuated and lost.

As technology progresses and more solid-state lasers are developed, single-mode fiberoptic cables are expected to dominate many long-distance requirements due to their extremely wide bandwidths and multichannel abilities.

Information transmitted via fiberoptic cable travels under the name of *incident light photon*, a somewhat formidable title meaning "sourced light in the form of radiant energy moving at the established speed of light": 299.8×10^6 meters/second, or 186,280 miles/second in free space. The detector/receiver must then convert this energy into an electron flow that is not impeded by mismatch, leakage, noise, or poorly designed electronics, and it must have considerable reliability.

Thereafter, it is up to connectors to couple these detected signals within or without the system—a considerable problem initially because modified RF connectors for cable were seldom satisfactory and often produced more than considerable losses (Fig. 3-1). Those units available today are much less than 1 dB on the average, and even less than 0.5 dB for those of better quality. At first, stainless steel and nickle-plated brass were used as improvements continued. At that time, a cable's jacket was removed, fibers were coated with epoxy and inserted into the connector. After epoxy curing, core trimming took place, and a coupling nut added and secured.

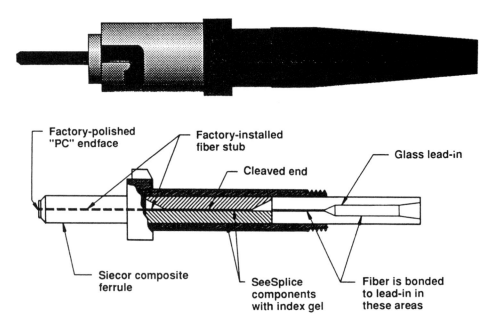

3-1 Field-installable multimode connector that requires no fiber sizing, heat suring, or polishing. Siecor Corp.

Advantages and disadvantages

There are a number of advantages to fiberoptic cable that place it in a distinct category, Fig. 3-2. It features very wide bandpass, no short circuits, noise immunity, absolute electrical isolation, message security, no crosstalk, small and lightweight properties, competitive prices, capability for huge transmission content, rapid propagation rate, little service, and few amplifiers compared to coaxial cable. And once the telephone companies are allowed to use fiberoptic cable in private dwellings, picture telephones and many other handy services will be immediately available, much to the chagrin of some competing video and data carriers.

There are some difficulties, however, in realizing all these advantages. The transmitter's LED driver must generate sufficient current for ade-

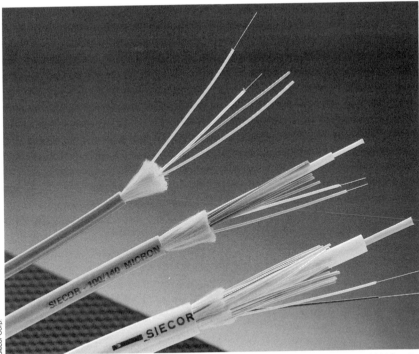

Siecor Corp

3-2 Indoor/outdoor multifiber cable with protective jackets in the 100/140 micron series.

quate optical operation along with data signal switching. LED and optical connectors need to operate as a single function, all immune to power supply changes and temperature variations, along with logic to enable and disable the input bitstream. The cable must be of adequate quality and devoid of mismatched couplings and leakage, in addition to adequate supports and positive strain relief along its route.

All this is relatively simple compared to the receiving mechanism. Here, optical energy has to be current-source changed and then current-to-voltage converted. The initial detector is often a high-impedance device with small signal output that reacts linearly to optical energy fluctuations. This invites the possibilities of both noise and interference, which can affect critical signal-to-noise (S/N) ratios. The current-to-voltage converter (CVC) has to furnish signal gain proportional to input current, even with a low-input impedance and the obligation of properly following the detector's fast/slow transitions. The linear voltage amplifier must then stay within limits dictated by the detector's threshold divided by the CVC noise output, or both signal and noise are unfortunately amplified. Rise times and bandwidths in this stage are also critical, as well as settling times. In other words, adequate amplifier response with careful attention paid to RC factors among time constants between the amplitude detector and voltage amplifier.

Once all this is done, it's a simple trick to display whatever has been transmitted and hope for a bit-error rate of less than 1×10^9, which, according to Motorola, is a signal amplitude of $6.15 \times$ rms noise. Anything less will probably permit noise to appear in the readout. Should both data and threshold outputs be capacitatively coupled, Motorola says their baselines float and "maintain an average value of zero." The signal-to-noise-derived equation then amounts to:

$$S/N = 20 \log \text{peak signal/rms noise}$$

At least that's one way of evaluating the recovered information; by now there are probably others. This basically serves to illustrate and warn of possible problems involved in recovering and amplifying an optically carried signal. Quality systems are therefore not necessarily cheap but, apparently, most effective.

In choosing detectors, both fiber cable runs and data/frequency rates initially determine selection. For instance, ordinary bipolar phototransistors are inexpensive and have high gain, but millisecond rise and fall times couldn't handle high-speed photons. FET phototransistors were available, too, providing considerable amplification and vastly improved rise and fall times (medium nanoseconds). But pin photodiodes offered linear responses, picosecond rise and fall times, and seemed eminently suited for fast signal detection. (You might have noticed frequent use of the past tense in describing fiberoptic cable operations to this point. That's because we're still absorbing and reporting on developments in the late 1970s and early 1980s. Therefore, there'll be considerably more to tell as we continue.)

Packaging

Due to the many entrepreneurs in the early days of fiberoptics, large, awkward couplings, discrete-device semiconductor modules, and other hardware proliferated in the usual effort to outdistance competition. As usual, however, printed circuit boards, ICs, and somewhat standardized hardware has finally prevailed—with the usual claims and differences, as you would expect. Monolithic optoelectronics appeared, followed by hybrids with better noise figures as well as larger and more diverse-valued RC components that can handle greater currents. Emitters and detectors were often integral parts of the optical cable connectors, and when one failed, the entire module and/or its associated electronics would require replacement. This proved costly, and most emitters and detectors are now replaceable without disturbing associated components and connectors. There is and has been the usual problem of exact alignments between fibers in cable connectors or splices. Axial and angular offsets result in unacceptable losses, and there is also the critical problem of hermetic seals. Epoxy, unfortunately, isn't good enough, and some light emitters require heat sinking for even milliwatt power dissipation. Optical connectors, therefore, are often made of brass that, although soft, will do the job.

Fiberoptic measurements

Basically, there are three fundamental measurements applicable to fiberoptic cables for attenuation that are described in International Electrotechnical Commission (IEC) documents. They include:

- Cutback
- Insertion loss
- Backscatter

In *cutback*, constant optical power enters the fiber's input and is measured again at the output. Then 2 m is severed from the input, and power is again measured there. This suggests a power equation, but with P_1 divided by P_2:

$$10 \log P_1/P_2 = \text{attenuation in dB}$$

Unfortunately, cutback doesn't readily deliver reproducible tests and is therefore somewhat unreliable.

Insertion loss connects optical source to optical receiver with a short piece of fiber and measures P_1. A test fiber then replaces the reference fiber and P_2 is measured using the same $10 \log P_1/P_2$ equation for attenuation. Here, however, a mode scrambler/mixer fiber is used for stable distribution. Another means is with a lens-aperture stop system to illuminate approximately 70 percent of the core's diameter. After a few meters of fiber, stable distribution is established.

The *backscatter* measurement uses Rayleigh light scattering, which results in measuring a sample of the light as it returns to its origin, allowing optical power and time delay to permit:

$$\text{Attenuation} = 5 \log P_1/P_2 \text{ in dB}$$

As you might have recognized, only one end of the fiber is used, permitting a power attenuation of 5 log rather than 10 log, as before. The method, however, needs pulses in powers of watts for large fibers and high receiver sensitivity, with some signal averaging required, along with fiber dimensions remaining constant. See Fig. 3-3.

Bandwidth is the next important consideration for fiberoptic cable parameters, with measurements either in frequency or time. Usually evaluated in 1 km sections, sourced modulated light must enter the cable's input and traverse to the other end where the usual P_1, P_2 properties are ratioed as a complex transfer function $H(f_m)$, where the modulating frequency is f_m. The equation then becomes the *magnitude* of $H(f_m)$ = $P_2(f_m)/p_1(f_m)$ and represents the frequency measurement.

When measuring time, very short light pulses into the fiberoptic cable

Siecor Corp.

3-3 One of three compact Siecor power meters, all battery operated, for both single and multimode fiberoptic cable systems used in fault isolation and troubleshooting.

result in expanded pulses at the cable's end. By this means, and with several equations, you can obtain the pulse area, center, and rms pulse widths. All are contained in the integral between minus infinity and plus infinity, and they probably interest only those who regularly work with calculus, which is normally a very small portion of readership.

You can also find fiber dimensions and near-field responses, which are complex equations that have to be left to those actively working in more theoretical situations than I care to undertake. In the meantime, there should have been standard sweep/frequency methods devised to do all or most of these exercises without the application of pure mathematics. One can, however, offer a simple log ratio for allowable power loss in a fiberoptic cable if you know the power input and receiver sensitivity. The allowable cable loss between transmitter and receiver in dB becomes:

$$L_T = 10 \log \times \text{power in} \div \text{receiver sensitivity}$$

Just remember that P_1 and P_2 are in microwatts (still power only). When considering scatter losses, diffractions, beam bending about buildings, and signal security, guided and enclosed transmissions do have significant advantages. But fiber users also have to be aware of coupling and scattering attenuation, as well as multifiber "bundling," which is always dependent on the various refractive index profiles. Bandwidth saturation is another limiting factor with multicables saturating in the low GHz. Whether this continues to remain a problem can't be known at this time due to ongoing manufacturing and research developments.

Applications

In the digital sphere, fiberoptic systems have sales predicted at over $20 billion for the globe by the middle 1990s due to their low losses, tiny size, noise and signal immunity, lack of radiation, and considerable flexibility.

For microwave applications, they'll appear in phased-array scanning, sequential scanning, antenna/receiver connectors, missile-guidance systems, and even spectrum analyzers. In typical systems, you'll find a laser-diode transmitter, the fiber cable, connectors, modulator, receiver (photodiode), optical coupler, and switches. Then, if you commence with an analog signal, optic A/D converters can already operate in the very low gigasamples per second range, and acceleration will probably improve in the coming decade. In the meantime, further work with GaA/As and Ga1nAsP continues for injection materials, especially at 1300 nm and 1550 nm, where minimum chromatic dispersion and fiber losses have been found to occur. However, light-emitting diodes are less linear and efficient than lasers and have a direct modulation bandwidth of less than 100 MHz. Consequently, very high speed microwave applications tend to depend more on injection lasers. Because of their very small sizes and high gains (optically), such lasers accept GHz modulation directly once bias has been established above the lasing threshold.

All this requires very fast photodetectors that deliver currents proportional to optical signal intensities, thereby converting radiation patterns into electrical information. These are often pin and avalanche photodiodes and include such semiconductor materials as silicon, germanium, gallium arsenide, and quarternary material such as InGaAsP.

Analog signals This is another separate and very important application of fiberoptic cable, along with transmitters and receivers. But you still need such electronics as RF combiners, laser drivers, and AGC control, in addition to power controllers and temperature compensation. The latter is very necessary when variable thermistors ride levels on the laser output. Here, frequency division multiplexing (FDM) systems are popular for analog systems that require the usual optical transmitter, fiberoptic cable and the usual detector. Multianalog inputs are first summed, then broadband-amplified for best noise and distortion operations. The thermistor supplies automatic temperature control while AGC maintains needed signal levels for laser diode drive. Pin or avalanche photodiodes do the detecting, with their outputs changed from current into voltage for analog reception. If single mode fibers are used at 1300 nanometers, bandwidths are predicted above 10 GHz. Prime distortions are reportedly second and third intermodulation products existing below 30 dB and 45 dB, respectively. Therefore, special laser selection for linear operations is essential because nonlinear corrections are either difficult or nonexistent.

Holographic optics   Also called *holographic optical elements* (HOEs), they are still of considerable interest and are formed by dual laser beams. As laser beams are HOE intercepted, the diffracted beam changes shape in whatever form that's desired. A good example is that of the compact audio disks where the laser beam is divided into three by a grating. The center beam picks up information from the record while the other two track any errors that might occur. If the center beam goes off center, a tracking-error signal causes electrical recentering. The two outside beams are formed by diffraction.

HOEs in today's laser scanners record interference patterns between two laser beams. This is difficult due to the necessity of a highly stable optical table, and waveforms sometimes aren't possible from some components. Even a computer arrangement to solve these difficulties is often a problem in itself. At the moment, HOEs are most useful for "unique functions" that can't be generated by reflective methods.

Multiplexing   Multiplexing aids in completely filling channel fiberoptic capacities, but bandwidth is limited accordingly. Similarly, routing optical inputs and their addresses delays data transmission and even causes interrupts. But if optical processing takes the place of electronic processing, then this condition could be avoided. However, the optical processor seems complex in itself and might be difficult considering the information available at this writing.

Evaluations

You can call the following either *tests* or *evaluations*, whichever seems appropriate. But engineers, technicians, and installers should have an outline of what's needed to determine the quality and operating ability of fiberoptic cable. Of course I can't possibly cover the waterfront in any actual analysis, but at least you should have some of the parameters required for intelligent operating assessment.

Go-No-Go   These tests are especially important for quick cable checks. You only need a suitable light source and optical level meter.

Identifying the particular fiber   This is probably next in importance, both installed and in splicing trays or storage. Optical power meters are available, but test tones and light directions are another method. The power meter measures the actual power as a function of optical wavelength, which usually requires standard wavelengths in nanometers and possibly internal calibration. LEDs or lasers connect to a dc current source with output through a fiberoptic to the power meter. The optical power can also be measured as a function of input current using a GPIB controller.

Optical losses also need a known reference so their power reductions can be evaluated in terms of incident light and are wavelength dependent. Operating temperatures and other conditions might be variables during such tests. Optical time domain reflectometers, like standard cable instruments, find faults, splice problems (similar to connectors in CATV), poor cladding, and/or glass/plastic signal cores. Backscattering describes the technique entailing a power-pulse excitation into the fiber, and then backscattered light returns to the measuring device. All this involves fiber aperture, core diameter, wavelength, and optical return loss. These ODTRs are connected to only one end of the cable, so they have a singular advantage over power meters. If attenuation is required, they can be inserted in the cables, the fiber ends can be separated, or optical filters can be added on line.

Connectors for fiberoptic cable are many and varied, but single-mode fibers must be held firmly to reduce stretch strain and insertion loss. Reflections are also of more than passing concern and can be evaluated by the simple equation:

$$L_R = P_{reflected}/P_{incident}$$

Copper cable

Already a multibillion-dollar industry with many diverse sources, a list of this highly diversified signal and power-carrying medium would involve more pages of manuscript than contained in some moderately-sized chapters. Therefore, instead of including such items as intercom cable, magnet wire, rip cordage, FEP teflon and other specialty items, we concentrate primarily on the signal-carrying variety, including both RF/video and audio. This should be sufficient to offer a comprehensive explanation of prime consumer and commercial products regularly available in the marketplace. We also continue concentrating on fiberoptic and copper cable comparisons that are necessary to a worthwhile understanding of what can be used where, how, and why.

Coaxial cable (also called "coax") originally consisted of copper, lead, and insulators, including a center conductor and shielding. Lloyd Espenschied and Herman A. Affel are said to have been its inventors, with first installations in Phoenixville, Pennsylvania during 1929. Both were Bell Telephone engineers. One wonders how many millions of miles of coax have been produced and strung since that date of over 60 years past. Copper (from the Greek *Kyprios*, an island where it was initially produced) has appeared in ornaments, munitions, early armor, and many other soft-metal applications. But it was not until the advent of electricity, and later electronics, that its prime utility as a superb conductor of electricity and heat was recognized.

One of the major users of cable, CATV served some 4.5 million sub-scribers in 1970 with 2,490 systems. In 1990, it's estimated 9,000 cable tele-vision systems are operating with 50 million subscribers, which con-tinues to increase some 10 percent each year. That's a formidable number and growth pattern in the short span of 20 years. As you might expect, cities and suburban areas, especially those with anti-TV and satellite convenants, are the greatest beneficiaries, in addition to certain very hilly rural areas where standard broadcast television reception is all but impossible. And although the Federal Communications Commission has outlawed such restrictive practices, most or many local county governments are against enforcing the satellite earth station restrictions, and any action will probably have to originate with the various states, who might also be timorous in bucking their more affluent citizens.

Nevertheless, coaxial cable in one form or another will continue to be installed wherever useful throughout the country and abroad, and a great deal of time will probably pass before it is seriously challenged in most applications. The main reasons are because it's presently less expensive than fiberoptic cable, much less complex in usage, has better than pass-able bandwidth, and a majority of terrestrial RF systems in the country will continue to buy and install it.

High/low frequencies and impedances

In the RF world, cables are available in various sizes and three primary impedances: 50 ohms for TV broadcast and microwave; 75 ohms for regu-lar video/satellite (after the block down-converter) conduction; and 600 ohms for audio. Among the three, there are vast differences and all sorts of interesting applications. Let's discuss broadcast and microwave types and then offer a fairly stiff evaluation of contemporary video and audio carriers to keep the discussion at a relatively familiar level.

For broadcasters, cable must be both efficient and capable of consid-erable power delivery, require little maintenance and moderate cost, and have rigid but modest mechanical flexibility. Very high frequency (VHF) and power, listed between 30 and 300 MHz, usually requires 50-ohm impe-dance, while some low-power UHF in special applications can work at 75 ohms with frequencies between 300 and 3,000 MHz. Microwave and satel-lite uplinkers also operate at 50 ohms, but after downconversion below 2 GHz, 75 ohms is again the composite video/audio RF carrier. The larger cables with waveguide or considerable center conductors usually allow both greater power and less loss than smaller varieties whose copper or steel-clad copper inner conductors are seldom larger than AWG 10, and often no more than AWG 18, as specified by American Wire Gauge (AWG) standards.

There will be no attempt to expand on the topic of twisted pairs other than to say they are often low-frequency transmission types that have been used for data and telephone connections. They are almost as antiquated now as the "electric effluvia" of Stephen Gray who discovered a damp string rubbed by a charged glass tube at one end would attract particles at the other, which occurred in 1729, followed by Benjamin Franklin's discovery of positive and negative electricity in 1747. But it wasn't until 1912 that Lee DeForest developed a triode amplifier capable of sufficient amplification to permit laying transcontinental telephone lines. With vacuum-tube amplifiers there came wireless telegraphy, radio, radar, television, and satellite transmissions as vacuum tubes were supplanted by semiconductor electronics. Also a greater understanding of the transverse electromagnetic (TEM) propagation in two-conductor transmission lines composed of E (electric) and H (magnetic) fields representing currents and voltages in coaxial cable. As always, these are 90 degrees out of phase, with the E field operating clockwise, and the H field perpendicular to it, just as any representation of sine-wave voltage and current will show, with current lagging voltage by 90 degrees. Both, of course, are time-related.

The terms current (I) and voltage (E) can denote a cable's ohmic value and/or impedance (Z) from the $E = IR$ venerable Ohms law about electricity. Simply substitute Z for R, adding the usual j operator and its omega (ω) motivator for capacitance and inductance, and you have the time-honored equations for characteristic impedance of a transmission line:

$$Z_o = E/I \quad \text{(with matching termination)}$$

$$Z_o = \sqrt{\frac{R + j\,\omega\,L}{G + j\,\omega\,C}} \quad \text{(relative to distributed circuit constants}$$

where R is resistance, G is conductance, L is inductance, C is capacitance, line and no reflections. Omega is the frequency rotator and represents 2π times frequency, or angular velocity. You should know, however, that frequencies up to the higher kilohertz can cause wandering impedances, whereas those in MHz and above maintain reasonably constant values provided inductances are kept low. So watch your audio transmissions diligently. At MHz, poor shielding, bad coupling, extended lengths, and cheap lines with small center conductors are the bad guys. For microwaves, leakage, too many abrupt curves, and couplings constitute the worst headaches. Below 1.5 GHz, the newer UL-approved coax with AWG 18 center conductors and at least 60 percent shielding is a real joy to work with, especially cable with over 80 percent propogation velocity.

We could continue on to explain standing waves, mismatches, quarter- and half-wave reflections, and shorted and open stubs, but suffice it to say that any line terminated in other than Z_o has reflections and loss of energy. This can be calculated by the rather simple equation:

$$E_r = E_i \left(\frac{R_L - Z_o}{R_L + Z_o} \right)$$

where E_r is the reflected voltage, E_i the incident (driven) voltage, R_L the terminating resistance, and Z_o the characteristic impedance of the line. Impedances are often found by inducing a voltage of some frequency into a circuit or line, halving its value with a variable resistance, and then measuring the value of that resistance. This method is certainly not exact, but it's in the ballpark for general operations, requiring only a signal generator, oscilloscope, and a suitable potentiometer. You can also calculate characteristic impedances by this notation:

$$Z_o = 138 \log_{10} D/d$$

where the inside diameter of the outer conductor is D, and the diameter of the inner conductor is d.

It then follows that on lossless lines, voltage standing-wave ratios (VSWR) of reflected and incident waves are:

$$VSWR = \frac{E_{max} + E_{min}}{E_{max} - E_{min}}$$

Where losses are apparent, the equation becomes considerably more complex, with solutions in hyperbolic functions, which are somewhat similar to trigonometry but based on e^x rather than the familiar terms θ and sides a, b, and c. Hyperbolics, nonetheless, does apply to triangles projected within a circle, thus the similarity with trigonometry. The newer scientific calculators can handle such mathematics rather easily. But terms such as sinh, cosh, tanh, and coth do take a minute or two before becoming familiar. Should you have occasion to work with this branch of mathematics, you'll find a close relationship between it and calculus as well as logarithms.

Since impedance matching between cable and antenna produces more or less VSWR, it's most important to couple these components as electrically and physically tight as possible, providing a continuation of the shielded conductors and minimal leakage. Cable flexing is another problem, and although standoffs driven or screwed into building sidings are not as necessary as with twinlead, they will help prevent considerable cable whipping by the wind that always results in deterioration. Further, loose couplings invite water absorption or "wicking," as it's called, and this always results in signal loss at the receiver. Just because a cable is coaxial, this doesn't mean it's always watertight. Consequently, adequate precautions are always necessary in any installation or replacement.

According to some authorities, a VSWR for AM radio can be as much as triple with no appreciable effects. For FM radio, VSWR less than 1³/₄, and for television, less than 1:1 is considered good.

Sweep checks

Few writers today remember that coaxial cable has to be swept if you need to know exact terminations or discover any discontinuities along its length. While the great cable manufacturers such as Comm/Scope have highly sophisticated equipment for this purpose, you can really do an equivalency at home with a simple sweep generator and internal/external markers that will easily offer an acceptable substitute.

Select 100 feet of coax, connect the sweep generator's RF output to one end and its diode detector to the other via the necessary fittings. On the left vertical is a high reference voltage, probably generated by the beginning of sweep, followed by a 41.67 marker, a 44 MHz center marker, and a 47.25 MHz marker on the right (Fig. 3-4). Since the generator is tuned to 44 MHz, a beat between the generator and oscillator produces what looks like a basic cw peak. This is okay because the baseline of the display is generally parallel to the baseline reference below, both of which are illuminated via the *x-y* amplifiers of a dual-trace oscilloscope.

The next sweep photo was taken with center marker at 80 MHz (Fig. 3-5). Here, the generator might be somewhat nonlinear, or there's some line tilt at this frequency. You could try several terminations here to see if the generator's baseline pulls down on each side of 80 MHz, parallel with reference sweep. If not, the generator is at fault.

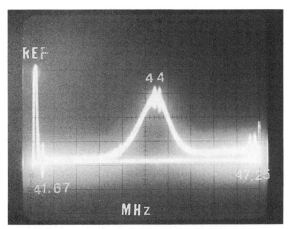

3-4 Sweeping coaxial cable with appropriate markers indicates outstanding faults and discontinuities.

3-5 A 6 MHz bandwidth sweep with a center point of 80 MHz ref. indicates sweep beginning.

The third waveform in the sweeper series demonstrates high-frequency coax fidelity because it matches that of the generator almost perfectly, at 5 MHz sweep width, that is (Fig. 3-6). Center frequency here is 200 MHz.

Although this is a simple check, many TV or stereo systems can be easily examined similarly in a very short time with basic equipment. For low sound-type frequencies, you can probably use a function generator with variable sweep. So, many seemingly complex cable problems can be solved very easily with just a little thought and ordinary TV-shop equipment. I prefer simple test procedures so that most of you can readily duplicate these fundamental measurements. This is also a basic means of checking notch or bandpass filters for interference elimination or frequency passbands, especially where critical wavelengths exist. Amplitudes of such responses would be obvious, but dB attenuation can easily be recorded by using the simple equation:

$$dB = 20 \log \times \text{voltage apparent}$$

The only catch would be, reactance to what input level? This has to be determined according to filter requirements as ac, or even with dc in combination. When dealing with filters of many descriptions, each has to experience operating parameters before becoming totally predictable. Iron-core inductors are effective at low frequencies, whereas air-core inductors operate best at HF and RF. Coaxial cable, consequently, might be considered in the upper category if there are discontinuities along the line. Therefore, with proper filtering and little dc ripple, low-value dc becomes acceptable as a power source in company with high-frequency ac. Satellite block downconverters are an excellent example of coexistence with no interference apparent. Here you're dealing with frequencies

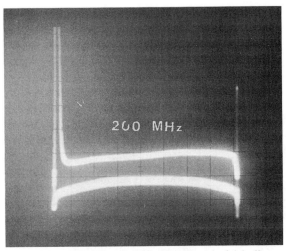

3-6 At 5 MHz sweep width, the trace is fairly linear for consumer-type equipment. Large voltages on either end denote bandwidth limits.

between 950 and 1450 MHz and dc at levels between 16 and 20 volts. Noisy ripple, I strongly suspect, could become disastrous and even ruin hempt or gallium arsenide semiconductors within the downconverters. An oscilloscope on line can quickly determine whether there's unusually low dc ripple. Should this occur, there are evident problems in the 16 to 20 V power supplies, requiring a quick fix.

In any coaxial line analysis, recall that resistance and inductance are series circuit elements, whereas capacitance and leakage conductance are shunts. Therefore, be guided accordingly when examining line characteristics extolled by the various manufacturers. Line conductances add up to power loss potential differences in lengths of line, while line resistances are power losses related to current, as in:

$$\text{power} = I^2R \text{ for series}$$

$$\text{power} = E^2/R \text{ for potential}$$

E is in terms of dc or rms ac.

Inductive loading, by the way, is great for CB and allied radio-frequency antennas to increase their electrical lengths, but don't try this on transmission lines due to nonuniformity, because phase velocities are reduced and distributed inductance is increased. Magnetic tape wrapping should also be avoided.

Cable characteristics

This chapter concludes with a good summary and chart of some outstanding coaxial cable characteristics (Fig. 3-7). Over-the-air and CATV elec-

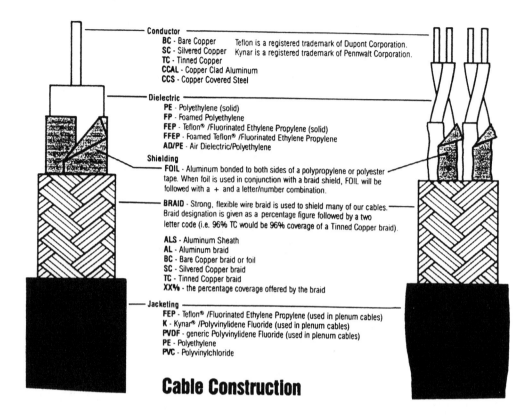

Conductor
BC - Bare Copper   Teflon is a registered trademark of Dupont Corporation.
SC - Silvered Copper   Kynar is a registered trademark of Pennwalt Corporation.
TC - Tinned Copper
CCAL - Copper Clad Aluminum
CCS - Copper Covered Steel

Dielectric
PE - Polyethylene (solid)
FP - Foamed Polyethylene
FEP - Teflon® /Fluorinated Ethylene Propylene (solid)
FFEP - Foamed Teflon® /Fluorinated Ethylene Propylene
AD/PE - Air Dielectric/Polyethylene

Shielding
FOIL - Aluminum bonded to both sides of a polypropylene or polyester tape. When foil is used in conjunction with a braid shield, FOIL will be followed with a + and a letter/number combination.

BRAID - Strong, flexible wire braid is used to shield many of our cables. Braid designation is given as a percentage figure followed by a two letter code (i.e. 96% TC would be 96% coverage of a Tinned Copper braid).

ALS - Aluminum Sheath
AL - Aluminum braid
BC - Bare Copper braid or foil
SC - Silvered Copper braid
TC - Tinned Copper braid
XX% - the percentage coverage offered by the braid

Jacketing
FEP - Teflon® /Fluorinated Ethylene Propylene (used in plenum cables)
K - Kynar® /Polyvinylidene Fluoride (used in plenum cables)
PVDF - generic Polyvinylidene Fluoride (used in plenum cables)
PE - Polyethylene
PVC - Polyvinylchloride

Cable Construction

Attenuation

Attenuation is the loss of electrical power as a signal travels along a cable. There are two types of losses that affect the attenuation of a cable: loss due to conductivity of conductors (center conductor and shield) and dielectric loss. Both losses increase with frequency.

Attenuation is measured in decibels per 100 feet (db/100′) and is calculated by:

Nominal
$$\text{Att. (in db/100')} = \frac{(2.386)\,(\sqrt{E_r}\cdot\sqrt{F})}{\log_{10}\frac{D}{ad}}\left[\frac{\sqrt{\varrho_i}}{ad}+\frac{\sqrt{\varrho_o}}{D}\right]+(2.772)\,(F)\,\sqrt{E_r}\,(d_f)$$

where E_r is the dielectric constant of the cable core, F is the frequency of the signal in megahertz, D is the dielectric diameter, d is the conductor diameter, a is the conductor stranding factor (.939 for 7 strands, .970 for 19 strands), ϱ_i is resistivity of the inner conductor, ϱ_o is the resistivity of the outer conductor and d_f is the dissipation factor of the dielectric.

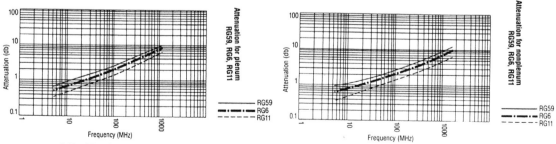

3-7   Explanations and statistics are in understanding cable characteristics. Comm/Scope

tronics should improve and develop with considerably more uniformity. This isn't a disparaging comment, but certainly deliberate, because all sorts of RF and baseband signals have floated into consumers homes in the past with mediocre regard for quality, and some continue to do so now. Cable television even bucked multichannel sound for a period, but many systems today can adequately carry HDTV. Their trunk amplifiers had better be good, connections superior, and cable absolutely dry. Otherwise, present NTSC might look even better.

RF transmission lines transfer energy from one point to another at specifically designed frequencies. Above those frequencies, losses increase; below those frequencies, there could be no signal at all. Therefore, as of 1991, there are no perfect transmission lines, only increased hope for superconductors, especially those that might conceivably operate at room temperatures. Now, all transmission lines have characteristic impedance (Z_o), which allows maximum current flow when voltage is applied. Z_o has already been determined in a prior paragraph using logarithms, but it can also be evaluated by the approximate equation:

$$Z_o = \sqrt{L/C}$$

where L and C are inductance and capacitance values per unit length of line. Both depend on line size and spacing. Large conductors close together normally result in high capacitance and lower inductance. And due to possible mismatches, terminations, etc., there can be resistive and/ or reactive elements that reduce cable effectiveness. With these VSWR problems, a higher VSWR means additional mismatch between line and load, and therefore a loss of power on the line.

Velocity of propagation is another term that's not often explained but remains highly important. True, RF energy on cable does travel at less than the 186,000 miles per second (the speed of light in free space), but maximum velocity (K factor) tells you the *efficiency* of the transmission line, which is its wavelength multiplied by frequency. A factor of better than 80 percent, therefore, signifies excellent cable, which depends on dielectric materials, conductors, shielding, and probably the diameter of the inner conductor at higher frequencies. In plain language, this all means that more information is delivered to its destination in a shorter time!

To maintain these desirable characteristics, cables connected to other devices such as antennas should have impedance-matching devices such as transformers, capacitors, or even solid-state devices that neutralize undesirable impedances and make the union appear purely resistive. Thus, except for line losses, all energy introduced at the input will be delivered to the load. In the past, two-wire parallel conductors were preferred for frequencies up to 250 MHz. But today, characteristics of coax have proved so efficient, convenient, sun and earth/water resistant, and price competitive, that most RF is carried coaxially rather than by other hard-wired methods. Radiation losses are minimal. Not so long ago, velocity factors assigned to different cables were:

Cable	K factor
dual open wire	0.975
coaxial (air dielectric)	0.850
coaxial (plastic dielectric)	0.660
twisted pair (rubber dielectric)	0.560

With the coax illustrated next, the K factor is 82 percent. How times have changed in just a few years!

However, compared with waveguides, coax isn't all that great above 2 GHz. Its inner conductor's resistance is initially small, but it's even smaller than the cross-sectional area of the outer conductor. But since conductive resistance is inversely proportional to the cross-sectional area, the *effective* resistance of the inner conductor is necessarily considerable. This increases with frequency until the skin effect causes resistance to rise above acceptable limits as frequency approaches 2 GHz.

Conversely, waveguides have no dielectric losses, they don't radiate energy, there's little skin effect, they have high-power-handling ability and consequently they easily accommodate high frequencies. But waveguides are expensive, they can leak, and they're of little benefit *below* 2 GHz. So coaxial cable and waveguides have totally different uses other than that they transmit RF energy.

Comm/Scope cable

North Carolina's Comm/Scope manufactures first-quality coaxial cable that is consistently used for both satellite and television antenna-to-receiver coupling (Figs. 3-8, 3-9, and 3-10). It is approved by Underwriters Laboratories, which is somewhat more expensive because it requires stranded, instead of rigid, wire and a more expensive jacket.

Satellite and TV cable has copper-covered center steel conductors, a gas-expanded polyethylene dielectric, and an inner shield of aluminum-polyprophylene-aluminum tape bonded directly to the dielectric, with an outer shield of AWG 34 bare aluminum braid. The actuator cables are shielded with aluminum polyester tape and a copper drain wire. The signal cables are totally waterproof and rated to 60 degrees C. In the UL versions, the two motor-current drive cables are separately insulated and covered.

The simplest test for any and all of these cables, since some carry signals and some do not, is a dc voltage of not less than 20 volts. If they pass that, they are neither shorted nor open. All receiver-antenna-positioner connections, however, should be checked for secure grounds and the least

Comm/Scope TVRO Cable Specifications

Part No.	Coax Type/ Cond Dia.	Shield Coverage	Rotor # Cond/AWG Construction	Actuator # Cond/AWG Construction	Power # Cond/AWG
8502 UL listed	single RG/59 .0032″	67% alum. braid and alum. tape	3/20 stranded shielded drain wire	3/22 stranded shielded drain wire	2/14 stranded
8510 UL listed	dual RG/59 .0032″	67% alum. braid and alum. tape	3/20 stranded shielded drain wire	3/22 stranded shielded drain wire	2/14 stranded
8530 UL listed	dual RG/6 .0040″	60% alum. braid and alum. tape	3/20 stranded shielded drain wire	3/22 stranded shielded drain wire	2/14 stranded
8003	single RG/59 .0032″	67% alum. braid and alum. tape	3/20 stranded	3/22 stranded shielded drain wire (jacketed together)	2/14 stranded
8133	dual RG/6 .0040″	60% alum. braid and alum. tape	3/20 stranded	3/22 stranded shielded drain wire (jacketed together)	2/14 stranded
8123	single RG/6 .0040″	40% alum. braid and alum. tape	3/20 stranded	3/22 stranded shielded drain wire (jacketed together)	2/14 stranded
8130	dual RG/6 .0040″	40% alum. braid and alum. tape	2/20 stranded shielded drain wire	3/22 stranded shielded drain wire (jacketed together)	2/14 stranded
8136	dual RG/6 .0040″	40% alum. braid and alum. tape	3/20 stranded	3/22 stranded shielded drain wire (jacketed together)	2/16 stranded

Electrical Characteristics of Coax (measured at 68°F/20°C)

	Max. attenuation (dB/100′) at these frequencies (MHz)			Return loss (to 1450 MHz)	Nom. cap. pf/ft	Nom. imp. (ohms)	Nom. vel. prop.
	450	950	1450				
RG/59	5.40	7.90	10.40	15 dB	16.2	75	82%
RG/6	4.40	6.54	8.40	15 dB	16.2	75	82%

	RG/59	RG/6	20 AWG stranded	22 AWG stranded	14 AWG stranded
DC Resistance (ohms/1000′)	56.4	35.5	9.9	15.7	2.5

Comm/Scope offers a complete custom capability to manufacture TVRO cables to your specifications. Please call for details.

Both the RG/59 and RG/6 coax cables have a copper covered steel center conductor surrounded by a gas-expanded polyethylene dielectric. They have an inner shield of aluminum/polypropylene/aluminum tape bonded directly to the dielectric and an outer shield of 34 AWG bare aluminum braid.

All acutator wire configurations are shielded with aluminum polyester tape and include a copper drain wire.

All TVRO cables are jacketed in a high-grade PVC that is sunlight-resistant, totally waterproof and rated to 60°C.

Comm/Scope, Inc.

NETWORK CABLE DIVISION

PO Box 1729, 1375 Lenoir-Rhyne Blvd.
Hickory, NC 28602
(704) 324-2200
(800) 982-1708
FAX (704) 327-3577

3-8   Cable specifications and characteristics of quality cable. Comm/Scope

Satellite TVRO Recommended Coaxial Cables

Comm/Scope. Inc.
NETWORK CABLE DIVISION

Product Description / Qualifications	Part Number	Center Conductor AWG or Dia. in in. / Wire Type / Nom DCR Ohms/1000'	Dielectric Nom O.D. in inches	Shield Construction / Nom DCR Ohms/1000'	Jacket & Nom O.D. in inches	Nom Cap. Pf/Ft	Nom Vel. of Prop.	Nom Imp. (Ohms)	Nominal Attenuation MHz	db/100'
RG59 (1450 MHz) CL2	5575	20 Solid CCS 56.4	FP .146	FOIL + 67% AL 10.3	PVC .242	16.2	82%	75	5 50 300 450 900 1000 1200 1450	0.88 1.80 4.26 5.30 7.70 8.13 9.20 10.20
RG6 (1450 MHz) CL2	5730	18 Solid CCS 35.5	FP .180	FOIL + 60% AL	PVC .272	16.2	82%	75	5 50 100 300 450 900 1200 1450	.65 1.44 1.98 3.38 4.21 6.14 7.20 8.26
RG11 (1450 MHz) CL2	5916	14 Solid CCS 14.29	FP .280	FOIL + 60% AL	PVC .405	18.0	84%	75	5 50 100 300 450 900 1200 1450	.35 .94 1.28 2.20 2.75 4.04 5.00 5.90
RG59 DUAL (1450 MHz) CL2	5586	20 Solid CCS 56.4	FP .146	FOIL + 67% AL 10.3	PVC 2/.242	16.2	82%	75	5 50 300 450 900 1000 1200 1450	0.88 1.80 4.26 6.30 7.70 8.13 9.20 10.20
RG6 DUAL (1450 MHz) CL2	5786	18 Solid CCS 35.5	FP .180	FOIL + 60% AL 9.0	PVC 2/.272	18.2	82%	75	5 50 100 300 450 900 1200 1450	.65 1.44 1.98 3.38 4.21 6.14 7.20 8.26
RG11 DUAL (1450 MHz) CL2	5918	14 Solid CCS 14.29	FP .280	FOIL + 90% AL 4.8	PVC 2/.405	16.0	84%	75	5 50 100 300 450 900 1200 1450	.35 .94 1.28 2.20 2.75 4.04 5.00 5.90

3-9 Types of satellite cables with single or dual signal conductors. Comm/Scope

Comm/Scope, Inc.
NETWORK CABLE DIVISION

Satellite TVRO Recommended Flat Cables

NOM. IMP. (OHMS)	NOMINAL ATTENUATION MHz	db/100'
75	5	0.88
	50	1.80
	300	4.26
	450	5.30
	900	7.70
	1000	8.13
	1200	9.20
	1450	10.20
75	5	.65
	50	1.44
	100	1.98
	300	3.38
	450	4.21
	900	6.14
	1200	7.20
	1450	8.26
75	5	.35
	50	.94
	100	1.28
	300	2.20
	450	2.75
	900	4.04
	1200	5.00
	1450	5.90
75	5	0.88
	50	1.80
	300	4.26
	450	6.30
	900	7.70
	1000	8.13
	1200	9.20
	1450	10.20
75	5	.65
	50	1.44
	100	1.98
	300	3.38
	450	4.21
	900	6.14
	1200	7.20
	1450	8.26
75	5	.35
	50	.94
	100	1.28
	300	2.20
	450	2.75
	900	4.04
	1200	5.00
	1450	5.90

DESCRIPTION: TVRO flat cables consist of single or dual 1450 Mhz coaxial cable extruded in line with a rotor control cable and either separate or combined actuator and power cables. The finished cable may consist of as many as five or as few as three component cables.

— Power cable
— Actuator cable (combined with power cable in non UL styles)
— Rotor cable
— Single or dual coaxial cables

PRODUCT DESCRIPTION QUALIFICATIONS	PART NUMBER	COAX TYPE/ COND DIA	SHIELD CONSTRUCTION NOM DCR OHMS/1000'	ROTOR # COND/AWG CONSTRUCTION NOM DCR OHMS/1000'	ACTUATOR # COND/AWG CONSTRUCTION NOM DCR OHMS/1000'	POWER # COND/AWG NOM DCR OHMS/1000'
DUAL RG/59	8510	dual RG/59 .032	67% alum. braid and alum. tape	3/20 stranded shielded drain wire	3/22 stranded shielded drain wire	2/14 stranded
UL listed			56.4	9.9	15.7	2.5
SINGLE RG/59	8502	single RG/59 .032	67% alum. braid and alum. tape	3/20 stranded shielded drain wire	3/22 stranded shielded drain wire	2/14 stranded
UL listed			56.4	9.9	15.7	2.5
DUAL RG/6	8530	dual RG/6 .0403	60% alum. braid and alum. tape	3/20 stranded shielded drain wire	3/22 stranded shielded drain wire	2/14 stranded
UL listed			35.5	9.9	15.7	2.5
SINGLE RG/59	8003	single RG/59 .032	67% alum. braid and alum. tape	3/20 stranded	3/22 stranded shielded drain wire	2/14 stranded
			56.4	9.9	15.7	2.5 (jacketed together)
DUAL RG/6	8133	dual RG/6 .0403	60% alum. braid and alum. tape	3/20 stranded	3/22 stranded shielded drain wire	2/14 stranded
			35.5	9.9	15.7	2.5 (jacketed together)
SINGLE RG/6	8123	single RG/6 .0403	40% alum. braid and alum. tape	3/20 stranded	3/22 stranded shielded drain wire	2/14 stranded
			35.5	9.9	15.7	2.5 (jacketed together)
DUAL RG/6	8130	dual RG/6 .0403	40% alum. braid and alum. tape	2/20 stranded shielded drain wire	3/22 stranded shielded drain wire	2/14 stranded
			35.5	9.9	15.7	2.5 (jacketed together)
DUAL RG/6	8136	dual RG/6 .0403	40% alum. braid and alum. tape	3/20 stranded	3/22 stranded shielded drain wire	2/16 stranded
			35.5	9.9	15.7	3.7 (jacketed together)

Electrical Characteristics of Coax (measured at 68°F/20°C)

	MAX. ATTENUATION (dB/100') AT THESE FREQUENCIES (MHz)			RETURN LOSS (TO 1450 MHz)	NOM. CAP. pf/ft	NOM. IMP. (ohms)	NOM. VEL. PROP.
	450	950	1450				
RG/59	5.40	7.90	10.40	15 dB	16.2	75	82%
RG/6	4.40	6.54	8.40	15 dB	16.2	75	82%

3-10 Attenuation and makeup of various types of TVRO and video cables including electrical characteristics.
Comm/Scope

amount of strain on the mating portions. In addition, coax seal should cover all signal F connectors to prevent oxidization and water wicking. Then, if ground burial is anticipated, place it securely in 1.25 inches or less of PVC 40 formulation pipe to keep it out of water and nullify the effects of winter freezes and spring thaws. You'll be glad you did, and so will the customer.

4

Video

INSTEAD OF SIMPLY RESTRICTING THIS CHAPTER'S CONTENTS TO PURE television, a general discussion of video and RF might prove somewhat more helpful and reach a broader audience, especially since we can then add cathode-ray tubes and modulators for a considerably better understanding of the entire subject. The modulator concept is often confusing to those who don't work consistently with video, but it occupies a fair portion of signal investigations when assessing linearity, noise, bandwidth, sidebands, and shielding. Cathode-ray tubes and associated passive components are another especially important factor in judging video because the eye cannot see pictures without a panel or cathode-ray tube display. Unfortunately, no matter what specialized instruments reveal, it's the human eye that's the final judge, and it has some odd peculiarities that oscilloscopes and analyzers really don't measure. It's the eye, for better or worse, that has become a main part of video, especially high-definition television, which should be reaching market by 1995 or 1996.

In the meantime, we can "suffer" with improved definition television (IDTV), which offers a refinement over ordinary NTSC but so far only at the receiver. True, the broadcasters have spruced up both linearities and bandwidths, but there are still artifacts that could be eliminated, along with better and even more powerful transmissions. For terrestrial broadcast video, all this costs a great deal of money to modify studio and transmitter equipment, and TV stations have a difficult time competing with the better cable and satellite systems that can process HDTV immediately in preliminary electronic arrangements. Examples are the Japanese FM MUSE system and Scientific Atlanta's HDB-MAC, which are designed to deliver video "in excess" of the present 4.5 MHz bandwidths assigned by the Federal Communications Commission. The final HDTV RF expansion for the foreseeable future probably will be no greater than 6 MHz for video/audio transmissions due to channel availability and transmitter/ receiver costs. It is now expected that two TV channels and one fairly broadband satellite transponder are needed to adequately serve terrestrial and spacecraft emissions. Even today, 20 MHz closed-circuit TV systems are not uncommon, but they do cost more than a few buffalo nickels. HDTV 30 MHz companded systems, however, do promise something in between, especially Zenith's 3XNTSC simulcast with NTSC format.

Video, however, will be coming into commercial and consumer homes in even more forms than appear today, especially when the telephone companies have gained FCC approval for fiberoptic picture phones across the land. At that juncture, what with TV, satellites, video conferencing, VSATs, videocassette recorders, cameras, camcorders, video games, possibly high-definition facsimile, teletext, computers, and a few unnamed other media, you will have all the sight and sound available for your residence and business that can readily be put to use. And as we progress into the nineties, more two-way, talk-and-view devices are sure of welcome introduction and use. Much of it, however, with the exception of high-definition television, will be based on the National Television Systems Committee (NTSC) basics, with which we should all become completely familiar. Therefore, let's begin with radio frequency (RF) carriers and continue on into pure video, both modulated and otherwise.

Carriers

The subject of carriers "seems so well understood" that relatively few electronics enthusiasts comprehend the actions of carriers and their sidebands to any real degree of useful insight. A broadcast carrier is the prime current-induced electromagnetic energy developed to transmit signals through air and space at a constant frequency, phase, and amplitude. Unmodulated carriers are said to have zero bandwidths, while modulated carriers have specific bandwidths, depending on the type of modulation, intensity, and relation to the carrier.

Other portions of this book show the action generated by amplitude modulation and frequency modulation and how they respectively vary RF amplitudes or stretch and compress the carrier at a constant amplitude. A third method has to do with television transmissions and is a combination of vestigial (one sideband removed) AM sideband and FM audio sideband emissions that are combined into a single over-the-air signal.

To expand the topic somewhat and offer a fairly lucid explanation of these various electronic emissions, I've set up a laboratory "broadcast" consisting of a 5 MHz carrier for two of these modulation techniques followed by off-the-air "live" signals for television. In this way, one can describe exactly the relationship of sidebands to their carriers to develop a fairly thorough indoctrination into rather straightforward techniques. Done with a spectrum analyzer and a Polaroid camera, the following waveforms should be almost self-explanatory.

Figure 4-1 shows the traditional AM-modulated carrier with two prominent sidebands and another two that are almost obscured by noise. At 100 kHz/division, the modulation appears at approximately 140 kHz on either side of the carrier. Occupied bandwidth is determined by the highest modulating frequency, and since there are two prime sidebands, the

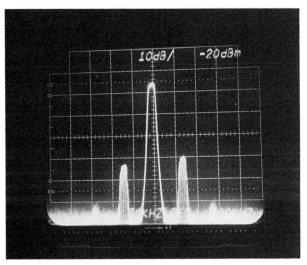

4-1 Traditional AM modulation with two prominent sidebands.

total bandwidth actually measures 280 kHz. The second example is that of frequency modulation (Fig. 4-2), which operates at 27 kHz. Observe how the sideband pairs seem to virtually climb the carrier with this much deviation. Here, maximum frequency occurs during the greatest positive swing of the modulation, and sideband pairs separate according to the modulation and its harmonic multiples. And unlike amplitude modulation, which has but a single pair of significant sidebands, FM has a number, as illustrated. Maximum FM deviation amounts to ± 75 kHz, but it's only ± 25 kHz for monaural TV sound and increases to 50 kHz for stereo (MTS) television.

The combination of video and sound carriers creates an entirely new situation whereby amplitude and frequency modulation are placed 4.5 MHz apart but usually broadcast from the same antenna. AM and FM transmitters produce the two modulated signals, which may either reach superturnstile antennas with two inputs (through a *bridge diplexer*) or single-input antennas (via a *notch diplexer*). Omnidirectional antennas have circular patterns, *peak power* refers to instantaneous power at the peak of

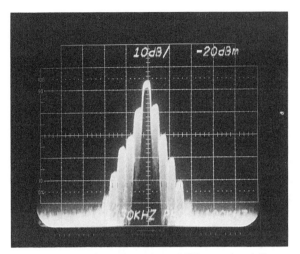

4-2 A 27 kHz deviation of a 5 MHz carrier delivers many sidebands in FM modulation.

the video sync pulse, horizontally polarized patterns predominate, and the amplitude difference between video and audio carrier levels is typically 10 dB, with video being the strongest. Lower TV sideband energy outside 6 MHz is absorbed in television broadcasting by a vestigial sideband filter that's often combined with a notch-diplexer and called a filterplexer.

Taken directly off the air, Fig. 4-3 shows channels 4 and 5 operating in Washington, D.C. The one on the left has a video carrier appearing at 67.25 MHz, while the marker on the right reads 77.44 (actually 77.25) MHz for channel 5—just a slight discrepancy in marker tuning. At 2 MHz per division, modulation running up and down the carrier is not especially obvious for video and certainly not for audio. The 6 dB blip between the carriers for channel 4 denotes the "suppressed" 3.58 MHz chroma signal, with the usual band of noise beneath. As you can see, chroma restraint is considerably better on channel 5, but since both "carriers" are more than 30 dB down from even the audio carrier, there's no interference possible.

If we "spread" the video carrier to 1 MHz/div, however, you have a better idea of this carrier's appearance and its accompanying modulation (Fig. 4-4). Decreasing the span/div further, sidebands would become abundant. So you see there is a good deal to this signal analysis, including carrier-to-noise, which is over 40 dB in each instance for video and almost that for audio. If you want signal-to-noise, just add 4 to 6 dB and you have it.

However, the extremely important factor in these two illustrations is the signal level. You can have all the signal amplitude in the world, but if the level isn't sufficient to put a signal into some receiver, then there's no picture. As discovered through many evaluations, a satisfactory level for many or most television and C-band satellite receivers amounts to – 40

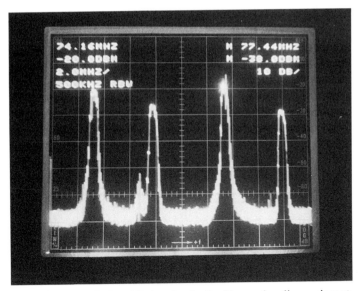

4-3 TV channels 4 and 5 showing both video and audio carriers at better than − 40 dBm levels for good pictures.

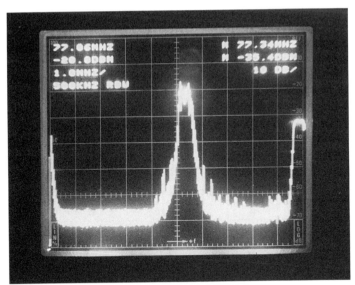

4-4 An expansion of channel 5's carrier with modulation.

dBm. If you go much below that figure, poor pictures are bound to result, although audio is not that easily affected because of lower frequency information. For the Ku band, you might back off another 5 dB in totally clear weather.

Video modulators

Modulators are not totally simple subjects, and there must be a thousand and one varieties, beginning with vacuum tubes and working up. In the middle and late 1950s, vacuum tubes were king, and all sorts of strategems were introduced to avoid multiple problems, especially in single-tube modulators bumping along at low frequencies. To recall a pair of these, we had to regress to a 1958 Air Force manual to pick up suitable diagrams to illustrate what tubes did during and following WWII (Fig. 4-5). Here you see both plate and grid-modulated stages, the former having a separate oscillator with the modulating signal introduced at the grid of V1, which then modulates the output of oscillator V2. Here, when oscillator plate voltage varies at the signal input rate, it produces an amplitude-modulated carrier through the tuned primary transformer coil at the output. V1 is so biased that it is a class-C amplifier, and the resultant becomes a carrier and its sidebands, the effect of delivering two signals to a nonlinear impedance.

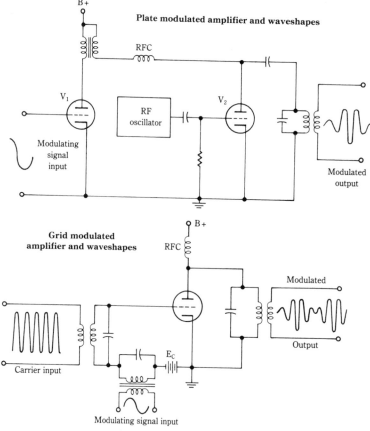

4-5   Plate and grid modulators from the 1950s. Okay for low frequencies but too basic for higher RF.

Grid modulation can occur with a single triode and a trio of isolating transformers in the grid/plate circuits. In this instance, grid voltage varies with signal input, resulting in tube plate power output, delivering a varying carrier to the plate output transformer. In each instance, the RFC coils prevent these oscillations from also modulating the power supply. Although grid modulation requires less modulating power, distortion can easily appear at the tube's plate. Bias and plate supplies require considerable regulation for this scheme to be successful.

Contrast these hot, high-voltage, high-current vacuum tubes with today's cool, small, and highly effective semiconductors and the comparison is startling. Instead of bulky (and expensive) transformers, Signetics, for example, furnishes a little eight-pin IC with modulator, clamp, and oscillator, then sound and video inputs do the rest. You do need an LC tank circuit for the modulator plus a tiny output transformer, but the IC does the remainder at a V_{CC} supply voltage between 4.5 and 5.5 volts at about 10 mA drain. Enclosed in this tiny package is a balanced modulator, symmetrical oscillator, and a video clamper, all with a frequency range from 50 to 800 MHz (Fig. 4-6). It can be used with both video and computers and has output voltages between 10 and 13 mV. It will support negative, positive, and general-purpose modulation. The actual schematic, unfortunately, is not available, but the block presents a general idea.

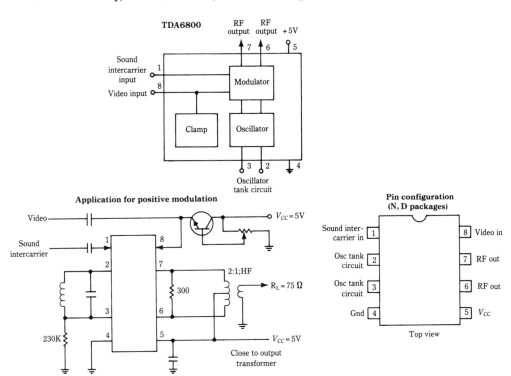

4-6 A modern, solid-state modulator contained in a tiny eight-pin IC.

In TV work, sideband systems often have a pair of double-balanced mixers for a suppressed carrier double sideband output. These are usually MOSFETS, sometimes arranged as a commutation mixer that very much resembles a vacuum-tube grid modulator but with a few added transformer windings for broadbanding and four metal-oxide semiconductors arranged much like a diode bridge. We don't go into details, but this is obviously another version of these modulator-mixers that probably could be described continuously for a week. For instance, in microwave signal processing, matched pairs of mixers do the work, especially for the military.

The FCC's set-aside station/channel passbands for television are 6 MHz, FM radio 200 kHz, and AM radio from some 10 kHz, depending on the point of measurement. What is not generally known is that the carrier and transmission bandwidth must fully accommodate these signals at a carrier power density (for video) measured at 26 dB down from carrier peak, according to FCC regulations. So when investigating resolution bandwidths with your trusty spectrum analyzer, see if the bandwidth is really this wide and is giving you everything you justly deserve. In radio, however, you'll have to include sidebands in your measurement.

Analog versus digital

When servicing digital systems, huge integrated circuits make up the bulk of active components, and capacitors and resistors are mere accessories. Progress is forever a wonderful advance and experience, but general signal processing is turning completely around, requiring new thinking, new techniques, and a revised means of troubleshooting. Current methods of creating sound and pictures are miracles compared with the 1980s.

It has also made me very aware that hard-board, soldered-in receivers, especially those from Asia, are almost unserviceable by consumers and require expensive work whenever there are problems. Zenith, on the other hand, is to be highly commended for its socket-mounted integrated circuits and removable, functional circuit boards, making home service possible with trained technicians. This is especially true of expensive digital receivers where chassis removal could involve major undertakings and whole cabinet pickups of 31- and 35-inch sets would require a truck and at least two strong men. Even 27-inch receivers with heavy picture tubes are more than an armload for any single individual. And now that the public has a taste of these excellent, larger-tube direct view sets, home service will become more important than ever because of shop charges and down times. High-end Philips receivers also have a removable digital section, but they are not otherwise modular.

We also have the distinct problem of field-test equipment usage, and this must be upgraded if TV is to be serviced in business establishments and homes. For the better receivers, color bars, gray scale, multiburst, dothatch (or crosshatch), video, and RF outputs are mandatory, as well as an audio tone or two. Whether oscilloscopes are mandatory is an arguable point that should be resolved by the individual agency. But certainly, high-impedance digital voltmeters, a few selected components, and a soldering iron or gun are musts. For the serviceman's NTSC generator, I recommend B&K-Precision's Model 1251, which has all the necessary patterns and more, including white and black raster plus red, blue, and green outputs (Fig. 4-7).

Digitized colors

Regardless of whether a television receiver is analog or digital, signals reaching the cathode-ray tube's cathodes are analog. This means that you watch waveforms of varying descriptions when looking at a crt during a broadcast, but only steady-state excitations with color bar generator signals applied. For this sort of oscilloscope analysis, a six-bar NTSC display is not necessarily helpful because you'll only see a series of step levels *without* the usual modulation, and that doesn't help a great deal when requiring changing signals denoting demodulator action on both red and blue outputs. Green is a matrix of the other two and does not have the necessary 90-degree phase angle separation from R and B to qualify.

Therefore, for oscilloscope work, a gated rainbow generator that's crystal controlled with an accurate 10-color, RF-modulated delivery is all that's usually needed, and each of the better ones today seem quite stable and responsive. However, those with separate three-way red, blue, and green outputs often have odd phase shifts that are not satisfactory and seem to confuse a receiver's detection system, even though those colors do emerge on the set's crt. So the full 10 petals that appear for red and blue

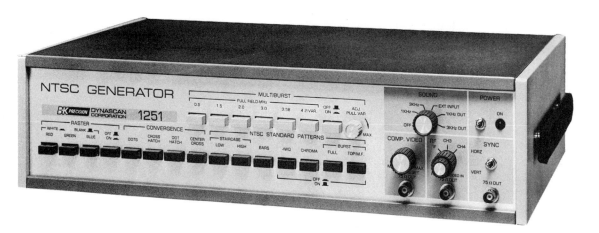

4-7 A Model 1251 NTSC color bar generator. B&K-Precision

amplification on an oscilloscope can tell you a great deal about the equipment you're investigating.

In this particular instance, we were examining a 31-inch digital Zenith receiver that developed the undesirable habit of sporadically casting a greenish veil over the entire picture without substantially changing other colors showing at the time. Since suggested retail for such a receiver amounts to some $2,000, the owner became somewhat annoyed that his expensive toy wasn't always delivering superb video to go with its excellent sound. Such a problem could originate from the picture tube, the final RGB amplifiers, or even the color circuits, so there are a number of "what ifs" with which to contend. Much of the ultramodern service literature today doesn't bother to offer accurate oscilloscope waveforms, so you have to rely on techniques developed many years past when color difference signals were divided between crt grids and cathodes (R-Y, B-Y, and G-Y), with the crt being the color matrix. In short, you have a subsystem checkout approach rather than a miserable IC or transistor-by-transistor silicon hunt. Here, if a symmetrical diagram with 10 petals doesn't appear, then you again have stepped into the barnyard quagmire.

Inserting a rainbow-modulated RF signal into the receiver's antenna terminals results in the usual 10 color bars and will appear on the face of any oscilloscope as a series of "hound's-tooth" excitations of varying amplitudes from the red and blue connections to the receiver's cathode-ray tube (Fig. 4-8). Observe that the red or Y connection nulls at the sixth bar

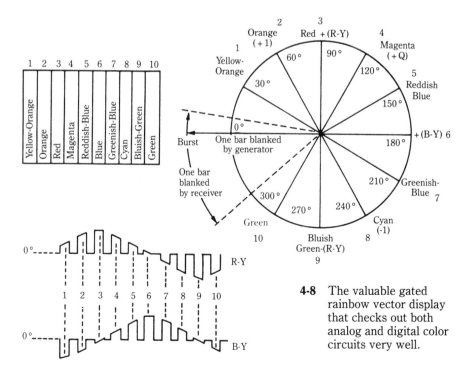

4-8 The valuable gated rainbow vector display that checks out both analog and digital color circuits very well.

and the blue or X connection nulls at the third and ninth bars; provided your receiver's tint (or hue) control is properly adjusted so that the magenta bar is fourth from the left. And do make sure you can see at least parts of the first and tenth bars; otherwise, your receiver is horizontally overscanned and probably has poor high-voltage regulation. Brightness (or black level), contrast, and color (including tint) must be adjusted properly, or the display will look like a splattered egg (Fig. 4-9). If controls make no difference, then you have either a noncompatible generator or amplifier-demodulator problems within the set itself.

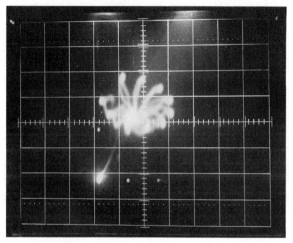

4-9 Misadjusted color and luma controls foul the vector pattern.

Vectors

The next step involves the output of the color detector and the D/A (digital-to-analog) converters themselves. If vector examination produces a symmetrical, equal amplitude pattern spaced at 30-degree intervals, then color processing needs no further consideration. The remaining part of the investigation centers on the RGB amplifier/drivers and the 31-inch cathode-ray tube. See Fig. 4-10 for a good color demodulator pattern. Note the symmetry; there's just a little "hammerhead" at the tips, resulting from either saturation or instantaneous phase reversal, and full 10 color bars are in evidence. Tint is off a little more than 30 degrees, owing to receiver hue control adjustment because the third red petal and sixth blue petal should be positioned at 90 degrees and 180 degrees, respectively.

As with most color receivers of today, RGB color amplifier/drivers are located on a printed circuit (PC) board that also supports the cathode-ray tube mating socket. This design both reduces noise and offers additional heat dissipation because of its separation from other processing components such as the digital section and low/high voltage. In this particular

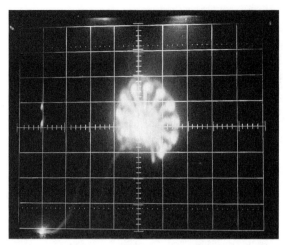

4-10 Vector pattern from demodulators shows excellent chroma detection and no D/A faults.

examination, be positive of your ground connections. Otherwise, all kinds of miserable apparitions can appear on the scope's screen.

Here, the No. 1 channel probe connects to the red (R) cathode input and channel No. 2 to the blue (B) input. Then simply push your scope's *x-y* switch and admire or marvel at the results. They might not all mirror what you've already seen from the demodulators. The one in Fig. 4-11 certainly does not! Recall that green is formed from a matrix of R and B. In the photo, much of the tenth green petal has disappeared, the vector is generally distorted and phase separations are by no means consistent. Looks like there is, indeed, a strong case for green overcast problems in the amplifier section and probably not in the cathode-ray tube. To check, adjust all color out of the crt and see if there are any changes in the black and white picture, especially gray scale. If there are none, return to the driver/amplifier board and begin looking for faults. In this Zenith receiver, you can easily substitute the entire board for a replacement and that should ordinarily cure your difficulties.

In working with color problems, we can't stress enough that a system approach is absolutely necessary if you're going to solve faults quickly and accurately. In color receivers, and especially these digital ones, hit-and-miss random replacements just won't cut the mustard. An analytical approach is your one and only hope.

Before leaving vectors, however, you should be made aware of several conditions: an amplitude reduction of the top or right sides of the pattern definitely indicates a red or blue amplifier condition; any non-30-degree phase shifting of petals shows poor demodulation; and any considerable internal expansion of petals usually denotes defective channel tuning. You can readily see, therefore, that chroma investigation with a decent gated rainbow genera-

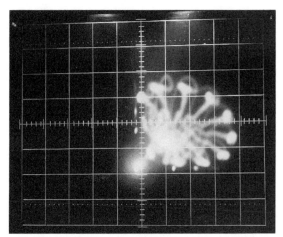

4-11 A passable vector into the cathode-ray tube, but there is some lack of symmetry.

tor and almost any dual-trace oscilloscope with at least a 1 MHz *x* channel bandpass can help solve many faults that could take literally hours or days of futile parts substitutions, which often generates more problems than they solve, especially when working with digital.

The final caution involves oscilloscopes that will not invert both channels 90 degrees. In order to look at a vector and its blanking in an upright position, inputs to the scope's horizontal and vertical channels have to be reversed. If there are only twinlead cables to the crt plates, then a pair of reversing switches can easily be installed between final amplifiers and the crt's V/H plates. But you should be forewarned this will cut the scope's bandpass considerably because of switch capacitance. Other alternatives would be to flip the scope on its back or simply learn to read patterns upside down. Vectorscope readouts illustrated are all done with an old, but very handy Telequipment D66 that's been a real "buddy" of mine for many years (courtesy Tektronix). Just turn the four preceding photos over on the page and you'll see what I mean.

Occasionally, this vector procedure results in a slip up due either to misinterpretation, basic design faults, or an intermittent condition that is difficult to judge. In that case, you're either going to pull the chassis or carry an expensive gray scale/NTSC color bar/dot hatch/staircase gray raster and possibly externally modulated audio/video to a customer's place of business or residence. Should you have to do this, pray the receiver isn't some Japanese hard-soldered IC arrangement with bare-bones procedure instructions and oddly drawn service information. This is why U.S. receivers with modular assemblies and socket-mounted principal ICs that can be exchanged in the field fairly easily without logging a good many hours on the bench and lots of unpleasantness with the receiver's owner. When such an occasion unfortunately arises, use B&K-Precision's Model 1251

NTSC generator, which has very close tolerance outputs and a multitude of signal variations.

For digital TV servicing, the intermittent condition reappeared, and it was necessary to use gray scale, low value raster, red, blue, and green screens (independently), color bars, and multiburst between 0.5 and 4.2 MHz to evaluate such signals directly on the receiver's screen. The green cast had become very prominent now, and replacement of both the comb filter video processor and the video codec A/D and D/A converter was mandatory. Both are 40-pin ICs so only factory equipment setups can check them (Fig. 4-12). Nonetheless, such ICs can be replaced in the field at considerably less cost to you and the customer if they are pluggable!

In the future, when servicing such digital equipment, it might be considerably easier to use a good NTSC generator first, if you can see test patterns on the TV's crt. But both gated rainbow and NTSC equipment will be a positive must for anyone servicing video units running on 1s and 0s. A look at some of the waveforms encountered might aid your thinking or astonishment. High IC impedances, however, could present some expected problems because these ICs use many MOSFETS in a number of configurations, and there are no special diagrams to look inside. If high

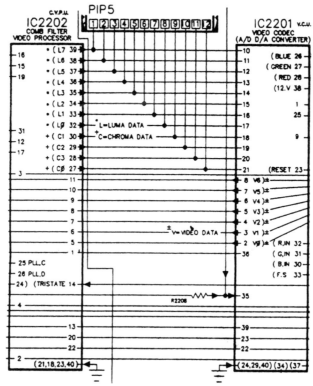

4-12   ICs 2201 and 2202 video and codec processors were the problem.   Zenith Electronics Corp.

impedances do present insurmountable problems when using inexpensive equipment such as handy ditigal switches, then a digital storage oscilloscope (DSO) becomes your only salvation, and these are still somewhat expensive. Perhaps, later, some combination of waveform analyzer can fill the bill once engineering costs are amortized.

Capturing digital waveforms on an oscilloscope isn't as easy as you might believe. The problem arises from varying frequencies, fast blanking intervals, lock-operated ICs, and bus-driven interchanges. Figure 4-13 is a

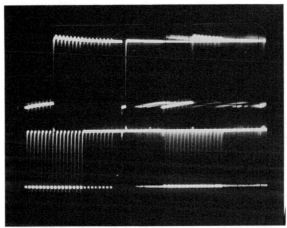

4-13 Typical digital displays from a nonanalog receiver. Both are complex, with more than one frequency apparent.

working example. In a simple four-pin stake connector, there were three prominent signals and ground. A 1-to-8 multiplexer switch dropped the value of each signal until maximum oscilloscope inputs had to be used, and this resulted in sync problems because of tiny waveforms. My only resort, therefore, was to return to a dual-trace oscilloscope and look through its 10-megohm probes at the test points in question. Operating points of these complex signals are obviously at different frequencies, and positive sync lock is almost impossible, even with the various kinds of equipment used in the laboratory. My conclusion, therefore, suggests that either you have an oscilloscope with independently sync'd channels or you simply accept the display of one channel at a time. Another look at the schematic of this receiver indicates there are so many operations in process simultaneously that synchronization of uncommon digital bit streams with one another is probably impractical except with exceedingly expensive equipment.

Swap parts

This is not the kind of report that is either helpful or appealing, but in the case of a modular television receiver or simply a digital data board with plug-in ICs or removable sections, you'll save a great deal of time just exchanging parts and let the factory worry about the individual defect. Otherwise, either probe the motherboard's external stakes with an oscilloscope or use subsystem checkouts such as a vectorscope. Where everything is firmly soldered (no plug-ins) like most Japanese devices, you have your week's work laid out for you. Plus, they often supply inadequate waveforms. Unfortunately, these problems usually worsen rather than improve because complexity keeps the software people in business, and the IC houses delight in executing the latest fancy designs. I'm not complaining but simply pointing out the direction commercial and consumer products are taking. Fortunately, with today's reliability, ICs usually afford relatively few difficulties. When these do appear, there's little to do but change the entire integrated circuit if the related fault is even probable.

Before leaving the discussion of color altogether, let's compare a top-of-the-line 1986 analog color receiver with the digital responses I've just shown (see Fig. 4-14). The vector pattern here has both crossovers in the pattern—and this means crosstalk and nonlinearities—and the actual disappearance of the green petal No. 10. Further, oranges are pushed toward reds (even with auto-color disconnected) for greater fleshtone spreads, which inevitably appear in adjacent scenes other than simply faces, arms, and hands. On the screen, some of these effects are not particularly noticeable, but the vector and its "hounds tooth" red and blue signatures that actually form the vector show fairly good blue reproduction (top), but it's not so hot for red on the bottom. The reds are far from symmetrical, and their amplitudes following blanking are obviously poor.

I suggest that those servicing color receivers become used to this vectorscope procedure and learn to work with it on most chroma and regenerated subcarrier problems. If the vector spins, then you have a bad 3.58 MHz

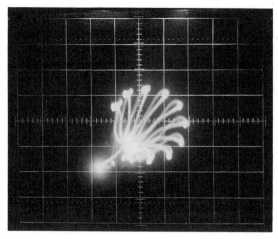 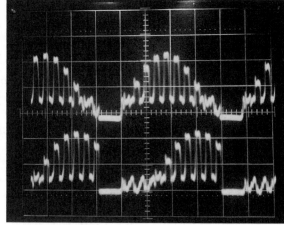

4-14 A 1986 analog receiver delivers both a poor vector pattern as well as a defective red demodulator response.

color oscillator fault, and an immediate check of the subcarrier should find the failure. Looking at the vector pattern at inputs to the picture tube offers chroma information not otherwise available and is also a full system check, including channel tuning, that instantaneously reveals a large bite of overall receiver operation because these color bars must pass through the IFs, too. But don't forget that receiver contrast, brightness, tint, and color controls must be properly adjusted for suitable patterns. If such patterns cannot be adjusted, then you can narrow receiver difficulties to the subcarrier, final amplifiers, or chroma processing. With just a little experience and effort, vector interpretation falls neatly into place.

If you're not using vectors for field or bench signal analysis, then a good NTSC generator with all the patterns suggested must be applied, whether analog or digital receiver. Here there's no real difference because all final information appearing on the crt is analog anyway. Even bandwidth-measuring multiburst patterns are very crt-evident and are highly useful in determining luminance response throughout the system. B&K-Precision also furnishes a series of generated patterns and explanations available to those who purchase the 1251 and 1260 generators. It would be difficult to operate without them when servicing some of the "tough dogs."

Sync

If there wasn't transmitter-receiver sync, there'd be no picture, whether color or monochrome. And going back to the fifties and even the sixties, sync was almost the most critical part of the receiver. True, bandpass was relatively poor, picture tubes were not especially reliable, audio was somewhat scratchy, deflection yokes and high voltage transformers were vulnerable, and AGC/AFT was often atrocious. But keeping video displays from rolling one way or the other required a complete change of technology: from tubes to solid state. Furthermore, discrete transistors weren't the final answer, and it was not until special count-down integrated circuits were developed that stable sync in most receivers was born. So during the 1980s, there have been few sync problems and most electronics observers think all difficulties have faded into the morning mist.

With the advent of improved definition receivers, however, you might have second thoughts. For openers, how about double horizontal frequencies and noninterlaced scan? A number of the 1991 models could easily have these two features, and others with jack packs will have video bandwidths of 7 to 8 MHz (or would you rather think in terms of 350 to 400 lines?).

And with the advent of high-definition television, brand new sync patterns may develop that we know little of as yet. This is why, therefore, we thought it advisable to include a liberal dose of vertical and horizontal sync plus 3.58 MHz chroma in this TV receiver chapter.

V/H synchronism

Transmitters usually develop V/H sync from a countdown of the 3.579545 MHz crystal-controlled oscillator, or they may have a 1.0069 MHz oscillator and sampling system to produce horizontal and vertical sync. With color burst as reference, $2/455 \times 3.579545$ equals 15,734.26373 Hz horizontal, and this divided by half the scanning lines, or 262.49583, becomes 59.9410 Hz, which is the standard vertical rate.

As will become apparent in Fig. 4-15, all equalizing, vertical pulses and pulse durations are interrelated in terms of a single horizontal line. Vertical sync pulses in the NTSC system appear during the first nine lines of the vertical blanking interval, while a single horizontal pulse appears during each of the 525 horizontal scanning lines. When the two scanning line fields are added, the sum becomes 525 lines, and this is called a *frame*. In television, there are 30 frames per second interlaced.

But in some forthcoming receivers, the 15.734 kHz horizontal sweep will be doubled to 31.468 kHz, and the line scan noninterlaced to bypass

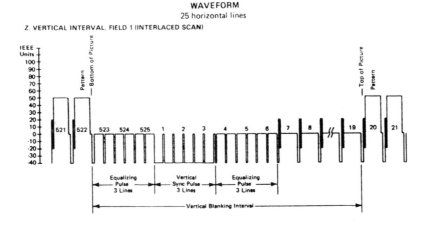

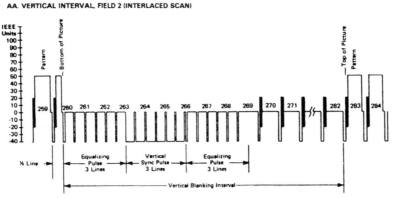

4-15 A two-field frame of interlaced scanning. B&K-Precision

any vertical picture jitter resulting from interlace reaction when counted down from the 3.58 MHz color carrier. All this should offer a smooth picture without apparent scanning lines and, with increased luminance resolution, produce a very fine picture indeed. Figure 4-16 illustrates a graphic of noninterlaced scan. Note that field 1 and field 2 scanning lines are now completely equal, just like field 1 in the interlaced display. Your signal generator during the coming years should adapt to both scan types, although 15,734 Hz may be doubled inside the newer receivers without outside stimulation. Only the B&K Model 1260 has noninterlaced scan; the 1251 does not. Note the I EEE units drawn vertically alongside each illustration. These can be helpful when examining sync amplitudes. A good oscilloscope will exhibit these same patterns if it can handle the *vertical* blanking interval. The horizontal sync pulse with chroma burst on the back porch occurs at the end of each scan line in the *horizontal* blanking interval, which is easily seen on any oscilloscope.

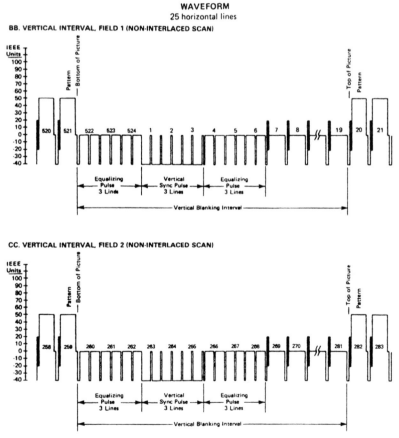

4-16 A noninterlaced pair of fields appearing soon in some of the "improved definition" NTSC receivers. B&K-Precision

You've undoubtedly seen several of these illustrations in the past; therefore, the horizontal portion will not be repeated. But you should remember certain displays that are helpful in recognizing faults and quality in any color receiver. In addition to troubleshooting, these patterns could become excellent sales aids for the better receivers if they are explained carefully to prospective buyers, especially the multiburst, gray scale, and raster patterns. All are essential to prime receiver operation on any broadband-transmitted program (Figs. 4-17 and 4-18).

This pretty well covers the sync portion as well as NTSC and gated rainbow generator usage. But we haven't said anything yet about the fully transmitted 6 MHz RF pattern with extended chroma, so that topic is due next. Effectively, you've so far learned about the parts, so let's briefly peruse the whole before continuing.

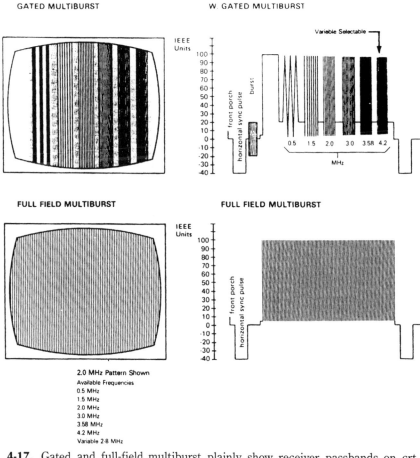

4-17 Gated and full-field multiburst plainly show receiver passbands on crt.
B&K-Precision

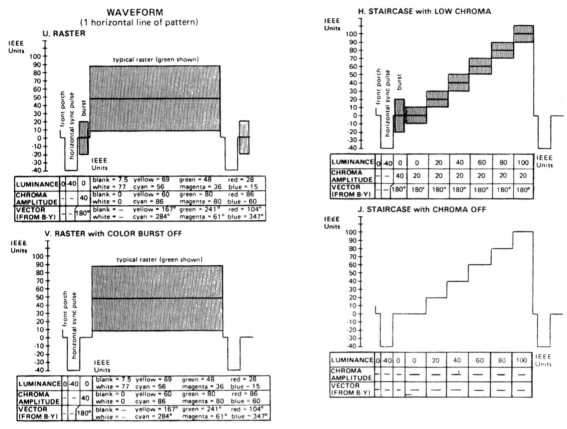

4-18 Rasters with and without chroma with modulated and unmodulated staircase to accurately identify gray scale. B&K-Precision

The complete RF signal

Now that you've seen off-the-air signals, troubleshooting test patterns, modulation of various descriptions, and other general characteristics, you should be ready for the total information broadcast. This is a 6 MHz composite waveform (Fig. 4-19) that includes 4.2 MHz of luminance (video) information, 2 MHz of chroma, and up to 50 kHz of audio (if stereo). Video and audio intelligence is separated by 4.5 MHz, producing a difference IF audio carrier frequency of 4.5 MHz, which has been identified as intercarrier sound. Between 1 and 2 MHz there is nothing but pure video, which is part of the fine (black and white) detail in any color picture. At 2 MHz, single-sideband I chroma appears, followed by double-sideband I chroma at 3 MHz, double-sideband Q chroma extending to 4.1 MHz, and the 3.58 MHz "suppressed" chroma subcarrier in between. Finally, the sound carrier is all by itself on the far right. Observe the relative positions of the several modulations, their carriers, frequencies, and bandspreads so you

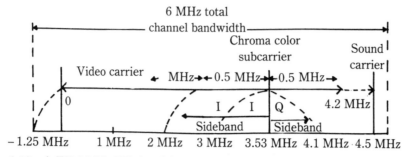

4-19 A TV 6 MHz RF signal from any broadcast station in NTSC format.

understand where each channel spectrum belongs. This pattern holds whether it's transmitting very high frequency (VHF), ultra high frequency (UHF), CATV, or C/Ku-band satellite under existing National Television Systems Committee determinations occurring between 1951 (reorganization) and 1953 (color). Should high-definition television come to pass by the middle of the decade, this NTSC spectrum will remain for the non-HDTV populace, but its extended-definition second-channel cousin will be altered radically for both expanded video and digital two- or four-channel sound. At this time, no solid HDTV diagram exists because we have no idea which system FCC's advisory Advanced Television Systems Committee (ATSC) or the FCC itself will select. But there are very strong indications it will be a dual-channel, simulcast system with NTSC on one channel and HDTV on another, probably UHF.

In the diagram, note that the sound carrier is always 4.5 MHz above the video carrier and must remain so for necessary audio/video separation, especially in the stereo system of BTSC-dbx or multichannel TV sound (MTS). And for your information, the various channels allotted to TV as well as CATV are provided at the end of chapter 5 for quick reference from information supplied by Zenith Electronics Corp.

VITS and VIRS

I have already explained what a multiburst pattern resembles, so this won't be repeated, but there are also VIRS and VITS signatures available on the very expensive color generators of which you should be aware. This is especially true of the vertical interval (color) reference signal (VIRS) that is sometimes still available on network vertical blanking intervals showing chroma, luminance, black, and color reference excitations on line 19 of the VBIs. Occupying between −40 and +90 IEEE units and lasting a full line in duration, this signal establishes the appropriate transmitter levels for outgoing color phase information, which should coincide exactly with burst on the back porch of the horizontal sync pulse. Black level reference is +7.5, and luminance is at 50 units on the scale shown. Times for a full line of VIRS illustrate the various segments' lengths in microseconds (μs) (see Fig. 4-20).

The VITS (vertical interval test signal) is not necessarily shown anymore because fields 1 and 2 of line 18 are no longer even reserved for this display because the FCC apparently doesn't think it's useful (Fig. 4-21). But because it shows full color bars, burst, the 2T and 12.5T sine² pulses, and an excellent 18 μs ripple- or ringing-apparent window, it's still useful. Color bar levels are both important as a full modulation sign and I EEE

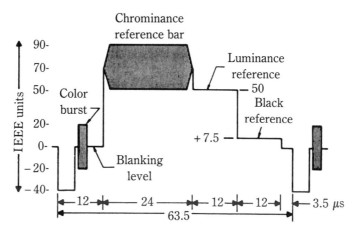

4-20 The VIRS chroma pattern for luma/chroma level and color phase adjustments on set-aside line 19 of the VBI.

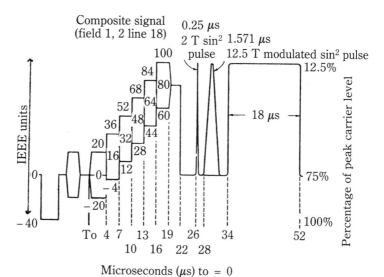

4-21 Another VBI pattern no longer required is the composite modulated staircase and 2T signals plus an 18 μs window former appearing on line 18.

level measurement, while the 2T and 12.5T spikes of voltage indicate luminance and color levels and/or chroma/luminance gain or delays. The small spike is for luminance. The wider pulse is for chroma and its differential loss or gain relative to luminance. Both amplitudes must match that of the window and staircase or you have problems.

These patterns are normally only visible on oscilloscopes at a receiver's video detector because further blanking removes them from transmission to the crt's cathodes. Sometimes, however, satellite transmissions run these patterns on normal horizontal picture scan lines. Then you can read their "numbers" directly on the cathode-ray tube of the TV receiver. Check a few transponders in the early afternoon or late at night and you'll see several test signals appear, although many are color bars only, or straight multiburst.

Nonetheless, all are useful in their separate makeups, and your interpretations will determine how the device under test passes or has some grievous fault. Try it and see; many of the satellite receivers will surprise you with their linearity, especially if you connect them to a broadband monitor-type TV.

Figure 4-22 should help you to visualize the various colors in terms of placement and nanometers. Note the large area of green, the red references below, and then observe that red is in 90-degree quadrature with blue on the left. You can now say that higher-frequency double-sideband Q signal reproduces colors from green through purple and the I signal covers hues from red/purple through yellow among the lower frequencies (or nanometers). The wide area of green above is where the greens merge, and this is how I and Q transmissions can be matrixed to form orphan green. This is also why a gated rainbow generator can show 10 color bars on the face of any color TV with hues from yellow to green, including magenta and cyan.

If many of these test patterns are applied with careful concentration and discrimination between occasional glitches and actual faults, you should be able to analyze or improve many electrical conditions that would otherwise escape notice. All variations from the perfect patterns aren't necessarily problems, and every slight or imagined glitch doesn't mean your receiver or system needs overhaul or should be canned. What they do mean is that your equipment should be in best operational order if you're going to reproduce a working replica of this chapter's waveforms and drawings.

Be aware that only the best video systems stand the test of near-perfect patterns, while inexpensive units with shortcuts often look somewhat "seedy." For instance, any TV set without a glass delay line or charge-coupled device comb filter probably has an LC chroma trap in its luminance channel and allows a bandpass of only 2.5 to 3 MHz regardless of signal input. Consequently, anyone with picture resolutions and definition appreciation should never purchase any television receiver without at least a comb filter, and super-sensitive souls ought to have first-class digi-

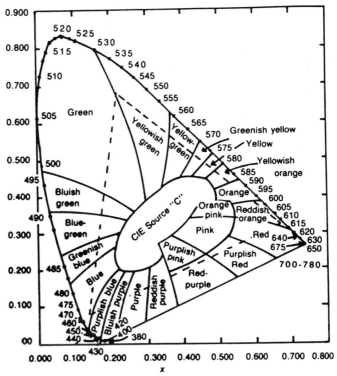

4-22 The standard and approved chromaticity diagram for NTSC color.

tal receivers with all their special picture programming, monitor jack-packs, and surround sound. There's still some good old USA design engineering here and there that can make your eyes and ears sparkle. In 1990 and 1991, my vote goes to Zenith without reservations. Their 31-inch chassis with surround sound is an absolute gem!

Picture tubes

This video chapter would be totally incomplete without some discussion of cathode-ray tubes, especially the newest ones that are now populating our top-of-the-line monitors and receivers. Their beautiful colors and broad resolutions are delightful to behold, and the coming years will see 31-inchers just as common as 25s and 27s are today. With production in millions of units, their $800 prices are bound to come down, and we should see many in the $1,500 brackets instead of $2,000 to $2,500 in the very near future. Analog supporting electronics will be less expensive temporarily, but as more digital receiver/monitors are produced, costs will steadily decrease here as well. Eventually, of course, pictures-on-the-wall will supplant the crt, but that is still possibly a decade or more in the future when these devices can become large enough and cost-effective enough to warrant general distribution. At such time, receivers should be virtually all digital and, without bothersome high voltage, servicing can finally become a science instead of an analog art.

Meanwhile, we do have very good cathode-ray tubes to contend with, and improvements here have been substantial also. In the beginning, there were all sorts of schemes in the color world beginning in 1928 with a mechanical field sequential receiver trying to scan 15 red and 15 cyan lines. Bell laboratories in the U.S. followed with a three-channel red, blue, and green system having 50 lines and 18 pictures/second. Then Dr. Peter Goldmark of CBS in 1940 became prominent with his field sequential receiver and whirling mechanical disk.

The Lawrence chromatron tube appeared in the early 1950s, where phosphors of red, green, and blue were placed in horizontal stripes. Deflection plates near these stripes deflected the beam accordingly. Afterwards, the shadow mask tube finally was developed with three electron guns exciting red, blue, and green deposited phosphors via a screen next to the faceplate of the tube with some 300,000 holes so that groups of three dots could be illuminated separately, depending on beam excitation. There was also the Apple single-gun tube invented by Philco that required a great deal of beam and signal processing to illuminate its vertically striped phosphor screen. Such stripes were about $1/16$ of an inch wide on a 21-inch tube, separated by black, nonilluminating (probably absorbing) coating in between.

This should basically bring you up to date with the cathode-ray tubes currently being produced by Philips (formerly Sylvania), Thomson CF (formerly RCA), and Zenith. There are also some prominent Japanese tube manufacturers such as Sony and Mitsubishi. In the beginning of the great import age (and the ruination of our balance of payments), all Asian receivers were shipped with mostly Japanese picture tubes. Then basic chassis were put on the boat for tubing in the U.S. Now, several Japanese companies are actually building crts for inclusion not only in their own receivers but U.S. sets as well, due to charges of dumping and just plain economics or, in the case of Sony, their own Trinitron common lens—not single gun—since this tube has three cathodes and, therefore, three guns with two electron lenses and two electron prisms for convergence.

It was not until 1973, however, that RCA was to introduce the first American vertically striped phosphors and closely spaced inline gun. This tube was to develop as a small, short-necked crt that was very rectangular and had a much flatter faceplate than its predecessors. Convergence was considerably simplified with a series of tab magnets mounted on the cathode-ray tube neck, and the deflection yoke was downsized to half of its former magnitude. With better convergence, brightness increased, center spot size for best resolution decreased, and power requirements diminished due to yoke and possibly video drives. High voltage, on the other hand, went higher for added brightness.

In the early 1980s, RCA further refined this display with its special Coty-29 crt assembly where tubes and deflection yokes were computer-matched for both efficiency and best convergence, at the same time reducing tube necks from 29 to 22.5 millimeters. Guns in these tubes now have slot optics for beam forming and generating precise focal distances for horizontal and vertical deflection.

North American Philips' Sylvania plant in Seneca Falls, NY also contributed to crt development in 1984 by introducing an ECG conical field focus assembly in one piece. Color tubes with this improvement were then offered in both 29 mm and 22.8 mm neck sizes and also internal magnetic shielding. Tricolor phosphor coatings are narrow, closely spaced phosphor lines separated by thin, black, opaque coatings, and they are aligned via appropriate slots in the shadow mask. Philips has also introduced varying horizontal scanning velocity. Today, all crt magnetic shielding is now inside the tube envelope, and most or all crts are shadow mask units except for a new development by Zenith, briefly described as follows.

Identified as a brighter, flat-face crt with welded-on high-tension foil shadow mask, Zenith so far has produced only a 14-inch industrial type for the more expensive high-resolution monitors. It is said to accept eight times the power of regular spherical-mask tubes, is 50 percent brighter, and exhibits 70 percent increased contrast.

It's flat face virtually eliminates reflections, double horizontal scans are 31.5 kHz, and characters can be displayed up to 80 × 25 lines, with an overall bandspread of 25 MHz. Frit-type glass cement secures the shadow mask support frame in place and all faceplate covering has a special tolerance temperature coefficient. Phosphor slurry is deposited by radial flow and suffusion. That's about the best description available at the moment, and this came from Zenith's patent award literature and not from any news release or engineering writeup. The three guns, yoke, and internal shielding are, apparently, conventional.

The final descriptive portion of the chapter will be devoted to the larger 31- and 35-inch crts appearing in receivers during 1989 and 1990 to see, if possible, why they present excellent images from such a large screen size. There obviously has to be a very valid reason.

The big ones

So far, these are Japanese-built and-marketed 31- and 35-inch crts coming principally from Mitsubishi and Matsushita, Panasonic's parent company. The initial information available to us involves a 33-inch, 29-kilovolt version with 110-degrees vertical deflection, a neck diameter of 29.1 millimeters, and quick-heating cathodes. This shadow mask is a slotted type whose phosphors are supplied current by quick-heating cathodes and protected by an internal magnetic shield.

Manufacturer Matsushita further specifies unitized grid electron guns with a center beam green, bipotential focus lens, and electrostatic focusing. Deflection, however, is magnetic at 110 degrees diagonal, 93 degrees horizontal, and 74 degrees vertical. The external conductive coating (aquadag, plus metal tension band) measures between 3,000 and 3,600 picofarads. Vertical-line tricolor phosphors on a metal-backed surface cover the inner faceplate with a matrix of black opaque material. Phosphors are of type x, supplying rare earth pigmented for red, sulfide for green, and pigmented sulfide for blue. Color coordinates for all are

	x	y
red	0.628	0.346
green	0.306	0.599
blue	0.150	0.070

Tube length is 19.346 inches with diagonals, widths, and heights of 33.165/27.551/21.814 inches, respectively, and faceplate light transmission at the center of 47.5 percent. Installed screen dimensions for this tube amounts to 30.827 inches, minimum; therefore, you could call this a 31-inch tube as enclosed in its cabinet. Center screen luminance measures 95 cd/m² at a total anode current of 1,500 μA. A standard TLY deflection yoke, model 15424F, supplies the sweeps. We could continue with additional statistics, but these should be sufficient for those nominally interested. Additional material is available from the manufacturer in Takatsuki, Osaka, Japan.

Mitsubishi currently furnishes the 35-inch version with square-corner design, a 32.5 mm neck diameter and external magnetic shielding. Convergence and deflection are both electromagnetic, along with a unibipotential focusing lens. The deflection angle measures 110 degrees supported by a 330P513 deflection yoke. Its aquadag coating and implosion hardware contains 3300 to 2700 pF in capacitance. The phosphor used is P2, with reds, blues, and greens similar to the 31-incher, and medium-short persistence delivers center light transmittance of 45 percent. Neck length for this tube measures 6.48 inches, with an overall length of 21.9 inches. Overall tube dimensions are 37.45 inch diagonal, 31.26 inch wide, and 24.66 inch high, with a usable screen area of 1370 square inch (or 3794 square centimeters).

The weight of this tube lists at 123 pounds, requiring an anode voltage of 25 to 32 kV and an average anode current of 2 mA. Shipment shocks are not to exceed 25G along tube axis and 30G perpendicular to tube axis, indicating careful handling. To replace this tube will certainly require two people or a mechanical hoist.

Dimensions and installation diagrams are not especially unique; therefore, they are not included. Just marvel at the resolution and definition of these large crts when viewing their video reproductions. Note that close coordination between accelerator voltages and cathode emissions are needed to prevent spot size enlargement and poor definition pictures.

Crt troubles

Many cathode ray-tube faults are clearly visible. It doesn't take a genius to spot electrode arcs, nor is it difficult to see when one or more guns are not lit. But it's the sophisticated troubles that always give problems.

For example, if the picture comes on slowly and gradually warms up to a murky display, what do you suspect? You could have a high-voltage lag, a flyback with a possibly shorted turn or two, and in the days of vacuum tubes, it might well be a horizontal output tube. Transistors seldom slump and usually work up to the time of total collapse. But what about final video amplifiers; couldn't these be a problem too?

If you can see the crt when it is first energized and the full screen is filled, especially if this is an older tube, you might as well suspect the crt itself. Conversely, a partial raster or one that's virtually all red, blue, or green would immediately indicate either RGB amplifiers or horizontal sweep which, of course, might involve the flyback, a leaky damper, or the hot transistor.

You must also be absolutely sure the aquadag coating on the picture tube is grounded because this is the usual 500 pf or larger capacitor that discharges tube electrical buildup. The same cautionary note goes for the degausser. If degaussing circuits are out, all kinds of swirls in a multitone picture immediately indicate crt shadowmask contamination. External degaussing and repair of the internal unit are the only options.

Where there are no obvious signs, such as the green overcast of several chapters ago, you'll have to find a worthwhile tube checker such as B&K-Precision's Model 467 or 490 with three meters that check all the guns simultaneously for emission, leakage, tracking, shorts removal, cathode cleaning, and even rejuvenation of old tubes, although the latter isn't always desirable or successful. When any tube with better-than-average mileage (hours) begins to show signs of exhaustion, a replacement is nominally required in almost all instances. The tube checkers use a surprising number of exchange fittings to examine all outstanding parameters. For my purposes, single-gun checkers don't really cut the mustard because all guns are not programmed equally and, therefore, there'll be some readjusting between tests, prolonging the agony. When it comes to triple-gun tracking, if all guns read within the given "good" area, then you can be fairly certain of that portion of the tube's operation.

Crt rejuvenation used to work fairly well for black-and-white tubes, but my personal experiences with color have not been especially good. Once in a while, the old crt responds, but any gassiness or interelement leakage usually returns quickly if tube restoration is not complete and there isn't enough cathode material to generate adequate emissions.

Occasionally, however, your crt checks out all right, but it won't operate. If the high voltage is sufficient, go immediately to the screen resistors and measure each one. You could likely find a virtual open, even though the voltage at the tube is within limits.

That is about all the substantive material available on cathode-ray tubes without stretching the obvious. We've covered video from the introduction of RF into the tuner to transmitter modulation, sync action, color troubleshooting, and on-screen display. This should be a pretty fair signal analysis for much of the receiver and normal broadcast transmissions.

Were it not an analytical description, one might further investigate the various workings of integrated circuits in detail for a more complete understanding of contemporary electronics, both analog and digital. We're tempted to place equal emphasis on signal origins compared with results, but the prime objective is to show what happens when specific electronics either bomb or deliver digestible fruit. While you can't physically digest waveforms and logic, a smooth, uncluttered appearance is usually pretty tasty to the systems and subsystems they serve. Glitches, aberrations, and artifacts are not digestible fruit, regardless of their origins!

5
Today's television antennas

WITH THE IMPENDING APPROACH OF HIGH-DEFINITION TELEVISION (HDTV) and hopeful public awakening to the mediocre-to-poor pictures they've been watching for some 50 years, it's about time attention was paid to the receiving device that's responsible for much of the problem: the TV antenna.

If all truth be known, there has been little antenna design or redesign, with several notable exceptions, for the past 15 to 20 years. Now the industry is beginning to awaken from its long Rip VanWinkle slumber and offer a hopefully new beginning. In the 1940s and 1950s, hi-lo folded diapoles with twinlead harnesses were popular from RCA. JFD had its own line, Jerrold engineered a log periodic with all driven elements, and others did whatever they were capable of (often, not much).

Then it was discovered that inline VHF receptors with corner reflectors or other UHF signal-capturing devices would operate even better than high/low/folded units, and a 300- to 75-ohm balanced-to-unbalanced transformer (balun) could match the impedances of these inlines to that of 75-ohm coaxial cable. Satisfactory coupling of inline antennas and coaxial cable were big advances, producing increases in gain, better front-to-back ratios, decreased wind resistance, stronger, moisture-protected signal elements, good UHF/VHF impedance matches, adequate shipping containers, and fairly reasonable pricing. After this came the introduction of low-noise, high-gain amplifiers that resisted overload in strong signal areas, much improved antenna rotators, along with price decreases, and finally a vast improvement in download cable for both attenuation and shielding. Additionally, to meet the need of housing development covenants and m'lady's objection "to those ugly old things on the roof," there are even developments in circular attic antennas that are rotatable, but they do not vary inductive lengths to operate well on the lower frequency channels. However, they have fair gain on the remainder and some ghost avoidance is possible with remote-control turning. So although most antennas are no comparative match for recent comb filter-equipped, microprocessor-controlled digital television sets, there is some progress and will very likely be more before the probable advent of broadcast HDTV in 1995 or 1996.

In the meantime, there'll be an opportunity later for readers to evaluate several of the better radiators with and without amplification receiving live, over-the-air broadcasts with results extolled in both graphs and explanations. I strongly suspect this has not been done recently, especially with good spectrum analyzers; therefore, I'll undertake the project for what it's worth to all of us: common knowledge of who's on first, second, or third. But since these are all very good antennas, differences in most instances should be negligible, although you might expect one or two happy surprises, especially among the amplifiers. And I just might be able to prove that even some smaller antennas with better amplification can do well or better than the big rigs. Certainly the beamwidths will be greater, but the front-to-back ratios might be less.

How they work

Antenna theory of operation is not too complex in the U/V spectrum, especially the receive-only types, because they only respond to a UHF/VHF range between 54 MHz and 806 MHz, less the usual band-reject slot of 88 to 108 MHz for FM and a bit more for other services. *Transmitting antennas* have a radiating element to convert RF currents into electromagnetic energy that propagates into terrestrial air space. This radiating element usually has a number of conductors called an *array*. As current flows in these conductors, both electric (E) and magnetic fields (H) are formed in space quadrature, expanding at nearly the velocity of light, with each field being proportional to the other. Together they are called a *radiation field* and expand initially as a wavefront that at some distance from the transmitter forms in right angles to the propagated energy.

Each antenna has a certain directivity with maximum intensity occurring at 0 degrees, followed by more-or-less uniform intensity to 30 degrees, where rapid dropoff begins. When graphed in concententric circles, this directivity and its resulting emissions are known as *polar coordinates*. The 30-degree angle is important because this is approximately the − 3 dB point where most transmit/receive measurements are taken (Fig. 5-1).

When transmission-line and antenna impedances match, transmit current flows freely, and when the antenna's impedance matches that of free space—approximately 377 ohms—maximum power results. Antenna effectiveness involves a number of configurations such as helical, super-

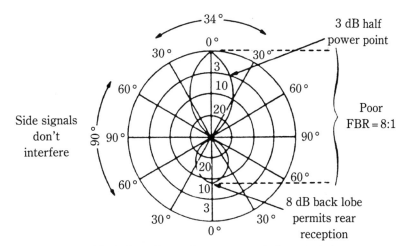

5-1 Typical receiver polar pattern and characteristics.

gain, superturnstile, cloverleaf, triangular, and square loops. Then beam shaping and beam tilt (from tower downward) often take place so that radiation covers specific areas, all of which must be approved by the FCC.

There is also vertical and horizontal emission known as circular polarization, but that is confined primarily to frequency modulation broadcast stations rather than TV. However, RCA (now owned by G.E.) has developed an effective Fan Vee circular polarized antenna, first used by WLSTV in Chicago in the 1970s, followed by Tetra Coil, TBK Quatrefoil plus TBJ types, and now TDM, TCL, and TCP. How many of these antennas are in active use we have no way of knowing. But we did want you to know that such CPs do exist. Harris Corp. also developed several CP antennas primarily for VHF. The Andrew Corp has UHF CP versions.

With the exception of JFD in the early days, afterwards bought out by Channel Master, there are no surviving CP receive antennas, and I know of none on the way. Apparently, CP TV is a hybernating science and art, perhaps to be revived in the next millenium. Right now, there's no real way of knowing. Could HDTV promote a resurrection?

Receiving antennas

Antenna theory and many practical applications haven't changed during these 15-plus years, probably because many parts of the country don't have that many TV stations, and receivers weren't up-to-snuff anyway. HDTV, the new, extended-definition VCRs, and the better camcorders are changing considerable thinking, and even though design revolutions aren't yet shaking the market place, a number of companies are considering their next moves as the nineties move toward century 21.

Generally, today's receive antennas originated from Hertz' free-air half-wave dipole or Marconi's quarter-wavelength design (Fig. 5-2). But

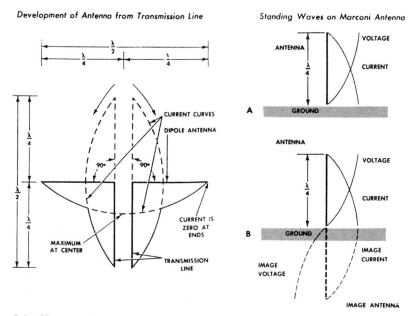

5-2   Hertz and Marconi antenna principles: half wave versus quarter wave.

Marconi's version has one end grounded or connected to counterpoise wires contributing a second quarter-wavelength. In television, the Hertz system is of prime interest because all TV receive antennas are various types of dipoles that simulate a half-wavelength. According to definition, a wavelength is the distance between similar-phased wavefronts known as lambda (λ). This is derived by dividing the velocity (300 meters or 984 feet) by the frequency in MHz (megahertz).

$$\lambda = \text{velocity/frequency}$$

In any Hertz antenna, as current becomes maximum impedance drops to minimum, center impedance measures 73 ohms, and end impedances are 2400 ohms. Pairs of such half-wave units folded in parallel with center connections measure 300 ohms, and even circles of such dipoles are acceptable for UHF. Interestingly, all three of these configurations have similar gains. Apparently, harnesses among present inline antennas produce the same 300 ohms, requiring 75-ohm baluns (balanced-to-unbalanced) transformers for cable conversion to 75 ohms.

Antenna elements in today's arrays are cut to certain lengths for specific frequencies and then harnessed in various ways to provide gain relative to an isotropic (omnidirectional) dipole. Elements consist of either driven or parasitic units. The former contribute to gain and the latter to receive-band shaping. On the front of modern antennas, you will see small elements known as *directors* and reflectors are often on the rear (Fig. 5-3).

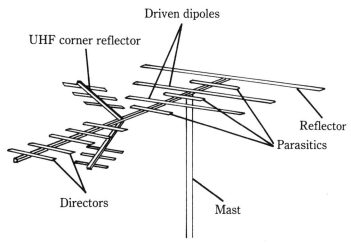

5-3 Common antenna parts: directors, reflectors, driven elements, and parasitics.

The directors attract and help shape incoming signals while the reflectors reject interference from the rear. What happens to sidelobe pickup is a matter of antenna design (explained later). You will also see the polar pattern of a typical low-gain antenna such as that used for small-city pickup having one or a few TV stations, relatively flat terrain, and few or no tall buildings. This, naturally, is the ideal situation and not of the real world around and about large metropolitan areas such as Philadelphia, New York, Chicago, Washington, D.C., Los Angeles, or other large cities. Here, ingenuity and careful understanding of overall signal conditions often solves most unusual circumstances, but some are so complex that no amount of compromise prevails. When that occurs, you're left with choice of either CATV or satellite reception, whichever is available.

If neither of these can come to your rescue, then a high-gain, narrow beamwidth antenna with a good rotor can assist considerably. But if there are maximum signal broadcast emissions, you'll have to reduce gain with some sort of attenuator suitable to the occasion. When all else fails, a single-channel Yagi can help with the worst offender, and a separate array probably can handle the rest. Notch-filter traps are also available if you care to use them, although this is normally not recommended.

Practically, an antenna should approach the frequency of a resonant circuit when tuned through its range, but all have losses that make antenna input impedances "somewhat" resistive. For maximum energy absorption, a half-wave dipole array has to be in the same polarization as the transmitting source. Electrical (E) and magnetic (H) fields arrive at the antenna, generating currents that are converted into electrical signals in the receiver.

To couple the antenna to the receiver use some sort of cable, usually coaxial (cable within a cable), that matches the impedance of the antenna, or you will lose signal gain due to VSWR (voltage standing wave ratios).

The greater the mismatch, the more loss. And since cable already has inherent losses due to resistances in its physical and electrical length, VSWR in any degree can profoundly affect signal strength and transmission fidelity. In twin or "bright" lead, secondary images (ghosts) became the principal problems due to bounce or other stray signals arriving microseconds behind the original. In coaxial cable, most electrical noise and secondary transmissions are denied entry because of shielding, but losses are somewhat greater in coax, and long runs often require amplification. Unfortunately, poor-quality amplifiers also supply noise along with increased gain, but because of recent improvements in such amplifiers today, it might be possible to furnish additional amplification to some of the smaller receive radiators, preserving broad beamwidth and at the same time offering about the same signal capture as much larger radiators without amplification. Initial investigation, however, already indicates that medium-gain antennas with above-average characteristics respond readily to selected amplification, especially over 35- to 50-mile distances, but they profit little when ranges extend beyond 50 miles. In other words, only so much signal can be captured by broadband, intermediate antennas regardless of additional electronics. Downlead cabling is also an important part of the receive-signal process, and you should select a specific type that's sunlight and earth-burial resistant, which also has the Underwriters Laboratories' approval since many county and state jurisdictions are requiring UL-approved conductors in accordance with the National Electrical Code.

In operation, antennas become resonant or almost resonant circuits. Near series resonance, input terminals approach zero impedance; but in parallel, the impedance is said to be infinite. Also, if antenna lengths are incorrect, they exhibit reactance as well as resistance. Consequently, any losses must be compensated in the design, which has to account for conductor resistance, principally skin effect at the higher frequencies as well as radiation resistance, although the latter applies more to transmitting elements rather than receivers. Therefore, larger-diameter, low-resistance conductors are desirable within electrical limits, which also increases their efficiency. Thereafter, a protective coating against oxidization and corrosion aids in maintaining this efficiency and prolongs antenna life. For antennas with nonzero reactances, their input impedances are the *vector* sum of both resistance and reactance ($R + jB$). For zero reactance, each side of an antenna has to be less than 1/4 wave in free space, and larger antennas offer less reactance when their lengths are not resonant. Lower Q (equal to X_L/R) allows resonance curves to be broader and allows better antenna response over wider frequency bands. The value Q, represented by the equation

$$Q = X_L/R \text{ or } 2\pi \, FL/R$$

is called the *figure of merit* or *storage factor* of an inductor and is the capacity of a coil to store energy in some magnetic field.

Types of antennas

Several types of receive antennas worth discussing (Fig. 5-4), are featured via signal analysis later in this chapter. Their importance lies mainly in the philosophy of design that, in turn, produces certain receive characteristics that can be useful. Interestingly enough, several of these antennas have almost identical appearances, especially those with UHF corner reflectors, which have somewhat similar gain and polar patterns. Beamwidths, however, differ, as will sidelobe suppression and front-to-back ratios in given situations.

Nonetheless, when all's said and done, "the proof of the pudding is in the eating," and I'll let you be the final judge of what suits you best. As with any other product, there are always trade-offs, and some are more attractive than others. Where gain and polar patterns are reproduced, all are generated on far-field antenna ranges by the manufacturers them-

5-4 Broadside, end fire, and collinear arrays symbolize various types of antennas.

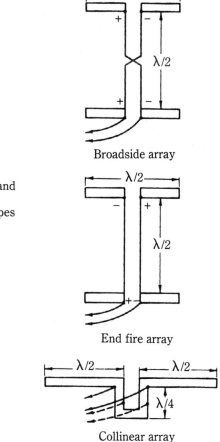

Broadside array

End fire array

Collinear array

selves. However, the graphs and Polaroid pictures are my own measurements taken from sample antennas on the roof and cabled down to a
$150,000 electronics laboratory below. The results are relatively accurate
for signal levels, beamwidths, and front-to-back ratios. Precise beamwidths are not available except on dedicated antenna ranges, but the best
possible using both antenna rotor and compass for generally reasonable
measurements, but not exact. Carrier-to-noise (C/N) information is always
signal-dependent so this parameter can vary considerably and is not especially accurate for this survey.

   Antenna types covered include crossfire, end fire, log periodic, a special rotor-controlled indoor/outdoor plastic (round) antenna, and a new
model from Zenith that's currently manufactured by Winegard. These
examples should offer a working cross section of available radiators now
on the market and readily available. One possible exception would be the
Jerrold/Cometic line now made in Canada and shipped south instead of
from former manufacturing sites such as Pennsylvania or New York. Of
the group, it remains the only true log periodic and deserves notable inclusion, especially with amplification.

Log periodic

Back in 1954, the first year of NTSC color television (approved December
17, 1953 by the FCC), a research group at the University of Illinois developed the log-periodic antenna that was initially marketed by the JFD corporation, then later by the Jerrold Corporation, and today produced to
some extent by Channel Master, a division of the Avnet Corp., Smithfield,
N.C., but not usually advertised as a log periodic in its Quantum series.

   The idea behind this design was to use advantageous driven elements
for maximum gain, phase-change front-to-back 180 degrees for backlobe
protection, and offer a reasonably priced array that would be generally satisfactory. All elements were cut within a half-wavelength of the specific
frequency, spaced so that each depended on the other, resonant at calculated frequencies, and harnessed together for smooth segue from one
channel to another. Unlike the original, however, which was designed for
VHF only, later models included a corner reflector with directors for UHF,
and some versions added parasitic elements for pattern shaping.

   The exact antenna on my roof at the moment is a Jerrold/Cometic log
periodic (Fig. 5-5) that has added the corner reflector, UHF directors, and
the other tuned and driven 37 (total) elements that follow. With a 5 to 6 dB
gain for the low VHF channels, gain jumps to 10 to 11 dB for high VHF
channels and at least 10 dB for UHF. Selected polar patterns show few
backlobes and no noticeable sidelobes, according to the manufacturer.
Breakaway signal blocking elements reduce any FM interference by a
maximum of 12 dB, which should be sufficient to negate all but the very
strongest frequency modulation signals. Thereafter, most name-brand
bandstop filters should fully relieve any residual.

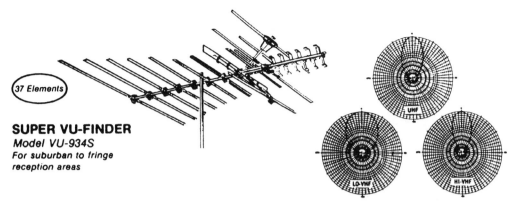

37 Elements

SUPER VU-FINDER
Model VU-934S
For suburban to fringe
reception areas

UHF

LO-VHF

HI-VHF

5-5   The original Jerrold VU-934S log periodic antenna with good gains, beamwidth, FB ratios, and superior polar patterns. Jerrold/Cometic

Generally, I have had excellent results with this antenna, although corrosion and oxidation will accumulate near water areas, especially salt water, which is to be expected. I suggest a change by the seventh year on this or almost any other antenna under similar circumstances. Log periodics don't have a lock on hostile environments any more than their immediate contemporaries.

End-fire array

As with any TV receive antenna, end-fire elements are interconnected with RF harnesses or lines. Leads to the various elements are connected directly and not reversed or crossed over to accommodate the accumulating phase shift. With half-wave spacing, each connecting line will be one-half wavelength long and deliver 180 degrees phase shift. Should quarter-wave spacing be required, connections are one-quarter wave in length, producing a 90 degree phase shift. Increasing the number of elements causes an antenna to become more directional, narrowing the beamwidth accordingly.

A pattern array for the end fire with elements spaced 180 degrees apart (Fig. 5-6) amounts to a bow-tie pattern along the z axis, or 90 degrees apart for a cardioid pattern as illustrated in Fig. 5-7. If elements receive in-phase instead of out-of-phase signals such as those in end fire, the array becomes a broadside antenna.

An interesting aspect of the end-fire antenna appears when looking down on the array in an x-z plane. Reinforcement of the two nondirectional patterns being 180 degrees out of phase actually combine, resulting in a field strength double that of a single antenna. Such maximum field strength occurs at the ends, hence the name *end-fire array*. In the cardioid case where half-wave elements are spaced one-quarter wavelength apart, signals reinforce in the forward direction but are totally out of phase in reverse.

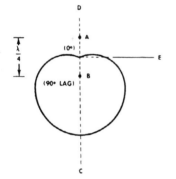

5-6   Example of end-fire, half-wavelength spacing in the *xz* plane.

5-7   Cardioid-shaped pattern forms with quarter-wave spacing and is another end-fire type.

In such antennas you will find parasitic elements that increase the directivity of an antenna but not its actual length. Such an element is usually a half-wave dipole placed parallel with and near a driven element. It will intercept a portion of the energy radiated by the driven element and reradiate it so that the two energies combine to actually modify the directional pattern of the driven element and produce radiation in a single direction. Maximum gain is said to take place when elements are spaced at 0.15 wavelength.

High gain and directivity are two prime antenna requirements, but there must also be substantial numbers supporting considerable front-to-back ratios. For instance, 10 dB FBR would be pathetic, but a 30 dB FBR would bring cheers. All of this means that you want to receive from the front and exclude signals from the back, completely blocking all interference. Many antennas, therefore, have reflectors at the rear that, tuned to a lower frequency than the antenna, block interference. That ordinarily generates backlobes. However, it's often necessary to sacrifice some antenna gain if you want maximum FBR, another trade-off in the design and development business. (You just can't expect everything.) Directors, conversely, are shorter, tuned to a higher frequency, and at spacings greater than 0.1 wavelength for maximum gain. Greater front-to-back ratios are possible with parasitic elements operating as directors rather than reflectors.

End-fire antennas are now manufactured by TDP Electronics in Swannanoa, NC (not far from Ashville). They feature blue and gold polyester finish, permanent electrical connections between elements, stout polypropylene insulators, nonslip mast clamps, an exclusive bow-tie corner UHF reflector, and all the original perma-tuned circuits bequeathed by dear old RCA, who originally engineered these radiators and manufactured them in this same plant on Old Bee Tree Road. The product, and its amplification, as you will see, is outstanding and colorful, too! But the best news may be in newly-designed variable-gain amplifiers and customer-switched FM trap. Both innovations are improvements over fixed gains and/or traps, and we expect more than casual results with these Permacolor Mod. 10G207 antenna-mounted amplifiers. Gains and performance figures come later with the various tests.

Indoor/marine

When first-class, substantial outdoor antennas can't be used, something else has to take their place besides last-resort rabbit ears. TDR also fabricates one of these that has a series of tuned elements and a motor/rotor that turns these LC parallel VHF components and the UHF bow tie (Fig. 5-8).

Operating from 120 Vac and/or direct current at 12 volts, direct current is furnished by a half-wave, transformer-coupled and regulated 8.3 V supply. The Mini-State antenna system is enclosed in a plastic radome, a rotator drive assembly with remote control, two transistor amplifiers, and a cam-driven, end-stop, bidirectional motor switch. When antennas inside the radome are rotated, lamps light various colors in the remote control for NSEW as coils and the bow tie assume different circular positions. With the 5M5740 home version, 60 feet of signal and rotor cable are supplied webbed together and terminated with respective F connectors and a five-pin plug for motor control. Usually, only one receiver is driven from this unit, but there is an optional amplifier available that drives at least two receivers. The schematic of the 5M5740 or 5MS750 illustrated is not especially clear, but it is the best currently available.

As indicated, the unit can be mounted outside on a pole or standard TV mast or it can even be hung upside down in an attic or other enclosed space. With amplification, the unit is substantially better than common rabbit ears, and its wavelength-tuned and rotatable receptors are especially effective if placed in front of a window facing many or most TV stations. We have yet to discuss nonrotor indoor antennas, but the lack of directional tuning is probably a handicap. As for marine installations, such TDP antennas offer small wind resistance, are sturdy, occupy little space,

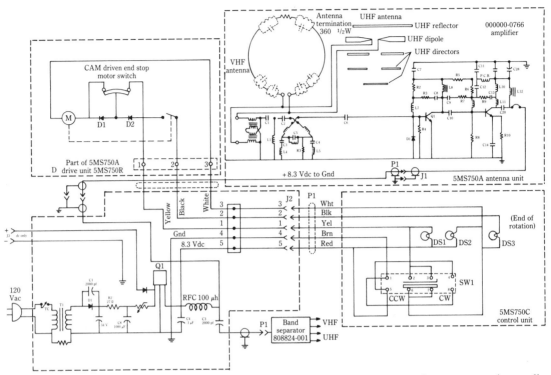

5-8 Schematic of TDP's Mini-State indoor/outdoor and marine plastic antenna that can rotate internally for best direction.

and should be satisfactory for distances up to 30 miles or so. In purely attic installations without an opening toward broadcast towers, you can expect a 3 dB drop during routine operation and up to 6 dB with heavy ice and snow. Therefore, if you can't have a first-rate outdoor antenna, the 5M5740 or one of its optional versions will certainly capture most VHF and all of UHF quite adequately. Marine versions operate equally well on 12 Vdc.

Crossfire and Quantum

While we don't dwell on the Quantum series in this report, it should have some coverage. Most of the information, however, concentrates on the Ultra-Hi Crossfire series, both types being manufactured and marketed by Channel Master, now of Smithfield, a few miles south of Raleigh, NC. This large plant was formerly the headquarters of Sylvania TV before it was assimilated by North American Philips, Knoxville, TN.

Crossfires (Fig. 5-9) are another among the inline series of television antennas with directors and a corner reflector for UHF, reinforced with driven and parasitic elements for VHF, all of which are harness-connected and electroplate-coated. VHF and UHF receptors, however, are isolated from one another to prevent UV channel interference. Nine of these Cross-

Channel Master

5-9 A heavy hitter: the Ultra-Hi Crossfire designed for far-fringe U/V reception.

fire arrays are offered by Channel Master, four large ones with double booms and five without. Operating characteristics range from deepest fringe U/V to near fringe U and suburban V.

Each antenna has spun-boom ends to eliminate wind whistles, corner reflector UHF, aluminum phasing crossover harness, insulated element spacers, reinforced element sleeves, and heavy-duty elements. Boom lengths measure between 77 and 173 inches, depending on antenna size and usage. These are broader bandwidth radiators than the Quantums, although gains are adequate with few sidelobes. And since corner reflectors have supplanted the simple dipole, UHF performance should be improved, with overall U/V response better for medium and strong signal areas. Where high directivity and narrow beamwidths are required, the Quantum should still be considered a highly desirable product.

The Quantum is especially noted for high interference rejection (meaning few sidelobes) resulting from patented front directors and high-efficiency rear reflector, plus specially tapered drive and high front-to-back ratios, which can be as great as 35 dB. Without amplification, our model 1162A designed for fringe V and deep fringe U performs well for most stations located in the general vicinity. It's heavy-duty elements and insulators are very adequate in all sorts of weather, and UHF response within reasonable limits is very good. Gold-hued alodine coatings seem to reject oxidation and corrosion. Parasitic elements are all mounted on standoff insulators, while driven elements are riveted and position-locked on the two electrical harness booms. These booms are then isolated from the mounting mast by large and durable plastic insulators. Quantums may be custom ordered according to circumstance. Boom lengths range between 111 and 189 inches, so if you want U/V and FM, be prepared for a rather large antenna.

In evaluating these two reflectors, let's observe an unamplified Quantum first and then work with both amplified and unamplified Crossfires.

Results could be interesting, especially in view of somewhat broader beamwidths and varied gains.

Amplifiers

There's no substitute for amplifiers. Most manufacturers offer a medium-gain variety such as the Channel Master's 0064C, which has three transistors, a 25 dB FM switchable FM trap that's also tunable, noise figures of less than 4, and a maximum microvolt input of 200 μV. Typical gain ranges from 16 to 17 dB on VHF to 23 dB on UHF. Designed to be mounted on the mast, it is fully weatherproof and outputs with a 75-ohm lead-in connector. The input, however, is 300 ohms and requires several feet of 300-ohm twinlead to complete the antenna-amplifier connection. Operationally, there's no fault to find, only good amplification, but unshielded cabling in dual conductors to the mast makes it subject to noise and adjacent channel pickup that could render problems in city areas. It would also be helpful to be able to vary gain at the receiver if there was either an overload or adjacent channel problem. An example of this appears next.

The TDP (Tandy Electronics) amplifier has both a customer-switchable FM trap as well as a screwdriver-adjust variable gain control. In addition, plastic fittings allow the unit to be clamped to three different varieties of booms near the UHF corner reflector. And although it, too, has a twin-lead input, the length is only several inches versus the several feet of its competitors. Wouldn't it be nice to have an antenna with good shielded, close-coupled connections switchable between the two impedances? The better television receivers now have a single U/V input, so why not a unified output from the good antennas? Would a built-in balun be that difficult?

At any rate, the Tandy is dandy except for an extra wide-range gain control. The model 10G 207 has VHF/FM gain at 25 dB and UHF 20 dB and comes equipped with special overload gain protection. The unit is attractively packaged and is custom manufactured by Tandy Electronics. Adjustable gain allows a 10 dB signal reduction, and there is a power LED on the indoor power portion that glows red when the amplifier is operating. Short-circuit protection is also provided, along with two pairs of inserts for varied boom clamping to secure the amplifier. Herringbone interference patterns from FM are easily restricted by switching in the FM filter, which is probably a notch trap that removes 88 to 108 MHz frequencies from the picture by blocking or shunt filtering. Operationally, there are no problems and little noise is amplified.

The Jerrold/Cometic amplifier is very similar to the Channel Master, but does have aluminum connector bars for direct antenna mounting as well as a secure boom clamp. Model 5287 has a noise figure of 4.5 dB VHF and 3.5 to 6.5 dB for UHF. Maximum inputs are 50,000 microvolts on VHF and 40,000 microvolts on UHF, usually very adequate for medium or distant locations from the transmitters. Cometic also has a more expensive version that can handle up to 85,000 μV on VHF. Here, again, this amplifier performs very well, is small enough not to be a boom obstruction, and works well with medium to higher gain antennas. Here, it is connected to a VU-934SR, which is a very good all-purpose reflector. The antenna itself has breakaway elements for FM rejection.

Antenna comments

Each receptor from every manufacturer has its own idiosyncrasies that can even vary among those in the identical group. Since I could not test them all, I selected only certain models, especially those antennas most probably used in general service: neither close-in suburban nor on a long-distance fringe. And, since our testing area used is approximately 30 to 35 miles from both Washington, D.C. and Baltimore, MD, checks on medium-range antennas makes reasonable logic.

Initial designs on these antennas are tested under much more precise conditions than occur here. But often in actual rather than simulated cw circumstances, advantages and disadvantages appear unanticipated and do help to evaluate the unit under investigation, especially if there are strong, medium, and weak broadcast stations around that offer a considerable variety of different signal strengths and programming. Everything doesn't simply depend on C/N, FBR, signal levels, etc., but the image itself and any adjacent channel intrusion is also one of the subjective facets that must be included. Video and audio marred by interference makes the job of viewing suffer loss.

With the exception of the 5M5740 indoor oval "frisbee," most of these antennas have similar dimensions and signal ranges. I have found, however, that every one of them produces considerably better gains and overall results when amplified, and interference such as noise is not appreciably increased. This means that the carrier signal portion of C/N has expanded, while noise has remained relatively the same. The noise floor in use for the measurements, however, was the noise floor of the analyzer rather than that of the TV channel signal under test. So we did subtract 2.5 dB for the spectrum analyzer's detector and amplifier as well as 3 dB additional for possible merging of signal and analyzer noise levels. Therefore, for every C/N measurement, 5.5 dB was subtracted from the 7L12's readings. This lowers the C/N figure, but it makes the measurement considerably more realistic.

When erected, all antennas had rotors and were placed at the same level on a roof some 25 feet above ground and fairly clear of trees except due north and due south. Without leaves, however, this makes little difference to TV-transmitted signals, so the readings should be reasonably accurate. West and northwest readings also took place over water, where most of the TV stations were located. So signal conditions were relatively good, mounting equivalent, and the various analyzer measurements combined with visual sightings should offer worthwhile analyses. Generally, the amplified versions of all antennas deserve the most scrutiny because this is a special aspect of the survey. I firmly believe that HDTV will require amplification and the best of antennas to operate as intended.

The larger antennas

Since larger antennas are of prime interest, let's examine signal and visual results together for a composite report. Most of these receptors have over 30 dipoles, with varying numbers of driven and parasitic elements. All are aluminum construction with single center support booms and elements attached to one another with either straight or crossover harnesses, depending on design. You'd think that a number of parasitic elements would force small beamwidths, but this is not necessarily true because waveshaping doesn't always determine signal ingress to the driven/active elements. So keep a wary eye on the comparator chart while advancing through the remainder of the discussion. Let's begin with Channel Master's contributions and work from there.

Channel Master manufactures several varieties of antennas from inexpensive to deluxe, and as you might expect, the more you pay, the better are the results. Top-of-the-line Quantum's have good unamplified signal characteristics but fairly narrow beamwidths. There are no problems, however, with adjacent channel interference, and they're both handsome and very sturdily built. I have analyzed one unamplified version just to see exactly what it would do and was pleasantly surprised. Actually, for a slightly limited range, especially on UHF, this antenna accepted signals from both Baltimore and Washington nicely with little necessity to move the antenna at all. Hence, it has broad and clean coverage with no amplification in one band and somewhat poorer response in another. With amplification, the 1162A fringe VHF and deep fringe UHF probably would have given equivalent competition quite a tussel. The price, however, is somewhat more, and with amplification, considerably more. Therefore, with an essential rotor and amplification, either the 1161A or the 1162A deliver excellent signals at considerable distances with more than adequate results. Good, firm mounting, however, is assuredly required for all weather operations because this is not a lightweight array.

Newest in the Channel Master line consists of the Ultra-Hi Crossfire, a considerably lighter antenna with a number of parasitic elements and a nice UHF corner reflector with plenty of out-front directors. My model, the 3674A, comes with both driven elements and parasitics. In setting up this antenna, be sure that criss-crossing members of the harness do not touch, and do be careful of the mast amplifier mounting. Between the two, by carefully adjusting the insulator separators and deleting the twinlead between mast and amplifier by mounting the amplifier on the antenna boom just in front of the UHF corner reflector, secondary images were avoided and possibly better gains realized.

The 3674A was designed for fringe UHF and far-suburban VHF and supports these advertisements very well. Actually, it was equal or better in VHF gain than most others we tested. It seemed to perform better in a broadband signal reception sense at VHF than when amplified, which decidedly does require a rotor where there are many stations and frequencies in close proximity. So designed gains do make a difference in both versions—something which bears considering when purchasing.

With the 0064C amplifier, you don't approach overload, but there is slight softening of images unless exactly tuned to some channels. In the unamplified version, this does not occur due to diminished gain. However, the more distant UHF channels could use a few more dBs, although widely dispersed VHF channels are very good indeed. Therefore, if you're choosing between Quantum and Crossfire, take into account all these considerations, remembering the design purpose of each.

TDP (RCA/Tandy) is the same line of quality antennas originally designed and manufactured by the great Radio Corporation of America before selling out to General Electric. I was especially anxious to test these reflectors to note any changes or improvements, and there is at least one obvious one: the amplifier. Otherwise, hardware appearance and specifications are similar, if not identical, and Tandy Corp. can remain happy with the product.

The initial radiator tested was the 4BG30, followed by the 4BG26 in both amplified and unamplified versions. The results, as you shall see, were not especially surprising and evolved very much as we remembered them from a number of years ago. The testing difference, however, is done by both visual and comparative examinations with a calibrated spectrum analyzer. The antennas themselves are a very good blend of signal-capture hardware, appearance, and price. But an outstanding result, especially on the 4BG26, involved TDP's new variable-gain amplifier. With this special amplification, the 4BG26 was most certainly equal to many of its much larger and more expensive contemporaries and is heartily recommended for many installations up to distances of at least 30 miles, depending on terrain or man-made obstructions. With its wide beamwidth and somewhat smaller front-to-back ratios, there is always a chance of cochannel problems and even sidelobes. But in fairly open territory, and especially with rotor, you couldn't ask for a better-performing, low-cost radiator that could be compact enough to grace many a nontrussed attic or open chimney with effective signal capture for most local TV stations. But don't forget the amplifier!

Comparative analysis

An analysis of the foregoing television antennas was conducted during the winter of 1990-91 on an island named Turkey Point just south of Annapolis, MD. At any one time, four were mounted at equivalent heights some 5 feet above the building's roof and all equipped with 360-degree rotators.

And three of the four were separated by distances of at least 25 feet or more to prevent interaction.

Most of the downlead signals passed through a pair of couplers and one splitter for the spectrum analyzer; consequently, you can allow a 10 dB loss in all measurements, and when computing exact figures, 10 dB should be *added* to each reading. For carrier-to-noise (C/N) evaluations, however, there was a *deduction* of 5.5 dB to allow for spectrum analyzer detector and internal losses including a 3 dB arbitrary subtraction for a probable instrument noise floor combining with that of the carrier under study (Fig. 5-10). You may not, however, change this figure because it is a requirement for factual calibration.

In such measurements, I have discovered that signal levels are often much more important than C/N if for no other reason that regardless of C/N, you can't receive working information unless the dBm power level is sufficient for an antenna to operate. Carrier-to-noise does offer a lesser or greater ratio between the two electrical conditions, and it also is directly proportional to signal-to-noise (S/N), which is an absolute figure that must be produced to render an agreeable picture.

In AM modulation such as broadcast television, the following equality exists:

$$S/N = C/N + 4 \text{ or } 6 \text{ dB (depending on the authority)}$$

In FM modulation, especially for satellite work where noise in color is considered triangular:

$$S/N = C/N + 37.5 \text{ dB}$$

These are two very simple equations that are thoroughly useful in determining if you have enough noise and signal separation to adequately view a decent picture.

Signal levels, however, are not arbitrary or especially flexible. On either satellite or terrestrial broadcast, such carrier levels must approach or surpass -40 dBm following the antenna and/or amplification to view good video. Usually, under such circumstances, C/N measurements take care of themselves.

Therefore, in viewing the graphs that follow, pay more attention to the levels rather than C/N amplitudes. But front-to-back ratios are also important because this indicates the amount of interference that could creep in from the rear of your reflector. As for sidelobes, an accurate assessment of these requires a sweep of all frequencies in the two VHF and UHF bands, and this was not practical in the examination. Generally, however, nothing unusual was noted throughout the tests except the huge signal wallop of channel 22, only a few miles away, compared with all other transmitters at 35 miles or more distant (Fig. 5-11). Without amplification, the channel 22 effect was negligible or nonexistent; but with amplification, channel 20

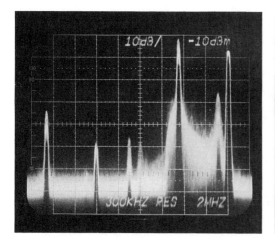

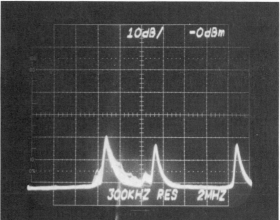

5-10 To find the noise floor of any spectrum analyzer, just engage a low-value kHz filter.

5-11 This much signal at −12 dBm can play havoc with adjacent channels.

5-12 Rotate your antenna for diminished gain or attenuation.

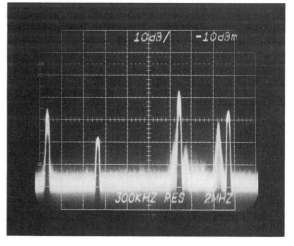

was affected considerably unless the antenna was tuned exactly. This was difficult owing to the broad range and angles of the separate transmitters in Maryland, the District of Columbia, and Virginia, the prime objective being to tune each antenna so that most or all could be received with little or no antenna movement. If this was possible—and in several instances, with the broader band antennas, it was (Fig. 5-12)—then an antenna rotor might not be mandatory for those who prefer only the major channels.

Now, bearing in mind that you must add 10 dB to each of the indicated levels in Fig. 5-13, let's begin our discussion of the various results and see what these connected dots actually mean. An amplified version of the Channel Master Ultra-Hi Crossfire could be a good starter. Measurement

Chart designation	Antenna name	Channel	C/N	−3 dB bandwidth	FBR
A (★)	Jerrold/Cometic VU934-SR	2	39.5	2 × 18	17
		11	36.5	2 × 20	17
		24	42	2 × 10	14
B (◆)	TDP (Tandy) 4BG26	2	44.5	2 × 31	12
		11	34.5	2 × 30	22
		24	54.5	2 × 20	10
C (✖)	TDP (Tandy) 4BG30	2	38.5	2 × 30	12
		11	38.5	2 × 28	18
		24	51	2 × 21	26
D (●)	Winegard/Zenith 973-4002 Crossfire	2	34.5	2 × 30	16
		11	28.5	2 × 15	22
		24	34.5	2 × 20	14
E (▲)	Channel Master Ultra-Hi Crossfire 3674A	2	44.5	2 × 20	12
		11	50.5	2 × 15	20
		24	49.5	2 × 22	28
F (■)	Channel Master Quantum 1161 A	2	30.5	2 × 22	22
		11	34.5	2 × 15	22
		24	29.5	2 × 14	15

Notes

1) Amplified (heavier lines)
2) Unamplified (lighter lines)
3) Due to two couplers and one splitter, all signals are 10 dB less than actual values. Therefore, add 10 dB for real levels and values.
4) Dots indicate signal levels in dBm. Where there are no dots or other symbols, signals were below −66 dBm.
5) Distances to Washington, D.C. and Baltimore transmitters are about 35 miles.
6) Noise floor is approximately 8 dB.
7) C/N measurements reduced 5.5 dB for analyzer internal losses.

5-13   Spectrum analysis of six of the better TV antennas in the U.S., covering 18 widely separated broadcast stations in the Washington, D.C. and Baltimore areas. Note that the heavier lines on the graph on page 129 are the antennas with amplification and the lighter lines are unamplified.

Channel number

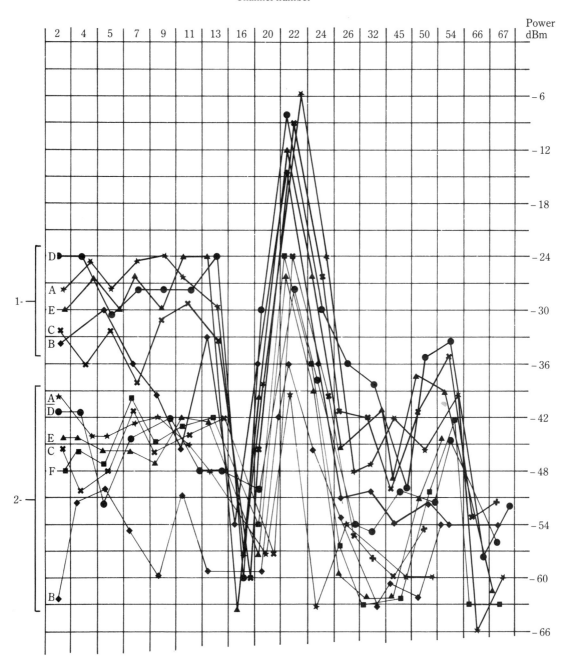

levels begin at − 30 dBm for channel 2, progress to − 26 dBm for channel 4, and continuing in a sawtooth up/down configuration to channels 11 and 13, where they peak in the VHF range at − 24 dBm.

For channel 16, however, this eastern shore station is considerably further distant than the D.C.-Baltimore group, and therefore there is a dip to −64 dBm. Thereafter, there's a sharp increase for channel 20 to − 40 dBm and a considerable jump to − 12 dBm for nearby, powerful PBS channel 22.

Channel 24 drops the signal to − 26 dBm, and channel 26 falls to − 46 dBm. But once again, the pattern increases to − 41 for channel 26, falls to −49 for channel 45, recovers to − 37 dBm for channel 50, to − 39 for 54, and finally bottoms out at − 62 for channel 67. Note that a signal for channel 66 was not recorded, but all others are there.

From this graph, you might conclude that VHF gains are especially good and relatively constant, but very distant stations aren't exactly first class. On the other hand, UHF reception is better than reasonable. The unamplified version follows along the same pattern at about 15 dB or less, and has no signal capture beyond channel 54.

Above the amplified 3674A graph is that of Jerrold/Cometic's 4BG30, an all-driven VHF element log periodic with 180-degree phase reversal for back signal rejection. It, too, exhibits high gain for VHF with only a modest drop for channel 16 on the eastern shore. But its channel 22 high point is − 6 dBm, and it appears quite uniform between channels 26 and 54, dropping to only − 48 dBm and then rising to − 40 dBm before finally resting in the − 50s for channels 66 and 67. This is a very uniform, high-gain antenna that was originally designed by Jerrold Electronics and remains one of the top performers in the industry. Unfortunately, it has to travel all the way from Delhi, Ontario, Canada instead of Pennsylvania or New York, which can become somewhat of a complication, making the reflector a little more expensive.

TDP's amplified version of the 4BG30 has somewhat less gain but is very good at VHF. A moderately priced antenna available from Swannanoa, NC, the channel 16 dip goes to − 60 dBm, recovers to − 46 for channel 20, and reaches − 9 dBm for channel 22, the strong one. The peak then recedes to − 24 for channel 24, − 41 for channel 26, − 42 for channel 32, takes a dip to − 50 for 45, then climbs in 6 dB increments for channels 50 and 54 before bottoming out at − 53 and − 52 for channels 66 and 67. I was able to adjust the pointing angle of this antenna so that virtually every one of the local TV stations was available with good results, excepting channel 16, which is in a totally different direction. Considering price and performance, this antenna is excellent!

The other graphs, you should be able to follow and judge for yourself. Nonetheless, refer to the amplified and nonamplified versions of TDP's 4BG26. This is actually a local (metropolitan) antenna with good beamwidth and only fair gain in the unamplified version. But study the amplified track of this little fellow, and its gains and uniformity will surprise you. Its maximum signal drop, for instance, only goes to -54 dBm, and its channel-22 high point is -14 dBm. The amplifier almost seems to have been designed to put the 4BG26 in the same league with the big boys who are not amplified. In addition, because of its small size, this unit should work well in many attics where larger reflectors would be unable to turn.

I therefore suggest that this antenna be used almost always with its variable amplifier, both indoors and out. Because its beamwidths are considerable, you may find antenna rotors are not a mandatory requirement as they have become with many of the larger radiators. If you add the suggested 10 dB removed earlier by couplers and the splitter, a true signal level of -48 dBm isn't a hindrance at all.

Figure 5-13 also shows comparative C/N, beamwidth, and front-to-back ratios (FBR) for the antennas at selected channels 2, 11, and 24. Overall, the Channel Master Quantum is the FBR leader, and the 4BG26 has the beamwidth and some of the highest gain. Channel Master's Ultra-Hi Crossfire does well in both gain and FBR. Observe that the least FBR measures 10, while the highest is 28, followed by 26 and 18. But also recall that these are some of the best intermediate-gain antennas in the land, and their statistics should be good!

As the world turns, I expect some realignment in both the TV picture as well as TV antennas and accessories. U.S.-based sources for TVs, receptors, cathode-ray tubes, fiberoptic cable, computers, and video games are becoming more predominant then heretofore, and we should see a substantial decrease in the eventual balance of payments that have caused such misery from overseas. Conversely, some of the weaker players in these categories will have to fall by the wayside due to price and the fast pace of product improvements.

Indoors

Neither the 10 dB loss nor other unlisted measurements apply to the 5MS740 Tandy indoor antenna or rabbit ears—only 4 dB loss in the receiver-spectrum analyzer splitter (see Fig. 5-14). Note that inside and outside figures correlate fairly closely if the disk antenna is placed close to a window. Regardless, however, inside a business or dwelling, you can count on at least a -3 dB loss, and considerably more if there is a slate roof.

When comparing the 5MS740 to rabbit ears, regular channels often cannot be received and there is a 16 to 20 dB difference in signal levels almost anywhere in the graph, making many people wonder why "rabbit ears" were ever domesticated in the first place. From the graph, it's apparent they still belong in a landfill.

Also included in this chapter are some antenna gain and polar patterns furnished by the manufacturers that should serve to further aid in analyzing what one reflector does and the other doesn't (Figs. 5-15 through 5-19). And as we continue toward the eventual arrival of HDTV, more than passing

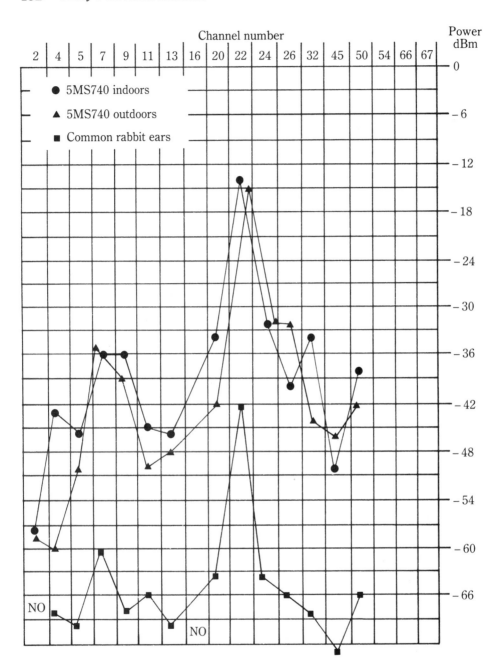

Notes

1) For actual measurements, *add* 4 dB for splitter loss for both Tandy and rabbit ears.
2) Transmitter distances are approximately 35 miles from Annapolis, MD.
3) Noise floor is approximately 8 dB.

5-14 Tandy's TDP Mini-State indoor/outdoor plastic antenna versus common rabbit ears. Note the 20 dB difference!

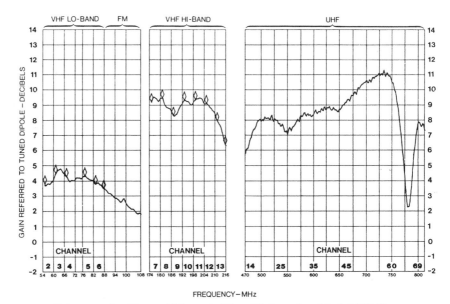

5-15 Gain chart for Channel Master's Ultra-Hi Crossfire, Model 3674B. Channel Master

attention should be paid to what each antenna does and how. Remember that an additional 3 dB gain is required as well as is good, broad beamwidth, a pair of incompatibles that are often hard to acquire.

The assessment

This chapter has been an assessment of the better antennas available today in a test setting that anyone with a good spectrum analyzer can accomplish. Testing simply requires considerable accuracy and patience. There's no trick to the proceedings at all. It's just a bundle of attentive work coupled with dogged persistence. (This study consumed about five days, followed by the write-up.)

In the signal comparison chart in Fig. 5-13, the dots illustrate the dBm signal level, with connecting lines drawn between. Where there are no dots, it means this channel bottoms out somewhere below the −66 dBm cutoff level. At −60 dBm, you'll see only a snowy (noisy) picture that's not worth viewing. At −50 dBm, however, the image is quite passable, and at −40 dBm, scenes are in full color and have good definition/resolution. Therefore, in any antenna signal measurements, aim for −40 dBm out of the antenna, amplifier, or block downconverter (in the case of satellites), and you should enjoy the results. Of course, the final image arbiter becomes your television receiver/monitor. Good signals into a worthwhile receiver usually bring happiness to the beholder! But even with the best antenna and downlead cable in existence, any receiver without at least comb filter luma-chroma separation can't do incoming signals justice. And for the forthcoming HDTV, I earnestly suggest UL-approved RG6/U cable

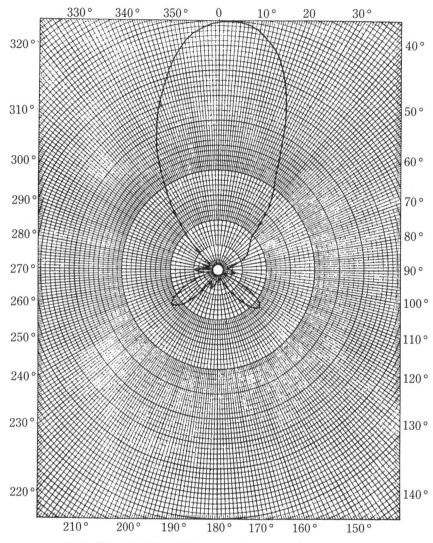

5-16   The 600 MHz UHF pattern for the 3674B. Channel Master

for maximum passband and all-weather protection. You'll need this, even inside the house.

Winegard/Zenith

Introduced in mid 1990, Winegard is now producing a brand-new television antenna for both itself and Zenith that promises some interesting innovations for the first major design change in many years. Introduced in seven models, the VHF portion has an impedance of 75 ohms, while UHF remains at 300 ohms. A matching harness connects the two for a regular

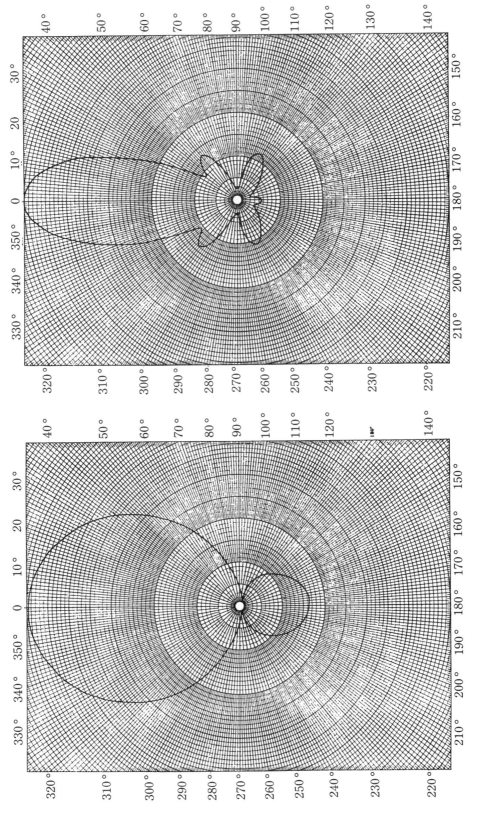

5-17 Channels 2 and 11 polar patterns for the 3674B. Channel Master

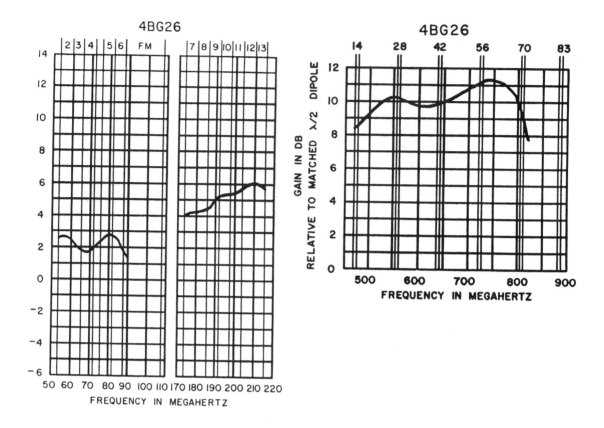

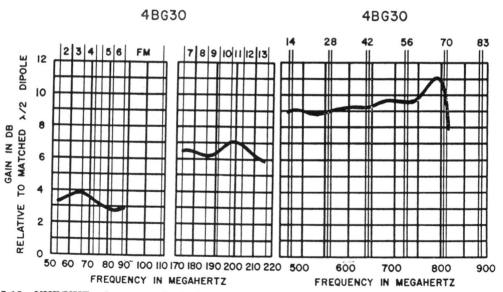

5-18 VHF/UHF gain patterns for both the 4BG26 and 4BG30 TDP antennas. TDP, a Division of Tandy Electronics

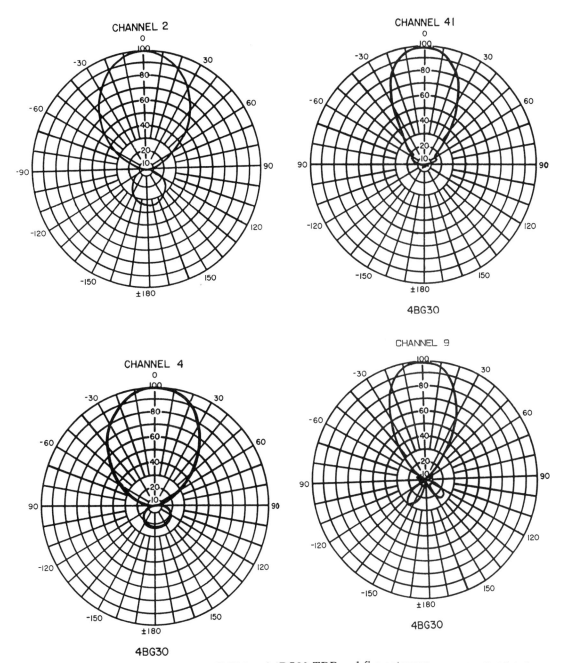

5-19   Polar pattern sampling for the 4BG26 and 4BG30 TDP end-fire antennas. TDP, a Division of Tandy Electronics

75-ohm downlead that requires no additional balun. This means that the latest receivers with a single coaxial cable input can receive inputs without splitters or other paraphernalia either directly or through one of the improved amplifiers which have been so successful throughout various tests in this chapter. If these direct connections have the singular advantage one strongly suspects, the additional 3 dB required for HDTV will have been realized without any special amplification other than that which might already be available. Testing, however, is believing, and one won't be positive until at least one of these antennas is on the chimney.

The particular antenna Zenith has authorized for testing is a "near fringe" 973-4002 unit with 27 elements: four driven and three parasitic for low VHF; four driven and nine parasitic for high VHF; and four driven and thirteen parasitic for UHF. Its boom length is 99½ inches, its turning radius is 71 inches, and it is UPS shippable. Low band gain averages at 5.7 dB, high band gain averages at 9.7 dB, and UHF averages at 10.3. All aluminum elements and booms are acrylic-coated to prevent oxidization and corrosion.

Thus far, that's all available of this new line except for the polar patterns for a number of channels (Fig. 5-20) as well as 3 dB beamwidths and the various front-to-back ratios that were tabulated from the patterns. Sampling I used was channels 4, 7, 14, and 50, which should cover both VHF and UHF as credible examples. The F/B of channel 14 isn't exactly a winner, nor is channel 7. But overall, except for sidelobes on channel 7, all polar patterns are reasonable and probably much more accurate than those ordinarily published as general examples of some antenna series. At least these are the individual plots and would appear to be taken directly from a calibrated far-field antenna range without retouching.

Two types of developmental amplifiers were sent with 973-4002 whose power supplies are identified as 9000 and 7070. Neither has adjustable gain nor customer-operated FM traps. Testing was not especially productive.

Regular antenna checks revealed very reasonable operation over the U/V bands, especially most of VHF. With amplification, however, some ghosting was noted in upper VHF and UHF, which seemed to be caused by the amplifiers, primarily, with a possibility of parasitic reflections (however, this was not conclusive during the short interval available for testing before manuscript delivery to the publisher).

Channel listings

The following constitutes a complete TV and CATV listing of all television channels in current use by Zenith Electronics and is published here for your selective use.

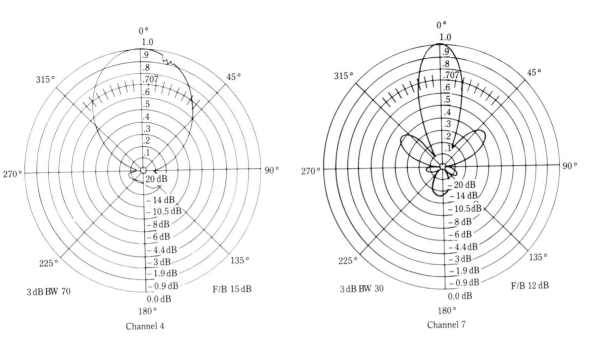

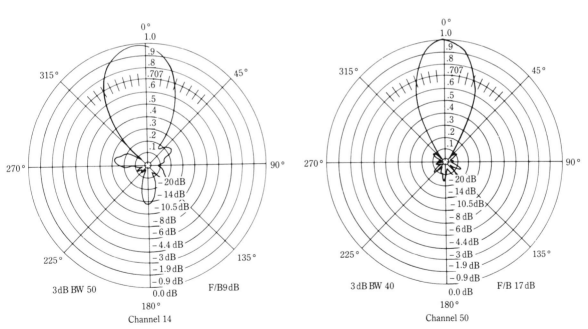

5-20 Characteristics polar patterns of the new Zenith/Winegard near-fringe 75/300-ohm antennas. Bandwidths and front-to-back (F/B) ratios are calculated on each pattern. Zenith Electronics

BROADCAST CHANNELS

\# \# \# ZENITH VHF FREQUENCY CHART \# \# \#

CHANNEL NUMBER	BAND	VIDEO CARRIER	AUDIO CARRIER	OSC FREQ.	DIVIDE BY 64
		\# \# \# LOW BAND VHF \# \# \#			
2	54 - 60	55.25	59.75	101	1.57813
3	60 - 66	61.25	65.75	107	1.67188
4	66 - 72	67.25	71.75	113	1.76563
5	76 - 82	77.25	81.75	123	1.92188
6	82 - 88	83.25	87.75	129	2.01563
		\# \# \# HIGH BAND VHF \# \# \#			
7	174 - 180	175.25	179.75	221	3.45313
8	180 - 186	181.25	185.75	227	3.54688
9	186 - 192	187.25	191.75	233	3.64063
10	192 - 198	193.25	197.75	239	3.73438
11	198 - 204	199.25	203.75	245	3.82831
12	204 - 210	205.25	209.75	251	3.92188
13	210 - 216	211.25	215.75	257	4.01563

\# \# \# ZENITH UHF TV BAND FREQUENCY CHART \# \# \#

CHANNEL NUMBER	BAND	VIDEO CARRIER	SOUND CARRIER	OSC. FREQ.	DIVIDE BY 64
14	470 - 476	471.25	475.75	517	8.07813
15	476 - 482	477.25	481.75	523	8.17188
16	482 - 488	483.25	487.75	529	8.26563
17	488 - 494	489.25	493.75	535	8.35938
18	494 - 500	495.25	499.75	541	8.45313
19	500 - 506	501.25	505.75	547	8.54688
20	506 - 512	507.25	511.75	553	8.64063
21	512 - 518	513.25	517.75	559	8.73438
22	518 - 524	519.25	523.75	565	8.82813
23	524 - 530	525.25	529.75	571	8.92188
24	530 - 536	531.25	535.75	577	9.01563
25	536 - 542	537.25	541.75	583	9.10938
26	542 - 548	543.25	547.75	589	9.20313
27	548 - 554	549.25	553.75	595	9.29688
28	554 - 560	555.25	559.75	601	9.39063
29	560 - 566	561.25	565.75	607	9.48438
30	566 - 572	567.25	571.75	613	9.57813
31	572 - 578	573.25	577.75	619	9.67188
32	578 - 584	579.25	583.75	625	9.76563
33	584 - 590	585.25	589.75	631	9.85938
34	590 - 596	591.25	595.75	637	9.95313
35	596 - 602	597.25	601.75	643	10.0469
36	602 - 608	603.25	607.75	649	10.1406

CHANNEL NUMBER	BAND	VIDEO CARRIER	SOUND CARRIER	OSC. FREQ.	DIVIDE BY 64
37	608 - 614	609.25	613.75	655	10.2344
38	614 - 620	615.25	619.75	661	10.3281
39	620 - 626	621.25	625.75	667	10.4219
40	626 - 632	627.25	631.75	673	10.5156
41	632 - 638	633.25	637.75	679	10.6094
42	638 - 644	639.25	643.75	685	10.7031
43	644 - 650	645.25	649.75	691	10.7969
44	650 - 656	651.25	655.75	697	10.8906
45	656 - 662	657.25	661.75	703	10.9844
46	662 - 668	663.25	667.75	709	11.0781
47	668 - 674	669.25	673.75	715	11.1719
48	674 - 680	675.25	679.75	721	11.2656
49	680 - 686	681.25	685.75	727	11.3594
50	686 - 692	687.25	691.75	733	11.4531
51	692 - 698	693.25	697.75	739	11.5469
52	698 - 704	699.25	703.75	745	11.6406
53	704 - 710	705.25	709.75	751	11.7344
54	710 - 716	711.25	715.75	757	11.8281
55	716 - 722	717.25	721.75	763	11.9219
56	722 - 728	723.25	727.75	769	12.0156
57	728 - 734	729.25	733.75	775	12.1094
58	734 - 740	735.25	739.75	781	12.2031
59	740 - 746	741.25	745.75	787	12.2969
60	746 - 752	747.25	751.75	793	12.3906
61	752 - 758	753.25	757.75	799	12.4844
62	758 - 764	759.25	763.75	805	12.5781
63	764 - 770	765.25	769.75	811	12.6719
64	770 - 776	771.25	775.75	817	12.7656
65	776 - 782	777.25	781.75	823	12.8594
66	782 - 788	783.25	787.75	829	12.9531
67	788 - 794	789.25	793.75	835	13.0469
68	794 - 800	795.25	799.75	841	13.1406
69	800 - 806	801.25	805.75	847	13.2344

CATV CHANNELS

* * * ZENITH VHF AND CATV MID BAND FREQUENCY CHART * * *

CHANNEL NUMBER	BAND	VIDEO CARRIER	AUDIO CARRIER	OSC FREQ.	DIVIDE BY 64	CHANNEL INDICATOR
		* * * LOW BAND VHF * * *				
2	54 - 60	55.25	59.75	101	1.57813	2
3	60 - 66	61.25	65.75	107	1.67188	3
4	66 - 72	67.25	71.75	113	1.76563	4
A-B(4+)	70.75-76.75	72.00	76.50	117.75	1.83984	00
5	76 - 82	77.25	81.75	123	1.92188	5
6	82 - 88	83.25	87.75	129	2.01563	6
		* * * MID BAND CATV * * *				
A-2	108 - 114	109.25	113.75	155	2.42188	0
A-1	114 - 120	115.25	119.75	161	2.51563	1
A	120 - 126	121.25	125.75	167	2.60938	14

CHANNEL NUMBER	BAND	VIDEO CARRIER	AUDIO CARRIER	OSC FREQ.	DIVIDE BY 64	CHANNEL INDICATOR
B	126 - 132	127.25	131.75	173	2.70313	15
C	132 - 138	133.25	137.75	179	2.79688	16
D	138 - 144	139.25	143.75	185	2.89063	17
E	144 - 150	145.25	149.75	191	2.98438	18
F	150 - 156	151.25	155.75	197	3.07813	19
G	156 - 162	157.25	161.75	203	3.17188	20
H	162 - 168	163.25	167.75	209	3.26563	21
I	168 - 174	169.25	173.75	215	3.35938	22
* * * HIGH BAND VHF * * *						
7	174 - 180	175.25	179.75	221	3.45313	7
8	180 - 186	181.25	185.75	227	3.54688	8
9	186 - 192	187.25	191.75	233	3.64063	9
10	192 - 198	193.25	197.75	239	3.73438	10
11	198 - 204	199.25	203.75	245	3.82831	11
12	204 - 210	205.25	209.75	251	3.92188	12
13	210 - 216	211.25	215.75	257	4.01563	13

* * * ZENITH SUPERBAND AND HYPERBAND CATV FREQUENCY CHART * * *

CHANNEL NUMBER	BAND	VIDEO CARRIER	AUDIO CARRIER	OSC FREQ.	DIVIDE BY 64	CHANNEL INDICATOR
* * * SUPERBAND CATV * * *						
J	216 - 222	217.25	221.75	263	4.10938	23
K	222 - 228	223.25	227.75	269	4.20313	24
L	228 - 234	229.25	233.75	275	4.29688	25
M	234 - 240	235.25	239.75	281	4.39063	26
N	240 - 246	241.25	245.75	287	4.48438	27
O	246 - 252	247.25	251.75	293	4.57813	28
P	252 - 258	253.25	257.75	299	4.67188	29
Q	258 - 264	259.25	263.75	305	4.76563	30
R	264 - 270	265.25	269.75	311	4.85938	31
S	270 - 276	271.25	275.75	317	4.95313	32
T	276 - 282	277.25	281.75	323	5.04688	33
U	282 - 288	283.25	287.75	329	5.14063	34
V	288 - 294	289.25	293.75	335	5.23438	35
W	294 - 300	295.25	298.83	341	5.32813	36
* * * HYPERBAND CATV * * *						
AA	300 - 306	301.25	305.75	347	5.42188	37
BB	306 - 312	307.25	311.75	353	5.51563	38
CC	312 - 318	313.25	317.75	359	5.60938	39
DD	318 - 324	319.25	323.75	365	5.70313	40
EE	324 - 330	325.25	329.75	371	5.79688	41
FF	330 - 336	331.25	335.75	377	5.89063	42
GG	336 - 342	337.25	341.75	383	5.98438	43
HH	342 - 348	343.25	347.75	389	6.07813	44
II	348 - 354	349.25	353.75	395	6.17188	45
JJ	354 - 360	355.25	359.75	401	6.26563	46
KK	360 - 366	361.25	365.75	407	6.35938	47
LL	366 - 372	367.25	371.75	413	6.45313	48

CHANNEL NUMBER	BAND	VIDEO CARRIER	AUDIO CARRIER	OSC FREQ.	DIVIDE BY 64	CHANNEL INDICATOR
MM	372 - 378	373.25	377.75	419	6.54688	49
NN	378 - 384	379.25	383.75	425	6.64063	50
OO	384 - 390	385.25	389.75	431	6.73438	51
PP	390 - 396	391.25	395.75	437	6.82813	52
QQ	396 - 402	397.25	401.75	443	6.92188	53
RR	402 - 408	403.25	407.75	449	7.01563	54
SS	408 - 414	409.25	413.75	455	7.10938	55
TT	414 - 420	415.25	419.75	461	7.20313	56
UU	420 - 426	421.25	425.75	467	7.29688	57
VV	426 - 432	427.25	431.75	473	7.39063	58
WW	432 - 438	433.25	437.75	479	7.48438	59
XX	438 - 444	439.25	443.75	485	7.57813	60
YY	444 - 450	445.25	449.75	491	7.67188	61
ZZ	450 - 456	451.25	455.75	497	7.76563	62
-	456 - 462	457.25	461.75	503	7.85938	63
-	462 - 468	463.25	467.75	509	7.95313	64

ZENITH ULTRA CATV BAND FREQUENCY CHART # #

CHANNEL INDICATOR	BAND	VIDEO CARRIER	SOUND CARRIER	OSC. FREQ.	DIVIDE BY 64
65	468 - 474	469.25	473.75	515	8.04688
66	474 - 480	475.25	479.75	521	8.14063
67	480 - 486	481.25	485.75	527	8.23438
68	486 - 492	487.25	491.75	533	8.32813
69	492 - 498	493.25	497.75	539	8.42188
70	498 - 504	499.25	503.75	545	8.51563
71	504 - 510	505.25	509.75	551	8.60938
72	510 - 516	511.25	515.75	557	8.70313
73	516 - 522	517.25	521.75	563	8.79688
74	522 - 528	523.25	527.75	569	8.89063
75	528 - 534	529.25	533.75	575	9.98438
76	534 - 540	535.25	539.75	581	9.07813
77	540 - 546	541.25	545.75	587	9.17188
78	546 - 552	547.25	551.75	593	9.26563
79	552 - 558	553.25	557.75	599	9.35938
80	558 - 564	559.25	563.75	605	9.45313
81	564 - 570	565.25	569.75	611	9.54688
82	570 - 576	571.25	575.75	617	9.64063
83	576 - 582	577.25	581.75	623	9.73438
84	582 - 588	583.25	587.75	629	9.82813
85	588 - 594	589.25	593.75	635	9.92188
86	594 - 600	595.25	599.75	641	10.0156
87	600 - 606	601.25	605.75	647	10.1094
88	606 - 612	607.25	611.75	653	10.2031
89	612 - 618	613.25	617.75	659	10.2969
90	618 - 624	619.25	623.75	665	10.3906
91	624 - 630	625.25	629.75	671	10.4844
92	630 - 636	631.25	635.75	677	10.5781

CHANNEL INDICATOR	BAND	VIDEO CARRIER	SOUND CARRIER	OSC. FREQ.	DIVIDE BY 64
93	636 - 642	637.25	641.75	683	10.6719
94	642 - 648	643.25	647.75	689	10.7656
95	648 - 654	649.25	653.75	695	10.8594
96	654 - 660	655.25	659.75	701	10.9531
97	660 - 666	661.25	665.75	707	11.0469
98	666 - 672	667.25	671.75	713	11.1406
99	672 - 678	673.25	677.75	719	11.2344
100	678 - 684	679.25	683.75	725	11.3281
101	684 - 690	685.25	689.75	731	11.4219
102	690 - 696	691.25	695.75	737	11.5156
103	696 - 702	697.25	701.75	743	11.6094
104	702 - 708	703.25	707.75	749	11.7031
105	708 - 714	709.25	713.75	755	11.7969
106	714 - 720	715.25	719.75	761	11.8906
107	720 - 726	721.25	725.75	767	11.9844
108	726 - 732	727.25	731.75	773	12.0781
109	732 - 738	733.25	737.75	779	12.1719
110	738 - 744	739.25	743.75	785	12.2656
111	744 - 750	745.25	749.75	791	12.3594
112	750 - 756	751.25	755.75	797	12.4531
113	756 - 762	757.25	761.75	803	12.5469
114	762 - 768	763.25	767.75	809	12.6406
115	768 - 774	769.25	773.75	815	12.7344
116	774 - 780	775.25	779.75	821	12.8281
117	780 - 786	781.25	785.75	827	12.9219
118	786 - 792	787.25	791.75	833	13.0156
119	792 - 798	793.25	797.75	839	13.1094
120	798 - 804	799.25	803.75	845	13.2031

HRC CHANNEL NUMBER	BAND	VIDEO CARRIER	AUDIO CARRIER	OSC FREQ.	DIVIDE BY 64	CHANNEL INDICATOR
		* * * LOW BAND VHF * * *				
2	52.75-58.75	54.00	58.50	99.75	1.55859	2
3	58.75-64.75	60.00	64.50	105.75	1.65234	3
4	64.75-70.75	66.00	70.50	111.75	1.74609	4
A-8(4+)	70.75-76.75	72.00	76.50	117.75	1.83984	00
5	76.75-82.75	78.00	82.50	123.75	1.93359	5
6	82.75-88.75	84.00	88.50	129.75	2.02734	6
		* * * MID BAND CATV * * *				
A-2	106.75-112.75	108.00	112.50	153.75	2.40234	0
A-1	112.75-118.75	114.00	118.50	159.75	2.49609	1
A	118.75-124.75	120.00	124.50	165.75	2.58984	14
B	124.75-130.75	126.00	130.50	171.75	2.68359	15
C	130.75-136.75	132.00	136.50	177.75	2.77734	16
D	136.75-142.75	138.00	142.50	183.75	2.87109	17
E	142.75-148.75	144.00	148.50	189.75	2.96484	18

HRC CHANNEL NUMBER	BAND	VIDEO CARRIER	AUDIO CARRIER	OSC FREQ.	DIVIDE BY 64	CHANNEL INDICATOR
F	148.75-154.75	150.00	154.50	195.75	3.05859	19
G	154.75-160.75	156.00	160.50	201.75	3.15234	20
H	160.75-166.75	162.00	166.50	207.75	3.24609	21
I	166.75-172.75	168.00	172.50	213.75	3.33984	22
		* * * HIGH BAND VHF * * *				
7	172.75-178.75	174.00	178.50	219.75	3.43359	7
8	178.75-184.75	180.00	184.50	225.75	3.52734	8
9	184.75-190.75	186.00	190.50	231.75	3.62109	9
10	190.75-196.75	192.00	196.50	237.75	3.71484	10
11	196.75-202.75	198.00	202.50	243.75	3.80859	11
12	202.75-208.75	204.00	208.50	249.75	3.90234	12
13	208.75-214.50	210.00	214.50	255.75	3.99609	13

* * * ZENITH SUPERBAND AND HYPERBAND HRC CATV FREQUENCY CHART * * *

HRC CHANNEL NUMBER	BAND	VIDEO CARRIER	AUDIO CARRIER	OSC FREQ.	DIVIDE BY 64	CHANNEL INDICATOR
		* * * SUPERBAND CATV * * *				
J	214.75-220.75	216.00	220.50	261.75	4.08984	23
K	220.75-226.75	222.00	226.50	267.75	4.18359	24
L	226.75-232.75	228.00	232.50	273.75	4.27734	25
M	232.75-238.75	234.00	238.50	279.75	4.37109	26
N	238.75-244.75	240.00	244.50	285.75	4.46484	27
O	244.75-250.75	246.00	250.50	291.75	4.55859	28
P	250.75-256.75	252.00	256.50	297.75	4.65234	29
Q	256.75-262.75	258.00	262.50	303.75	4.74609	30
R	262.75-268.75	264.00	268.50	309.75	4.83984	31
S	268.75-274.75	270.00	274.50	315.75	4.93359	32
T	274.75-280.75	276.00	280.50	321.75	5.02734	33
U	280.75-286.75	282.00	286.50	327.75	5.12109	34
V	286.75-292.75	288.00	292.50	333.75	5.21484	35
W	292.75-298.75	294.00	298.50	339.75	5.30859	36
		* * * HYPERBAND CATV * * *				
AA	298.75-304.75	300.00	304.50	345.75	5.40234	37
BB	304.75-310.75	306.00	310.50	351.75	5.49609	38
CC	310.75-316.75	312.00	316.50	357.75	5.58984	39
DD	316.75-322.75	318.00	322.50	363.75	5.68359	40
EE	322.75-328.75	324.00	328.50	369.75	5.77734	41
FF	328.75-334.75	330.00	334.50	375.75	5.87109	42
GG	334.75-340.75	336.00	340.50	381.75	5.96484	43
HH	340.75-346.75	342.00	346.50	387.75	6.05859	44
II	346.75-352.75	348.00	352.50	393.75	6.15234	45
JJ	352.75-358.75	354.00	358.50	399.75	6.24609	46
KK	358.75-364.75	360.00	364.50	405.75	6.33984	47
LL	364.75-370.75	366.00	370.50	411.75	6.43359	48
MM	370.75-376.75	372.00	376.50	417.75	6.52734	49
NN	376.75-382.75	378.00	382.50	423.75	6.62109	50

HRC CHANNEL NUMBER	BAND	VIDEO CARRIER	AUDIO CARRIER	OSC FREQ.	DIVIDE BY 64	CHANNEL INDICATOR
OO	382.75-388.75	384.00	388.50	429.75	6.71484	51
PP	388.75-394.75	390.00	394.50	435.75	6.80859	52
QQ	394.75-400.75	396.00	400.50	441.75	6.90234	53
RR	400.75-406.75	402.00	406.50	447.75	6.99609	54
SS	406.75-412.75	408.00	412.50	453.75	7.08984	55
TT	412.75-418.75	414.00	418.50	459.75	7.18359	56
UU	418.75-424.75	420.00	424.50	465.75	7.27734	57
VV	424.75-430.75	426.00	430.50	471.75	7.37109	58
WW	430.75-436.75	432.00	436.50	477.75	7.46484	59
XX	436.75-442.75	438.00	442.50	483.75	7.55859	60
YY	442.75-448.75	446.00	448.50	489.75	7.65234	61
ZZ	448.75-454.75	452.00	454.50	495.75	7.74609	62
AAA	454.75-460.75	458.00	460.50	501.75	7.83984	63
BBB	460.75-466.75	462.00	466.50	507.75	7.93359	64

6
Satellite signals

THESE SATELLITES ARE THE GEOSYNCHRONOUS VARIETY THAT ARE orbited and orbit-maintained by their launch vehicles and on-board hydrazine positioners at 22,300 miles above the equator. They are positioned by Geneva and national accords at certain longitude positions. In the Americas and Canada, such positions are west longitudes ranging from 62 degrees WL (assigned to AMSC) to 143 degrees WL (Aurora 1) for the United States and actively operating satellites of Anik D1, D2, Aniks C1 through C3 for Canada, and Morelos 1,2 for Mexico, all of which are within the U.S.-assigned overall western allocation.

Nominal channels number 36 for C-band spacecraft and between 10 and 16 for Ku. Hybrids such as the Spacenets have twelve 36 MHz and six 72 MHz transponders for C band and six 72 MHz transponders for Ku. But the early SBS series only had 10 transponders with max bandwidths of 43 MHz. An up-to-date listing of all these satellites in the Western Hemisphere is shown at the end of the chapter.

Both C and Ku band satellites belong to the Fixed Satellite Service, while the proposed D irect Broadcast Satellite Service has never flown and probably won't until almost all desirable parking slots have been filled for C and Ku. At the moment some 30 U.S. satellites are in position in addition to seven foreigners, most operating at least part time. If all were closed up to their required positions of 2 degrees spacing, there could be 82 geosynchronous spacecraft in heavenly orbit—something not problematical in the foreseeable future due to heavy launch costs in the millions plus design and construction tags that often add up to more than $100 million. Even the Japanese don't throw around that much loose change.

Present satellite life spans are projected for approximately 10 years or a few more, and this does make transponder rentals and sales a heavy levy.

But with more experience in design and possibly additional thruster fuel storage, even spacecraft refueling or repairs, we would expect these enormous costs to come down, perhaps substantially over time, and advertiser rather than scrambler backings to begin to make headway by at least the mid 1990s. In the meantime, although fiberoptics and the phone companies have reached a significant marriage of convenience and technical progress, there's room for almost all business communications everywhere, and many, many transponders will continue to carry B-MAC, VideoCipher 1 and 2, Orion, Leitch, and the rest of the brood as long as they're profitable. High-definition television, when it comes, will probably add another two or three scrambled signals for painful and/or expensive decoding.

Furthermore, you can't always operate cable and fiberoptics under oceans and among continents by the thousands, and so satellite communications is bound to prosper both nationally and internationally for the foreseeable future and then some. Therefore it behooves at least some of the more eloquent to become familiar with the territory and be able to at least talk the language coherently. With that in mind, let's begin with slant ranges—the distance between you and the satellite, and work up . . . And we'll include scrambling as well.

Slant range and location

Here you don't need heavy mathematics, just a hand calculator, a couple of constants, and the ability to add, subtract, and take a couple of square roots, plus knowing your position and that of the satellite (Fig. 6-1).

Simply, R_o represent the earth's radius of 3956 stature miles, then multiply this times 6.611 for the satellite's geostationary orbit in equatorial plane and subtract the longitude difference between your position and that of the satellite, knowing your own latitude also: The equation opens up to:

$$\text{slant range} = R_o \sqrt{6.611^2 + 1 - 2(6.11) \cos H \times \cos \Delta L}$$

And let's say the spacecraft you're looking at is GSTAR II at 105 degrees WL and you live in the vicinity of Las Vegas but not quite to the Mustang Ranch. Your respective latitude and longitude there would be 36.2 degrees N and 115.3 degrees W. You may either use the above equation or another and somewhat simpler computation where the earth's center to a satellite has already been computed and a second constant inside the square-root sign simply requires two basic trigonometric angles and the solution is at hand.

$$\text{slant range} = 14{,}414 \sqrt{3.389 - \cos \text{lat. angle} \times \cos \text{lon.}}$$

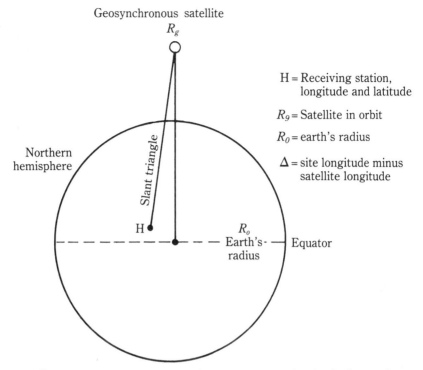

Geosynchronous satellite

R_g

Northern
hemisphere

Slant triangle

H •

R_o
Earth's-
radius

H = Receiving station,
longitude and latitude

R_g = Satellite in orbit

R_0 = earth's radius

Δ = site longitude minus
satellite longitude

Equator

6-1   Slant range measurements require no more than a hand calculator to locate
GSTAR II from Las Vegas.

with lon. being the difference between your site and that of the satellite. So:

$$\text{slant range} = 14{,}414 \sqrt{3.389 - \cos 36.2 \times \cos(105° - 115.3°)}\text{WL}$$
$$= 23{,}278 \text{ Stat.Mi.}$$

Unfortunately or otherwise, you can hardly see that far, but it does
give you an idea that another 1,000 miles (besides the earth's perpendicular distance) separates you from the spacecraft you're aiming for. But what
you really want to know is the relative position and look angle of this satellite from your bottom dollar vantage point in Las Vegas. Therefore, here's
how you go about that small chore by using a simple graph and drawing a
couple of lines (Fig. 6-2).

Once again, the longitudinal difference between you and GSTAR in
addition to the latitude are involved, and the readout is quite easy if you
follow the curving lines. It turns out your elevation angle approximates
46.5 degrees and azimuth 18° + 180° = 198° total.

So GSTAR II in reference to a spot about Las Vegas is fairly high in
the sky and at a relative bearing a little past due south. That wasn't difficult, was it? You really don't need to draw lines each time you want azimuth and elevation bearings, just a pencil spot will do where the latitude

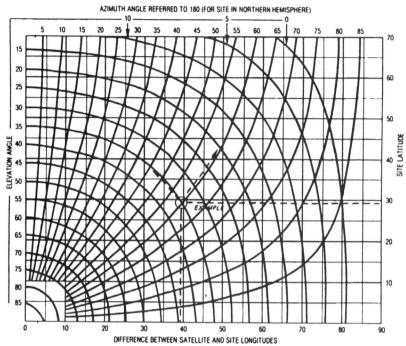

AZIMUTH ANGLE REFERRED TO 180 (FOR SITE IN NORTHERN HEMISPHERE)

DIFFERENCE BETWEEN SATELLITE AND SITE LONGITUDES

6-2   Locating azimuth and elevation of any satellite is simply knowing lati-
tudes and longitude differences, which you then read directly on the
chart. SATCOM 1, for instance, appears at 240 degrees relative at an elevation of 36 degrees. Harris Corp.

and longitude join forces, then read the appropriate lines above and to the
left. Note this projection applies only to the northern hemisphere, which is
the line dividing the globe into two hemispheres, above and below the
equator. If you're unfortunate enough to have elevation angles less than 15
degrees, be very careful you follow one of the three large lines marked off
at the top. Then, you can't miss. However, if you don't add routine variation figures to your calculated azimuth bearing, you won't find GSTAR II
either. In the vicinity of Las Vegas, variation amounts to 17 degrees east.
West variations add to the azimuth bearing and east variations subtract.
So your true bearing amounts to 198 – 17 or 181 degrees actual.

Declination

While supplying specific and general information for satellite earth station
locations, pointing angles, elevations, etc., your mount will also require a
declination angle offset to compensate for the polar mount's man-made
curvature. Table 6-1 prints a standard listing for the various states and
many of their principal cities. You must, however, *subtract 0.5 degrees* from
each figure to be accurate. This particular list is an earlier one that is now
off 1/2 degree.

**Table 6-1. Declination angles throughout the U.S. form 5.4 to
6.8 degrees, but subtract 0.5 degrees from each for best accuracy**

	State	City	Declination angle	Galaxy 1(H1) Elevation	Azimuth	Satcom 4 (F4) Elevation	Azimuth
1.	Alabama	Birmingham	5.4	26.8	242.9	50.0	175.0
2.	Arizona	Pheonix	5.4	44.5	216.1	41.0	135.0
3.	Arkansas	Little Rock	5.7	30.4	237.4	48.0	165.0
4.	California	San Francisco	6.1	44.6	198.5	30.0	127.0
5.	California	Los Angeles	5.5	47.0	206.7	36.0	129.0
6.	Colorado	Denver	6.3	35.2	220.9	38.0	148.0
7.	Connecticut	Hartford	6.6	12.6	250.0	40.0	195.0
8.	Rhode Island	Providence	6.6	11.6	250.9	40.0	198.0
9.	Delaware	Wilmington	6.3	15.4	248.6	43.0	191.0
10.	Maryland	Baltimore	6.2	16.4	247.9	44.0	190.0
11.	Florida	Jacksonville	5.0	24.0	248.7	55.0	182.0
12.	Florida	Miami	4.4	24.3	252.3	59.0	187.0
13.	Georgia	Atlanta	5.5	24.8	244.7	51.0	178.0
14.	Idaho	Boise	6.8	36.7	205.0	30.0	136.0
15.	Illinois	Chicago	6.6	23.0	237.5	41.0	173.0
16.	Indiana	Indianapolis	6.2	23.1	239.9	45.0	175.0
17.	Iowa	Des Moines	6.6	27.1	232.0	40.0	164.0
18.	Kansas	Witchita	6.1	32.1	230.6	44.0	158.0
19.	Kentucky	Louisville	6.1	23.6	241.1	46.0	175.0
20.	Louisiana	Baton Rouge	5.0	32.0	241.3	53.0	165.0
21.	Maine	Bangor	6.9	8.8	252.0	36.0	199.0
22.	Massachusetts	Boston	6.6	11.2	251.0	40.0	198.0
23.	Michigan	Grand Rapids	6.7	21.1	238.8	40.0	176.0
24.	Michigan	Marquette	7.1	20.0	235.3	36.0	175.0
25.	Minnesota	St. Paul	6.9	24.5	230.8	37.0	166.0
26.	Mississippi	Jackson	5.3	30.1	240.9	51.0	167.0
27.	Missouri	Kansas City	6.2	29.3	232.5	43.0	163.0
28.	Missouri	St. Louis	6.2	26.6	236.9	44.0	169.0
29.	Montana	Great Falls	7.2	31.2	209.6	31.0	143.0
30.	Nebraska	Omaha	6.5	28.8	229.9	40.6	160.8
31.	Nevada	Las Vegas	5.8	43.6	210.1	36.0	134.0
32.	New Hampshire	Manchester	6.6	11.3	250.5	39.1	196.7
33.	New Jersey	Trenton	6.3	14.7	249.0	42.0	194.0
34.	New Mexico	Albuquerque	5.7	40.0	222.0	42.0	142.0
35.	New York	Syracuse	6.7	14.5	246.8	40.0	190.0
36.	North Carolina	Hickory	5.7	21.3	246.4	48.7	183.4
37.	North Dakota	Bismark	7.1	27.3	221.9	33.0	183.4
38.	Ohio	Columbus	6.3	20.8	242.5	44.0	180.0
39.	Oklahoma	Oklahoma City	5.7	33.7	231.9	47.0	157.0
40.	Oregon	Eugene	6.8	38.1	195.5	26.0	130.0
41.	Pennsylvania	Harrisburg	6.3	16.2	247.3	42.0	189.0
42.	South Carolina	Columbia	5.5	22.0	247.1	50.0	184.0
43.	South Dakota	Rapid City	6.8	30.7	220.6	35.0	152.0
44.	Tennessee	Memphis	5.7	28.5	239.2	49.0	168.0
45.	Tennessee	Knoxville	5.8	23.4	243.8	48.0	178.0

Table 6-1 Continued

State	City	Declination angle	Galaxy 1(H1)		Satcom 4 (F4)	
			Elevation	**Azimuth**	**Elevation**	**Azimuth**
46. Texas	Abilene	5.3	37.4	231.8	48.0	152.0
47. Utah	Salt Lake City	6.5	37.9	211.9	34.0	140.0
48. Vermont	Montpelier	6.8	11.6	249.2	37.0	194.0
49. Virginia	Richmond	6.0	17.7	248.1	46.2	189.1
50. Washington	Spokane	7.2	33.0	201.9	27.0	137.0
51. West Virginia	Charleston	6.2	20.5	244.4	45.0	183.0
52. Wisconsin	Green Bay	6.8	21.7	235.9	38.5	187.1
53. Wyoming	Sheridan	6.8	31.9	215.9	33.2	147.8

With a third figure now available, this means you have three corrections to make each time you set up satellite earth station mount and reflector: true azimuth, true elevation, and declination. Miss any one of these and your mount will never track accurately. In the east, by the way, set up first on GALAXY 1, and the other satellites should follow reasonably well if G1 is accessed carefully. Others toward due south and high elevations can fool you and disrupt the azimuth curve completely. And once C band has been tracked, then Ku can be attempted with only minute changes in north-south polarization and a half-turn in elevation, possibly not even that, depending on the accuracy of your mount. As most or many of you have already discovered, unless your mount can generate a double count from its reed switch or other sensor device, accuracy will not be sufficient to access Ku band within 1/4 degree, and this means constant azimuth retuning because of inaccurate positioning whenever you're not using C band. The latter only requires about 1 degree accuracy, permitting linear actuators to operate satisfactorily. How you program Ku within 1/4 degree limits is a mystery using standard linear mounts. So far as we can see, horizon-to-horizon mounts with double counts seems to be the only way just now.

Compass variations

Because of magnetic influences in the earth, simple needle compasses do not read correctly when pointed to their usual, north, south, east, and west locations. Therefore, when setting up an earth station or simply servicing it, true compass readings are only obtainable if a predetermined variation is added or subtracted from these relative directions. An easterly correction from magnetic north is always subtracted and a westerly correction added. A listing of the variations follow for the entire 50 states in Table 6-2 for your convenience. When setting your mount for true north and south, the addition or subtraction of W or E variations ensure accuracy that is critical in orienting your earth terminal. In the middle atlantic states, it's normal to set declination and magnetic variations when the mount and its antenna are pointed due south. Then set up on G1 for minor corrections and you should

Table 6-2. E/W compass variation corrections for the continental 48 states.
(Easterly corrections subtract from magnetic readings, and westerly corrections add)

Alabama	2E	Kentucky	1E	North Dakota	11E
Alaska	26E	Louisiana	6E	Ohio	3W
Arizona	14E	Maine	20W	Oklahoma	9E
Arkansas	6E	Maryland	8W	Oregon	20E
California	17E	Massachusetts	15W	Pennsylvania	8W
Colorado	14E	Michigan	3W	Rhode Island	15W
Connecticut	13W	Minnesota	6E	South Carolina	2W
Delaware	10W	Mississippi	5E	South Dakota	11E
Washington, D.C.	8W	Missouri	6E	Tennessee	1E
Florida	2E	Montana	18E	Texas	10E
Georgia	0	Nebraska	11E	Utah	15E
Hawaii	11E	Nevada	17E	Vermont	15W
Idaho	196	New Hampshire	16W	Virginia	6W
Illinois	2E	New Jersey	11W	Washington	22E
Indiana	0	New Mexico	13E	West Virginia	5W
Iowa	6E	New York	10W	Wisconsin	2E
Kansas	9E	North Carolina	5W	Wyoming	13E
Alberta	22E	Manitoba	10E	Saskatchewan	17E
British Columbia	23E	Ontario	8W	Quebec	17W

track the azimuthal arc without major problems. It's well to remember that elevation controls the broad center of the arc while declination regulates the ends. But be sure your north/south compass readings and elevations with appropriate variations included are precise before declinations are set and mount hold-down bolts locked tight. Once again, declinations are added to your latitude for correct elevations.

Space signals and receiving hardware

All the foregoing should have enabled you to find the satellite and adjust your earth station to receive signals. So far, nothing has been said about the antenna, its feedhorn and block downconverters. Perhaps a few paragraphs describing various receiving operations and the equipment needed to process them should be added. In truth, they are part of the satellite signal process and do require some basic understanding other than a picture or two to lighten interminable print copy reading. Unless said picture contains related and significant information, however, it has very little value other than adornment, and that's not our style.

Therefore, what we really plan to do in this single chapter is actually a condensed version of several books your author has already written on the subject. In no other way can we cover the subject with any authority unless much of the information is presented and you can follow and appreciate signal development and passage from spacecraft to on-screen display. Signals from the satellite's transponders are first.

The downlink

C band operates from an uplink of 5.925 GHz to 6.425 GHz and a downlink of 3.7 GHz to 4.2 GHz. *Ku band* generates uplink between 14 and 14.5 GHz and downlink from 11.7 to 12.2 GHz, both of which are in the Fixed Satellite Service (FSS). The *DBS*, the Direct Broadcast Service, has been authorized by the Federal Communications Commission but has not yet flown. Its uplink is 17.3 to 17.8 GHz and downlink 12.2 to 12.7 GHz.

All standard C-band satellites have 24 channels or transponders with bandpasses of 36 MHz each. Ku satellites of more recent vintage have 16 transponders at 54 MHz each. And Hybrid (C and Ku banders) normally have 12 transponders at 36 MHz, 6 at 72 MHz, and 6 Ku transponders at a bandpass of 72 MHz. The older, SBS Ku satellites, however, have but 10 transponders at 43 MHz each and power outputs of only 20W/channel.

Ordinarily, the newer Ku band satellites have 45W/transponder, but this could increase to 60 W with some of the newer units to be orbited. Certain C banders also have power increases from 5 or 10 W presently to 16 W as they assume new geosynchronous positions or replace some spacecraft that has failed. More powerful satellites, of course, mean additional hemisphere coverage and could result in slightly smaller antennas at many locations throughout the country depending, of course, on the "footprints" they cast. Footprints are the satellite's signal coverage normally given in dBW (decibels with respect to watts) across the U.S., and sometimes Puerto Rico and Hawaii. From these footprint contours you can easily calculate the various access levels required for video, music, or data. We're now looking at a total of 29 satellites in orbit: 6 have been retired and 4 are replacements. Cumulatively, 16 are C band, 10 are Ku, and 3 are C/Ku hybrids. Among orbital assignments, however, the FCC has now authorized 51 DOMSAT satellites to occupy the Clarke Belt directly above the equator for the U.S. alone. When the rest of the Americas join in, we should have an enormous selection of programs, if they aren't initially scrambled by the ever-present programmers and associations.

To give you an idea of the relative ease with which one can translate a footprint into terrestrial field strength, let's analyze one so you can see exactly what goes on. Since we've long had permission from GTE Spacenet to use the GSTAR footprint, and since this satellite is a little difficult to handle at times, especially GSTAR II, let's work with its best contour in the center of the country, which is 44.1 dBW (Fig. 6-3). Both GSTARs1 and 2 have 16 transponders with bandpasses of 54 MHz each; 14 with TWT (traveling wave tubes) outputs of 20 watts and two with 27 watts for 50-state coverage. Called *effective isotropic radiated power* (EIRP), GSTAR 2 delivers this signal to earth where the terrestrial antenna system and electronics must pick it up and display its video on a television screen. We'll assume an elevation angle of 20 degrees so the reflector will be reasonably free of the earth's 290 degrees Kelvin temperature, and a 10 foot antenna.

First, you have to establish a Kelvin temperature for this antenna, and this can be done by the approximation:

$$T°K = 10 + 180/e \text{ (}e \text{ is the angle of elevation} = 20°)$$
$$T°K = 10 + 180/20 = 10 + 9 = 19°K$$

The midpoint C band gain for this 10-footer is 39.5, assuming a Ku gain figure of approximately 46 dB. Therefore, a figure of merit for the antenna only becomes

$$G/T \text{ (ant.)} = 46 \text{ dB}/19°K \text{ and } 19°K = 10 \log 19 = 12.79$$
$$G/T \text{ (ant.)} = 46 \text{ dB} - 12.79 \text{ dB} = 33.21 \text{ dB}/°K$$

Now let's look at the entire receive system using a considerably longer equation that takes in all components.

$$T°K \text{ (system)} = T(\text{antenna} + \text{feed}) + T(\text{LNB})/G(\text{feed}) + T(\text{receiver})/G(\text{LNB}) + G(\text{feed})$$

In this exercise, remember you're working with temperature, so dBs must be changed. Now let's get a "feel" for components in the system:

The Ku temperature LNB is specified at NF 1.2, or 95 °K
Feedhorn, 0.98 °K
Receiver, 12 dB, when changed to temp. becomes $T°K = 290 (10^{12/10} - 1) = 290(14.85) = 4596°K$
Feed gain (VSWR loss) = 0.98
$T°K(\text{system}) = 19.98 + 95/.98 + 4596/10^{-5} + .98 = 118.3°K$

and changing this back to dB:

$$10 \log 118.3 = 20.73 \text{ dB}$$
$$G/T \text{ system} = 46 - 20.73 = 25.27 \text{ dB}/°K$$

and that's not bad at all for Ku. Please note that the antenna and block downconverter are the principal noise contributors to the system, and the feed and receiver account for very, very little. So we're really talking 10ths of a dB as follows:

$$G/T \text{ system (short calculation)} = 46 \text{ (ant. gain)} - 19.78 \text{ (LNB)} = 26.22 \text{ dB}/°K$$

Compared to previous laborious calculations, the G/T difference is

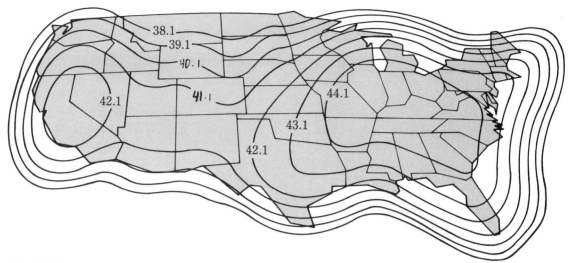

6-3 A CONUS footprint for GSTARS I/II. A good receiver can see − 49.5 dBm with good outside Ku band equipment.

26.22 − 25.27 = 0.95. A minor mistake in the long-form calculations could amount to more than 0.95 dB! So round figures in G/T are relatively simple if you just have the antenna and block downconverter characteristics.

Ku VSAT hard numbers

With the foregoing as background, assume a "typical" VSAT receive-only installation of a 1.2-meter (4-foot) reflector with a curvature accuracy of between 0.015 and 0.025 inches rms, preferably of solid fiberglass or first-class metal, with either an AZ/EL or double-count polar mount and reed (counter) switch. The block downconverter has a given noise figure of 1.2 dB, receiver is 12 dB, and the antenna efficiency is somewhere between 55 and 70 percent, depending on cost and side lobes. In heavy rain or snow, higher GHz frequencies will most certainly attenuate, so that between 5 and 10 dB (Miami, especially) must be factored in worst-case conditions. You must also consider whether transmissions are data, music, or video since video requires the higher signal level by 6 to 10 dB. Then you must remember that space loss for Ku amounts to 206 dB, instead of 196 dB for C band. Antenna gain for a 1.2 meter parabola is 41.5 dB.

With these considerations in view, let's pick a pair of small and medium power satellites and work with these for reasonably round figures, remembering that in some sections of the country, requirements are more stringent than others. A noise figure of 1.2 dB translates to 95°, and 10 log 95° = 19.8 dB. Therefore,

$$G/T \text{ (1.2 meter)} = 41.5 - 19.8 = 21.7 \text{ dB}°K$$

First, we'll go with a GTE SPACENET, which is a hybrid C and Ku-bander with a relatively low working Ku footprint but covers the continental U.S. nicely with a signal strength of 36.1 dBW. Such spacecraft have six 16 W transponders with bandwidths of 72 MHz (which could be split to 36 MHz, if required). A second example would be that of a GTE GSTAR with 14 20 W transponders and two 27 W transponders for full 50-state coverage. Average footprints measure between 39 and 44 dBW, depending on whether all of CONUS or just the east and midwest are covered. A compromise of 41 dBW should absorb most eventualities.

The downlink for Spacenet Ku is 36.1 dBW, and this subtracted from −206 dBm, or 36.1 + 30 = 66.1 dBm, or −139.9 dBm as the Spacenet signal reaching some earthly reflector. Now add 41.5 dB antenna gain, and 60 dB LNB gain, and you have a positive accumulation of 101.5. Therefore, −139.9 + 101.5 = −38.4 dB out of the block downconverter.

Take away another 8 dB for foul weather and a second 8 dB for cable loss, and your figures then become −38.4 − 16 = −54.4 dB, which the receiver "sees" as a working signal. You're still reasonably all right if your receiver operates between −60 and −20 dB. Its signal, however, will have to approach a level of −40 dBm. All else, therefore, depends on the receiver's threshold extension, which should not exceed 6.5 dB.

In the case of GSTARs, you can readily see how a 4 or 5 dB addition would pull all signals "out of the mud" for better-than-passable reception. Here, even a 10 dB weather fade wouldn't phase this well-fortified output.

On the other hand, if you planned to work some of the old SBS "birds" designed for voice and data primarily, their positions and 20 W/transponder outputs could become rather difficult, especially if transmissions were sporadic. SBS V, at 123 degrees WL, however, will have ten 43 MHz transponders of 20 W each and four transponders of 120 MHz bandwidth, with two 20-watters paralleled for 40 W output if desired.

The above calculations are for video transmissions, as are receiver statistics; consequently, music or data signals would appear that much stronger under all working conditions. I firmly believe, however, that most, if not all, satellite systems should be designed for picture carriers because there's no telling when video conferencing or just plain television will be required. Just a few dollars here and there can double the usefulness of any satellite system, be it in equipment cabling, or precise installations.

If you find these Ku computations interesting, just imagine what a power increase of from 5 or 10 W to, say 16 W will do for you at C band with all those 10-foot, high-gain reflectors and no weather losses to worry about. Ku sounds rather attractive now, but C band isn't a grandparent by any means. However, 2 degrees spacing for the 4/6 GHz spacecraft will certainly cause some problems unless strict polarity assignments are honored and small antennas with overly large focal distance to diameter ratios are either unknowingly or deliberately used. The results could become exceedingly messy, especially with indiscriminate trapping of offending channels and satellites. Let's see if we can't prove the point.

Carrier-to-noise and threshold

C/N isn't at all difficult after you've found carrier-to-system temperature (C/T), and this is simple once you know the EIRP (effective radiated isotropic power in watts), space loss and gain over temperature. The equation goes like this:

C/T = 36.1 (Spacenet Ku) − 206 (space loss) + 21.7 dB °K (G/T)

C/T = − 148.2

And, therefore,

C/N = C/T + Boltzmann's constant − 10 log IF bandwidth 27 MHz

C/N = 148.2 + 228.6 − 74.3 = 6.1 dB

Consequently,

C/N threshold = 5 + 5 log 0.5 × 27 MHz transponder BW/video baseband

or,

C/N threshold of receiver = 5 + 5 log 13.5 MHz/4.2 MHz

Receiver thresh. C/N = 6.34 dB

With a C/N of only 6.1 dB and a C/T of − 148.2 dB, according to these figures, Spacenet Ku either needs more output, or your antenna requires additional gain because sparklies show at 12 dB C/N, and you're not really safe until the figure is above 15 dB C/N. I am somewhat afraid the 206 dB space loss was a difficult factor. Otherwise, a considerably larger reflector is decidedly required for video. Conversely, data and sound probably would pass muster if we added an additional 10 dB for this transmission format or strapped a couple of transponders together for extra EIRP. Also, tighter antenna tolerances with up to 70 percent efficiencies and better feedhorns with especially matched block downconverters could help, too, when using 1.2-meter antennas for this purpose. If all goes well, we'll try and prove later that better equipment can help offset this very low C/N calculation.

The GSTARS, with their 20 to 27 W transponders, are in a much better position to offer considerably better service over specific or broader terrestrial terrain. At an average footprint of 41 dBW plus 30 for 71 dBm, then subtracted from −206 dB space loss, amounts to −135 dBm reaching the earth station (Fig. 6-3). Adding 41.5 dB antenna gain plus 60 dB LNB gain equals 101.5 dB total. Therefore, 101.5 − 135 = −33.5 dB out of the block downconverter. Then deduct 16 dB for foul-weather falloff and cable attenuation, and you have

signal reaching receiver = −33.5 − 16 = −49.5 dBm

That's an additional 6 dB over Spacenet's gain and should deliver a very reasonable amount of intelligence. Add a few more dB in the way of larger footprints and extra-gain antennas and electronics, and the heavens are yours. Don't, by the way, fall for the allegations of some who say very low noise block downconverters and high-gain amplifiers can't make a difference; we've just proved they can! (See Fig. 6-4.)

As you have now learned, all components in any microwave transmit or receive system are especially important in small-signal situations. In carefully impedance-matched feeds and LNBs, there is maximum performance that should always be conducted to the decoder/receiver with low-loss cable. Until fiberoptics are generally available for TVRO, I strongly suggest RG6/U stamped with Underwriters Laboratory approval. Furthermore, center conductors in this cable are best made of steel with copper flashing and protected with both aluminum foil wrap and thick braid for maximum signal containment and interference rejection. Grounding should occur at the receiver only because dual grounds invite circulating currents that play havoc with 950 − 1450 MHz first IF information.

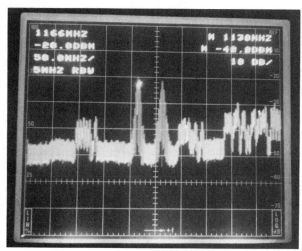

6-4 On a clear night in April, GSTAR II transponder 15 downlinks from program origination at Virginia Beach, VA. Signal level is 42.2 dBm with marker at 1130 MHz.

Feedhorns

Newest of the lot are products formerly offered by SBX Corporation (now Coast Hitech Corp.) and currently National A.D.L. Though different, each will play an important part in satellite signal reception during the 1990s: CHC as dual C/Ku broadband equipment, and A.D.L. with narrower Ku illuminations but special T.I. (terrestrial interference) rejection as well as a Ku-only feedhorn. We'll team them with a 1.2-meter Winegard antenna and a Hemt block downconverter from California Amplifier, a manufacturing and distribution affiliate of National A.D.L. All three of these products deserve special attention because they are both state-of-the-art and absolutely top quality.

CHC shines

Designed by engineers Harvey Hom and Richard Chou, recently of Grumman Aircraft, C- and Ku-band probes are fixed, with the entire assembly rotating 180 degrees for precise polarity control (Fig. 6-5). According to the designers, the C band portion doesn't even know the Ku probe is there, and there is no waveguide to cause SWR or other problems occurring in competitive receptors. Similarly, there are no moving microwave joints and all impedances between feedhorn and amplifier/block downconverters are carefully balanced, resulting in maximum gain and very minimum SWR.

The entire assembly mounts internally on an aluminum support frame, and the external cover is a press-fit aluminum cylinder with three

SBX-4120D

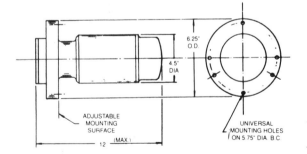

C/Ku-Band TVRO System

Product Features & Benefits:
- •Small Size
- •C/Ku-Band Reception
- •Low Noise
- •Low Cost
- •Easy Maintainance
- •Modular PCB Construction
- •Integral Polar Motor

System Specifications:

Interface Output Impedance	75 ohms Typical
3rd Order Intercept Point	+16 dBm Minimum
1 dB Compression Point	+5 dBm Minimum
Cross-Polar Isolation	30 dB Minimum
DC Power Requirements	+15 to +25 Volts at 265 mA
Weatherproof	Yes
Weight	5 lbs Maximum
Operating Temperature Range	-40 to +60 °C

6-5   Drawing and description of the new CHC broadband C/Ku feed.

plastic snap hooks for easy removal and replacement. Additionally, in the event of electrical failures, the low noise amplifier and downconverter sections are separately replaceable, lowering costs considerably. With typical gains of 64 dB and 55 dB, respectively, the C and Ku band sections have excellent low-noise figures and a focal distance extension of not less than 2.5 inches for accurately adjusting the f/D ratio, always required for proper illumination of any reflector. Accompanying scalar rings are conveniently bored for most, if not all, ordinary feed supports.

On strong signals, this feedhorn easily accommodates f/Ds between 0.28 and 0.42, and on weaker signals it peaks over the focal distance/diameters of 0.28 to 0.36. Deep reflectors such as Winegard's premier 10-foot perforated antennas can now be illuminated satisfactorily on C *and* Ku frequencies and produce excellent pictures on both.

California amplifier

The major marketing and manufacturing associate of Gerry Blachley's National A.D.L. design and production group, California Amplifier not only assembles and tests this very good C/Ku feedhorn but supplies excellent Hemt block downconverters to go with it. The unit easily illuminates antennas with f/Ds of from 0.3 to about 0.4 (Fig. 6-6), and also offers some significant terrestrial interference rejection due to its special hybrid

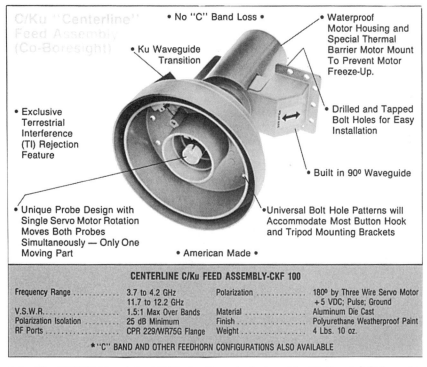

CENTERLINE C/Ku FEED ASSEMBLY-CKF 100			
Frequency Range	3.7 to 4.2 GHz 11.7 to 12.2 GHz	Polarization	180° by Three Wire Servo Motor +5 VDC; Pulse; Ground
V.S.W.R.	1.5:1 Max Over Bands	Material	Aluminum Die Cast
Polarization Isolation	25 dB Minimum	Finish	Polyurethane Weatherproof Paint
RF Ports	CPR 229/WR75G Flange	Weight	4 Lbs. 10 oz.

★"C" BAND AND OTHER FEEDHORN CONFIGURATIONS ALSO AVAILABLE

6-6 The RFI/EMI resistant C/Ku feedhorn is designed by National A.D.L. and is largely assembled and marketed by California Amplifier. California Amplifier

design. Prodelin's sturdy fiberglass 10-footer with a curvature accuracy of 0.030 inches rms, is a very good match for this feed when coupled with Hemt block downconverters. Correctly installed, you should be able to guarantee some 20 satellites and hundreds of transponders almost anywhere if you're using a double-count, high-accuracy horizon-to-horizon mount such as the muscled AJAK 180 or its smaller cousin, the AccuTrak for reflectors in the 6- to 8-foot grouping. For either the 10- or 11-foot Prodelin fiberglass reflectors, however, a 60 lb. counterbalance is recommended and furnished by AJAK to help with their hefty weights as they swing from low to high positions in the azimuthal arc.

Because all satellite-receive systems have to cope with 196 dB loss at C band and 206 dB loss at Ku, noisy, low-gain amplifiers and converters present a problem that can upset any satellite earth terminal. Consequently, gallium arsenide (GaAsFETs) field-effect transistors are rapidly being supplanted by new amplifiers called Hemts. This is a modulation-doped GaAsA1GaAs heterostructural expitaxy device with charge carriers remaining within a thin sheet of GaAs buffer layers. Having swifter electron mobility and saturation velocity, both higher cutoff frequencies and better transconductance is maintained. And with still further advanced techniques and manufacturing changes, such Hemt amplifiers are becoming tinier and more efficient with the passing months.

Terrestrial interference rejection by this feedhorn evolved from its chambered, hybrid design using the first and ninth orders arranged to propagate in phase. Internal corrugations in resonance balance the hybrid modes, producing a linearly polarized secondary beam of greater efficiency and less spillover. Such dual-mode feeds have a circular waveguide and two coaxially loaded waveguides. Each mode contributes phase alterations that change with frequency, forming very steep bandskirts that reject terrestrial EMI/RFI attempting to enter the feedhorn.

While this isn't necessarily a satellite book in itself, I thought that a few descriptive paragraphs might aid in selecting one or both outstanding designs that offer excellent service. And as part of any signal processing analysis, these two dual-band feedhorns have distinctive qualities their competition usually lacks. Furthermore, the very low noise Hemt amplifier/downconverters contribute considerably to much better than ordinary performance, delivering sharp, broadband signals to all receivers they service. Quality first is always less expensive than dissatisfaction in the future! As more dual-band systems are sold and installed, this statement will become more evident when much of the existing equipment in consumer/commercial hands must be replaced completely for combined C/Ku reception.

Antennas

Contrary to many light and airy opinions, mesh antennas are only the cheapest, not the best. Made of extruded aluminum with virtually no worthwhile curvature accuracy specifications, such antennas, unless 12 feet or larger, are nearly worthless for dual-band signal reception. Some of the 12-footers access the more powerful K-1, K-2 birds because of their large reflective surface areas, but the weaker satellites are never seen. Only the better-quality solid and perforated, strong-braced aluminum reflectors with at least 0.030 inch thicknesses appear to be reasonably satisfactory if fitted with correct mounts and feeds. An excellent example would be Winegard's 10-foot CK-1088 with good terrestrial interference rejection and precision construction.

This Pennacle antenna has the 0.030 inch rms curvature accuracy (Fig. 6-7) and sturdiness to handle most weather and signal conditions except that only recently has it been able to reflect Ku transmissions due to the CHC broadband feed. Now a complete antenna with 39.5 dB gain at C band, a wind survival of 125 mph, beamwidth 1.6 degree, depth of 27 inches, and efficiency of 67 percent, this smoked-chrome finished product weighs 92 pounds and is shipped in four quarters. With the CHC feed, very adequate operation on both 3.7 to 4.2 and 11.7 to 12.2 GHz frequencies have been observed and measured.

A fitting companion to the metal Winegard reflector is the specially formulated, sheet-molded compound (SMC) fiberglass antenna made by Prodelin Corp. of Conover, NC. This antenna is virtually indestructable, with high 0.030-inch rms curvature accuracy and has an f/D ratio of 0.3, which makes it suitable for both California Amplifier and Seavey C/Ku feedhorns and reasonably inexpensive block downconverters. Shipped in eight panels, this is a heavy reflector, weighing 295 pounds, and a guaranteed gain of 39.5 dB at midband for the 3.7 to 4.2 GHz spectrum. The Ku response is estimated at about 45 dBi. We would expect similar performance with the Winegard if both are using the same feedhorn and block downconverters. The photo in Fig. 6-8 illustrates both the 8-foot and 10-foot versions of this antenna erected several years ago at Anne Arundel Community College, MD. There have been no service calls on the installations in almost three years, proving that first-class equipment troubles neither the user nor installer. Both smaller and larger reflectors use the same focal distance length button hook feed support by simply changing the f/D ratio from 0.3 to 0.37 for the two radiators. The 8-footer, however, has only three molded panels and weighs but 120 pounds. Both are designed for 90 mph winds, and both can be painted. Special feed support cords prevent feedhorn shifts as the antennas traverse the geosynchronous arc. SMC panels for these antennas are formed at 300-degrees F temperatures under 5×10^6 pounds of pressure, and a textured surface scatters UV rays that would otherwise collect as heat at the assembled parabolic focal point.

We can now say that either of these reflectors—metal or fiberglass—will serve you well and for a considerable period after careful installation. Your formulation 40 king post must be precisely perpendicular to the earth and the mount's north-south position exact, particularly for Ku band reception. Installations, therefore, should be the next topic.

6-7 The Winegard 10-foot perforated aluminum Pinnacle can now operate at both C and Ku bands with the new SBX feed horn.   Winegard Corp.

6-8 Dual installations of 8-foot and 10-foot Prodelin fiberglass antennas at Anne Arundel Community College, Arnold, MD.

Satellite installations

Among antenna installers of all persuasions and abilities, you'll doubtfully receive identical answers (except from those trained by some specific organization) to perform one or a series of explicit tasks. Translated, that deliberately obfuscatory statement simply means most satellite people are going to do it their way unless told otherwise. My purpose, then, is to provide a few figures, words of caution, and some possibly helpful instructions for you to contemplate and execute if your time, inclinations, and pocketbooks are willing. Generally, the following information is followed literally by most people with more than average responsibilities and should prove successful in the majority of situations where oddball conditions are not taken into account, simply because we don't know what such circumstances might be. Nor will I dwell at any length on roof mounting because of the costs involved in nonpenetrating water or sand ballasts or building sidemounts that could require considerably more than casual structural engineering. For instance, try tacking a 12-foot reflector on some school wall's unsupported stack of bricks and see what happens. How about a pile of rubble and a smashed antenna. Next, who services this monstrosity and how?

The radiators of most concern are those in the 6-, 8-, and 10-foot classifications, which are the ones most likely to appear in the home and smaller commercial operations. VSAT types around 1.2 meters have many fewer installation problems with both hardware and wind resistance, and the majority of these are either roof or side building mounts and are easily secured. In addition, most are AZ/EL fixed-position installations that do not require separate king posts and horizon-to-horizon (H/H) motorized trackers.

Soils and/or rock

Clay soils are the easiest and best for good king post seizing. Sand is probably the worst. Under usual conditions and ordinary clay soil compositions, a 10-foot parabolic diameter antenna will require a 10-foot, 40 formulation steel king post (Fig. 6-9) that can easily be center-installed in a 4-foot hole, with $1/4$ cubic yard of 6-bag concrete, having a diameter of 18 inches. Adding about a dozen 12-inch reinforcing bars to the concrete as it is being poured, plus a 3-foot rectangular or square 2- or 3-inch deep platform above ground, virtually guarantees no movement of this king post even with winds exceeding 60 mph. Wind pressure here would be 9.5 lbs/ft^2 or 746 pounds. If you want to be extra cautious in obvious gale-force areas, add another 4 inches of hole depth and a little more concrete for 80 to 90 mile security. Here, you would have 20 lbs/ft^2 and the ability to withstand a force of 1540 pounds. Meanwhile, before the concrete sets up (hardens), recheck perpendicularity with a good angle finder such as Dasco's Pro to be positive you're within at least $1/2$ degree. North-south perpendicularity can be compensated, but not east-west, and Ku is much too critical for a simple spirit level.

A good rule of thumb for estimating wind velocity effects suggests multiplying every two feet increase in antenna diameter by 1.5. The same equality of course, would hold true for diameter reductions. An 8-footer in a similar 80 to 90 mph wind would undergo a force of 1027 pounds. So be governed accordingly.

As for rocky or very sandy soil conditions, you might have to drill holes in rock and, with the assistance of metal shims, install a metal frame of some description over a 4 to 6 foot area to successfully anchor both king post and antenna. All joints should be welded and large bolts firmly secured in either rock or very hard concrete. A first-class welding shop should be of assistance if you carefully explain your needs.

In relatively pure sand, either a considerably larger diameter king post hole is required or a triangular metal mount fixture with a fairly large slab

6-9 Fill your 18 × 48-inch king post hole with ¼ cubic yards of 6-bag concrete and ½-inch Rebars. Then add a 3 × 3-foot platform for maximum stability and security.

of concrete for its base or three cylindrical shafts of concrete for secure holddown. For a 10-foot reflector in sand, a concrete slab base of between 5- or 7-foot square is needed, varying from 42 inches to 12 inches in depth, and requiring between 3.24 and 1.81 cubic yards of concrete, respectively, all depending on your frost line. In warm climates the 7-foot square base would be adequate for a wind force of 3,000 pounds, but cold regions would need the 5-foot square unit which, by the way, would weigh 11,984 pounds. The larger slab would only weigh 6,713. These figures are based on fairly responsible calculations but are not gospel. Your particular situation could easily differ; therefore, your antenna manufacturer should be consulted before the actual installation begins.

Roof mounts are a different category altogether, involving relatively small reflectors, building roofs, esthetics, etc. We'll offer one good example that is proof positive, then let your antenna manufacturer do the rest. Our reasoning results from the number of VSAT offerors already in the market with more to come. Undoubtedly, they'll have many of their own methods, and one or two examples would certainly not cover the subject adequately.

Our single unit is illustrated in Fig. 6-10. It's actually a holdover from USCI days when Canada was broadcasting picture and sound information to mid-Atlantic U.S. from ANIK C-2. But it will easily support a 6-foot metal reflector in all sorts of weather, comes adjustable for virtually any

6-10 A simple, reliable three-section, adjustable roof king post that can easily support 6-foot reflectors on any roof.

angle of roof mounting, and can't cost much to build. So with all those requisites, this little galvanized single pole and dual-legged unit is sufficient unto the day. Originally devised and manufactured by M/A-COM, related units probably will appear on the market from AJAK before this text is published. Those of you planning to nail down a bevy of 1- and 1.2-meter reflectors may find its concept and cost very attractive. It also nicely accommodates an AJAK AccuTrak horizon-to-horizon mount for excellent Ku band access and accuracy within 0.133 degrees, almost double that of the 0.250 degrees you actually need. This same king post and leg assembly has been used during the summer of 1990 for both Ku and C band investigations with newly devised 4-foot and 6-foot reflectors.

Roof fastening can be either by lag bolts into the rafters (joists) or J hooks through the roof and snugged to the rafters. After that, it's only necessary to adjust the leg collars for a "perfect" antenna support. Just be sure you know where said rafters are located and use sealing cement in the bored holes to prevent ceiling leakage.

Substantively, that should offer a reasonable explanation of both antenna mounting and wind loading. There's some leeway in both topics, but what's on paper can be considered a reasonable guide.

Mounts

With a reed switch counting rotating magnets as mount gears revolve or "linear" arms contract and extend, the consumer or commercial positioner receives a stream of pulses pinpointing the east-west location of the antenna traveling its azimuth arc. This action is prompted by wider or narrower pulses from the indoor positioner instructing the mount's motor to turn clockwise or counterclockwise until the antenna reaches some programmed position and stops. Unless the reed counter can actually double pulse, the receiver receives only half the accuracy it needs for its electronic counter to register a precise position. Unfortunately, most mounts still do not have this advantage and, therefore, are not really suitable for Ku. They remain, nonetheless, fairly adequate for C band where only approximately 1-degree accuracy is required. To the best of our knowledge, AJAK Industries of Florence, Colorado is one of the very few or only horizon-to-horizon mount maker offering this necessary feature.

Note that we're not discussing either the 10-turns potentiometer nor the Hall-effect sensor, neither of which is involved in the double-count program. And while inexpensive reed switches are not necessarily the most reliable on-off devices in the switching business, they are cheap and also very easy to troubleshoot. To check one, simply ground one lead to an oscilloscope and connect the other lead to the scope's 1:1 probe. Then pass a small magnet across the face of the switch and watch the display go to zero as the magnetic field causes it to change, from open to closed. The scope's time base should be set to about 5 ms/div and the vertical amplifier to approximately 10 mV. External pickup should produce some sort of display, and the switch does the rest. A covered AJAK AccuTrak mount appears in Fig. 6-11 while supporting a 6-foot perforated 0.090-inch-thickness antenna. We wondered why this reflector did not receive well on C band and nothing at all on Ku. It turned out the f/D was 0.625! What feedhorn could handle that? Needless to say, this company is no longer in business. Wonder what the curvature accuracy might have been—possibly inches? Feet?

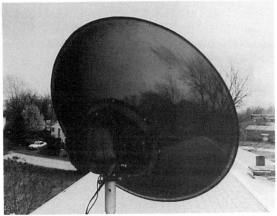

6-11   An AJAK Accu-Trak horizon-to-horizon (H/H) polar mount can comfortably support a 6-foot antenna in all kinds of weather.

A review

Let's break the electromechanical descriptions for now and look back over the satellite signal process. A satellite, any satellite, delivers electromagnetic waves earthward that can be traced in watts via some type of calculated or measured energy called a *footprint*. Ordinarily printed as a circular pattern covering part or all of the continental U.S. and possibly Hawaii, Puerto Rico, and Alaska, these footprints often vary in numbers from about 30 dBW to 48 dBW or more, depending on the spacecraft, its transponders, amplifiers, and the pointing of its antennas. Downlinked energy arrives as electronic (E) and magnetic (H, for oersteds) in a planar pattern that must be collected by the antenna and then radiated to its feedhorn (or reflector in the case of a Cassegrain arrangement), positioned at some focal distance away from the antenna's center or offset so that only a portion of the reflector is used. An offset receives the peak of any incoming signal so that maximum energy transfers to the following amplifiers and converters. Horn and reflector mismatches are thereby minimized for both gain and sidelobe improvements. However, these are for the flatter Ku-band antennas and often entail considerable focal distances from the reflector. Except for multifeed Torus antennas, most of today's antennas are the usual round parabolas, and the large ones (15 feet up) all have what are called prime/prime center focus feeds, usually either Gregorian or Cassegrain with comparable gains as sizes increase. The very expensive Torus radiators are rectangular and curved, often with similar-shaped rectangular multifeeds.

While geosynchronous (orbiting with the earth) are expected to station-keep within 0.5 to 1 degree, some other spacecraft, especially military, are not geosynchronous and large antennas must track these continuously with specially fabricated horizontal and vertical motors to maintain communications. Our television receive-only (TVRO) variety are only required to access the geosynchronous satellites, now numbering about 29 U.S. types, and program their predictable locations in some sort of non-destructive memory for eventual recall and programmed access. If our mounts, antennas, positioner logic, amplifiers, receivers, and television sets are adequate, that's exactly what happens. But one lousy TV with a luminance bandpass cutoff of 2.5 MHz and no stereo can ruin exceptional satellite reception, no matter how good the earth terminal equipment or its installation.

Since satellite energy usually has no terrestrial interference to contend with and delivers information to a satellite receiver's conventional IF band-pass of 27 MHz, it can carry maximum signals down to earth for decoding and introduction to your television set. And if such signals are pure audio and video at *baseband* and do not have to be remodulated on channels 3 or 4, a TV/monitor combination will reproduce maximum passband information from satellite electronics and present you with the best audio and video you've probably ever experienced. This is particularly true of the new Zenith digital TV/monitors, especially the 31- to 32-inch large-screen variety. Images and sound are exceptionally sharp and clean with no artifacts or other impediments. The satellite installation and its electronics, therefore, is really only as good as your television receiver will permit.

Some satellites, of course, do point and phase-shift their downlink patterns somewhat and/or operate in either vertical (V) or horizontal (H) polarities. This requires your receiver or positioner to electrically manage a skew control at the feedhorn that will change the angle of its probes to admit full-phased information. To do this, a small motor turns either the body of the feedhorn or its probes until the proper angle admits maximum energy. This motor usually operates on a dc supply of 5 or 6 volts, a ground (common) connection, and a pulse exciter. To turn the feed clockwise or counterclockwise, pulses in one direction or the other steer the motor right or left for best skew. Thereafter, transponder selection and fine tuning should bring picture and sound to your TV for display and audio reproduction.

Hardware

Many of you may also wonder why your large antennas seem to move very slowly when tracking the arc from their lowest positions. This is due to restrictions placed on satellite positioners to use low voltages and minimum currents. All dc- and not ac-operated, omnipotent Underwriters Laboratories have decreed that open-circuit voltages are limited to 30 volts and a short circuit current of 8 amperes or less after 1 minute, plus an overcurrent protective device of not more than 3.2 amperes. (They neglect the proven reliability of 36 volts at 3 to 4 amperes for the larger reflectors. Very sad!)

Effectively, either you market a 24 V system with increased current or a 30 V system with diminished current. This, of course, affects motor speed at the antenna, and the lower voltage also causes an added IR drop in cable actuator lines that sometimes even requires larger diameter replacement cable or forces additional power supply current and/or voltage from another source. Several years past, mechanical/electrical designers found that a 36 V, 3 to 4 A source would move the heavier reflectors with ease. Now, counterbalances and extra-diameter wire might become unfortunate necessities. If such cabling, however, was always faithfully buried in PVC pipe, even mighty UL might not object to some necessarily increased power rating. Safety first is great, but with much improved sunlight resistant and direct burial cable, all UL approved and now available from such excellent manufacturers as CommScope in Hickory, NC, some relaxation of this so-called "standard" certainly should be further considered and implemented. The TVRO industry is suffering enough without added straight-jacket restrictions. (From my standpoint, UL could use a good goose from a real gander.)

Webbed cabling, usually in 1.5-inch widths, accommodates motor drive and power, three-wire skew control and dual signal leads. The latter is always recommended for C and Ku receive combinations and even as a spare cable with C band only. Sometimes a faulty cable does develop problems and that extra link is very handy. When installing cable, do leave a loop or two at the antenna end for either repairs or replacing F-type signal connectors. If the ends aren't absolutely moisture-proof, even the best cables will "wick," that is, absorb moisture, and kill your incoming signal by degrees or altogether. Many a service person and earth terminal owner has repeatedly replaced expensive LNAs or block downconverters because of "wicked" cable. Both satellite and television signal cable should be of the RG6/U type, UL-approved, with firmly installed F-connectors for best 75-ohm impedance matching to avoid voltage standing-wave ratios (VSWR) accompanied by undesirable signal loss and pickup due to incompatible contacts and connections. And for those who still receive TV signals from their antennas via twinlead, this 300-ohm cabling should be discarded immediately and replaced with RG6/U, along with appropriate matching transformers (baluns) and sometimes splitters, although the latter are technically VHF/UHF frequency dividers. More of this is explained in chapter 8 on television antennas and MATV systems.

Actuators are the long, 18-inch and 24-inch arms that extend and retract to push and pull the reflector around, usually in only a 80- to 90-degree arc. The so-called "linear" is not really linear at all because it operates on counts per inch, and such counts vary with its extended or retracted arm. Therefore, we really can't precisely evaluate its accuracy other than to state that it cannot be as accurate as a double-count H/H mount because count numbers vary with arm positions.

The AJAK mount, on the other hand, guarantees 10 counts/degree and a proven accuracy of 0.133 degrees, which is considerably better than the $1/4$ degree that Ku must have for adequate programming. Furthermore, horizon-to-horizon mounts should cover an arc of 140 degrees, which is entirely adequate for currently assigned west longitude (WL) positions beginning with 62 degrees WL and ending with 146 degrees and 143 degrees WL. But most distressing among push-pull antennas is the usual sudden shift that occurs when moving from west to east or vice versa at the pinnacle of due south. An antenna with a "linear" simply flops over as it passes due south polarity, disrupting all accuracy and magnifying strain on the mount itself. Such differences should be reported since 1992 onward will bring more satellites to orbit, requiring additional pointing accuracies and even greater reliability and endurance. New mounts now in design appear to be all H/H types with considerable innovations and probably interesting price reductions as added incentives for change or new installations. These, coupled with several antennas in the works, could add some enjoyment to satellite sight and sound for everyone.

Concerning receivers and positioners: some are good and some are bad. We won't describe their electrical circuits, but certainly some of their prime characteristics are worth either a few cheers or warnings.

Top-of-the-line receiver positioners usually have very visible satellite and channel front-panel and on-screen displays, as well as audio tuning, polarity, a relative electronic arc position counter, format (horizontal/vertical polarity), channel fine tuning, and C/Ku switching. Under a front panel, you'll usually discover programming layouts, possibly sync and display adjustments, a setup mode for east/west electrical limits, and then either one or two methods of satellite, audio, skew, and counter number programming. At first, all this might sound somewhat confusing, but for accurate tuning and rapid transponder access, all of these facilities are more than necessary. Eventually, microprocessor control will have more reliable sensors and complexities consolidated and considerably reduced, especially channel fine tuning, which should be positively controlled even now by a good phase-locked loop circuit, which probably can be purchased on the open market. Display and receiver sync will also be automated in time, as skew control moves toward more positive function, especially with rotating feedhorns rather than simply moving probes. True, microwave phase is somewhat difficult to manage, but integrated circuits should eventually develop a comparison process that can automatically find the proper downlink angle. Later, someone will take the time to program positioner software so that antenna/mount setups involve only a single satellite, and the rest will automatically fall into place without further struggle. Whether such automation will substantially increase the cost of receiver/ positioners depends on IC availability, engineering design time, manufacturer's markup and indicated consumer/commercial acceptance. All of these advantages won't come at once, but eventually appear as features each fall and winter with new product announcements.

All of these simplified features should make overall satellite reception considerably more appealing, especially for those who've had neither electronics nor computer training. And for those of us who actually test the quality of such products with spectrum analyzers and the like, our results will prove considerably more accurate and much easier to tabulate and compare.

It's about time to rejoin reality and look at a few satellite signals directly off the block downconverters and also a few positioner pulses to keep you well informed. These will be taken at random from several unnamed satellites because some might be criticized rather severely should the occasion demand. Otherwise, this will be an exercise in illustrating "good" downlink information to guide you in the future.

Positioner evaluations

Many if not most positioners are configured so that the east/west (E/W) limits must be set up or logged before programming. This not only determines the tracking arc but it also adjusts your electronic log scale for special satellite and/or transponder identification. In the case of R.L. Drake, for instance, you can program the satellites in one mode but also program sound, skew, polarity, fine tuning, etc., in another. Therefore, if your electronic counter isn't working, you're not going to program. So the very first thing that should be investigated after mount and reflector installation is the switch, potentiometer, or Hall-effect counter at the mount/actuator to see if signals are traveling back through connecting cabling to the positioner.

All you need is a dual-trace oscilloscope or analog voltmeter with both attenuators set at about 10 V/div (this may vary with the equipment), and time base at 5 ms/div. If the results appear as shown in Fig. 6-12, you have evident problems. Motor rippling dc in the upper trace at 15 V is not the difficulty, it's the bottom squiggly trace that's the fault. Shown at 50 mV/ div, there's no way the positioner can react to this tiny response that isn't counting at all, even though we're using an old M/A-COM linear as an example, and a real one at that. Probes, of course, connect to one of the motor wires and one counter lead.

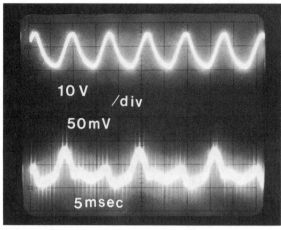

6-12 A good motor but defective reed counter illustrated on the graticule of a dual-trace oscilloscope. Amplitude and time base settings are
shown.

The upper trace, as reported, is all right in terms of volts ripple and a
dc level of 36 V. But if you had a current probe, the dc current would
appear in an entirely different waveform with considerably more meaning.
The bottom trace, naturally, has no similarity to the one in the previous
figure. So let's look at what happens when motor current begins to flow
and the counter normally counts (Fig. 6-13).

Surprised? The "squigglies" at the top now represent pulsating current flow, not voltage, and the bottom waveform has now grown from millivolts to 1 V/div, or about 5 volts due to the combination of reed switching
and inductive reaction of the lead-in cable. I had to speed up the time base,

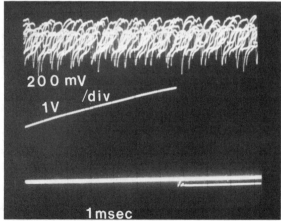

6-13 Current probes illustrate both motor drive (top)
and sawtooth counting (below).

however, to 1 ms/div to obtain the switching display. However, the upper trace now has to be characterized by milliamperes or amperes in terms of 2 mA/mV. Here signal peaks indicate approximately two divisions, or 400 mV. Therefore, the waveform power output at this point represents 800 mA. It would probably be in the amperes if it were not for the wire covering around which the probe is wrapped, and also if these were strictly dc probes, which they're not.

For those of you who do not have current probes, a dc meter in series with one of the motor leads would read the actual current drain, and your scope would only then have to reproduce the sawtooth in Fig. 6-13. But be sure your meter is on the amperes range and not mA; otherwise, you might have to purchase a new meter for a few seconds' mistake. Although we have used dc ripple picked up by ac probes to demonstrate visible current flow, the principle is there nonetheless, and you do know with certainty that the reed switch counter packs a nice wallop for the positioner to happily count as each magnet causes the switching counter to close from its normally open position.

Using this simple oscilloscope method, this is how the positioner can easily be checked as well as the mount or actuator. If the motor and reed switch are operating normally, you've probably won the battle. If not, immediately check cabling, hookups, and the reed switch itself with the scope and any handy magnet.

Receiver evaluations

What were once simple, hand-tuned channels, fine tuning, manual audio, volume and polarity/skew controls (Fig. 6-14) have now become either IC or microprocessor responsibilities that are becoming much more difficult to analyze and service. Fortunately, reliability for the better units is virtually remarkable, but that doesn't diminish the problem of troubleshooting any of the receivers delivered to the market in recent years. In addition, without waveforms to go by, who knows what when attempting even simple repairs. True, most receivers are returned to the manufacturer's factory for repairs, but when many additional satellite systems have been sold and installed, technicians outside the factory are going to have a real problem. And until you actually work on several representative types, manufacturer guidance is your only immediate salvation. For unusual faults, either you become very ingenious, or back to the factory goes your receiver/positioner for a full checkout.

Now let's review the M/A-COM block diagram of an older receiver that's no longer made (Fig. 6-15) since M/A-COM sold its consumer business to General Instrument, which now markets its own receiver/positioners. At the top left, the diagram begins with the second converter, or first intermediate frequency amplifier, which is attenuated by pin diodes, is converted from a bandwidth of 500 MHz to 140 MHz by the mixer, and is saw-filtered. The second IF further narrows this passband to 27 MHz, develops automatic gain

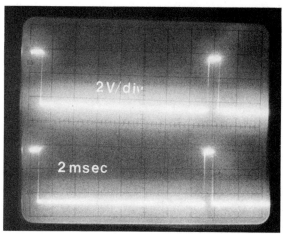

6-14 Skew movement is always determined by pulse widths in pulse-excited systems.

control (AGC) plus automatic frequency control (AF T), and detects the signal for video cipher and plain video outputs. Channel selection originates from microprocessor IDU in the second converter.

So far, much of this is similar to signal processing in a television receiver following the tuner except for the second downconversion, very wide bandwidths, and the obvious difference that satellite downlinks frequency modulate both video and sound, while terrestrial broadcasters AM modulated video and FM modulate sound. This means that even with a super-wideband oscilloscope, there'll be no demodulator probing of the IFs; you'll just have to wait until video is detected and brought out to a rear terminal. The video cipher composite output is a little different since it's not filtered or clamped to some specified level.

FM demodulation in the second IF also develops automatic fine tuning for the IDU as well as the sound output. This is passed through a 5 to 8.5 bandpass filter for a pair of mixers and phase-locked loop circuits also controlled by the IDU with feedback from both FM sound detectors following bandwidth switching that is selectable between 150 and 330 kHz. Mixer local oscillators are variable from 15.7 MHz to 19.2 MHz. Deemphasis is then applied to reduce preemphasized highs at the transmitter, and the stereo matrix now manually selects monaural, discrete, or matrix stereo, all of which continues under IDU control. (IDU simply stands for *indoor unit*.)

Next to IDU is the skew control that is subject to keyboard and remote control and outputs to the LED display units as well as the video SW drive and pulse channel to the mount or actuator. A main bus carries communications between the antenna positioner and skew, with the antenna positioner also outputting to the satellite indicator control panel. Other outputs include RF modulator channel 3/4, L and R wound, polarity, pulse, and the usual motor connections.

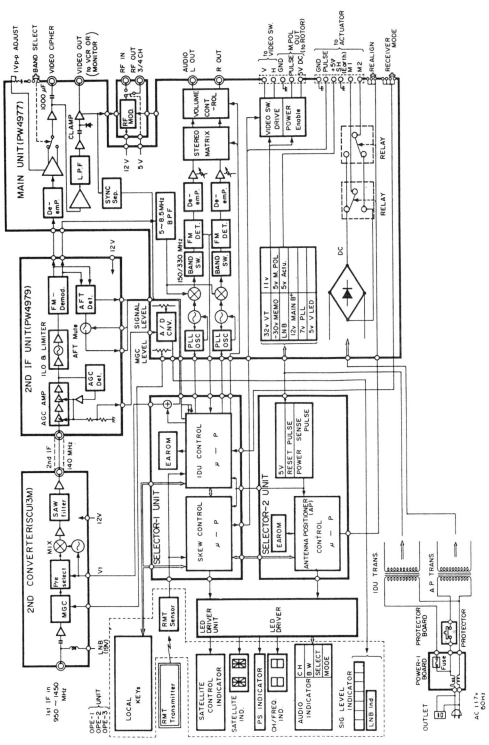

6-15 The old M/A-Com T-6 receiver/positioner is no longer made, but this should give a general idea of the operation of better integrated receiver positioners today.

Ac power supplies deliver parallel inputs to stepdown transformers for AP and IDU electronics, with IDU being the indoor electronics and AP, the actuator 5 V regulator that moves the M1/M2 motor currents. A 36 Vdc actuator motor drive, the current for the T6 was not given, but we strongly suspected it meets or exceeded 3 amperes.

Now that we've waded through an oldie, let's return to R.L. Drake's 2450 and look at incoming signal levels, several satellites, carrier-to-noise, and polarity skew. Skew comes first because it's no problem at all to execute and photograph (Fig. 6-14). Just by pushing the format control on the Drake, you have a change of polarity by rotating the polar probe's metal finger over approximately 100 degrees, depending on probe design. In one format position, the probe pulse measures approximately 1 ms in duration and lasts for 15 seconds. In the other position, this same positive pulse has a width of only 0.8 ms, but remains on the same length of time. Since both polarities are identical, it's obvious that pulse width determines the horizontal (H) or vertical (V) action. The amplitude of these pulses is about 4 volts.

You can therefore be certain that actuator/positioners and skews carry a fair voltage to drive their respective circuits. The scope, for your information, is simply connected to the skew output, time base selected, 2 V/div set on the vertical attenuator, and then photographed. There's nothing to it. Figures 6-12, 6-13, and 6-14, by the way, were done with a standard Hameg HM604 analog oscilloscope and not a storage scope. I hadn't seriously tried this before, but it isn't difficult, and anyone with a decent low-frequency scope should be able to handle it nicely. (A dc current probe would help considerably, but I don't have one.)

Satellite signals off the air

There are two ways to measure the worth of transponder signals, and it isn't what you see in Fig. 6-15. There are 17 active transponders on this Canadian D1 satellite, which downlinks a nice, strong signal here along the Atlantic seaboard. At 10 dB/division, our 7L12 Tektronix spectrum analyzer says signal tip levels are only −34 dB down, producing a whale of a picture since you'll have good responses at −40 dBm, or even less.

So what's the problem? Notice that the vertical transponders (the smaller ones) are barely 6 dB separated in amplitude from the vertical ones? You might get away with this on a strong satellite such as D1, but a weaker spacecraft will give you fits. Quickly go over to your receiver and work with skew so that the horizontal transponders appear as they should in Fig. 6-16. This polarity adjustment is just as clean as you can make them. Unfortunately, you can't expect such positive action all the time. The feedhorn assembly and its motor have a great deal to do with good, bad, or indifferent polarity adjustments, and this Seavey Engineering 124H feedhorn is considerably better than average (so is the R.L. Drake 2450 receiver/positioner).

The amplitude of all these transponders is very reassuring, and their incoming signal levels serendipity, but the critical signal measurement is carrier-to-noise (C/N) (Fig. 6-17). This is the decibel difference between the tip of any transponder and (in this instance) the center of its noise floor. One white and one black marker indicate the precise distance (amplitude) that must be taken into consideration. If you count carefully you'll observe the two marks are separated by 26 dB. What a C/N, you say? Unfortunately that isn't so. We're dealing with frequency modulation now, and the apparent C/N must also take into account the vagaries of the spectrum analyzer. This amounts to:

$$C/N = 10 \log (27 \text{ MHz}/3 \text{ MHz}) + 2.5 \text{ MHz}$$

a 2.5 dB corrects for log amp and detector because each transponder has a bandwidth of 36 MHz but the receiver's bandwidth is 27 MHz and resolution bandwidth is 3 MHz. We are not, in this case, evaluating a pure video signal. Therefore,

$$C/N = 10 \log 9 + 2.5 \text{ MHz} = 12 \text{ dB}$$

So instead of a magnificent 26 dB, the C/N becomes 26 dB − 12 dB = 14 dB.

That isn't bad considering studio signals are 54 dB (sometimes referred to as 56 dB in satellites). But the broadcast figure is good enough, consequently,

$$S/N \text{ (signal/noise)} = C/N + 37.5 \text{ dB, or } 51.5 \text{ dB}$$

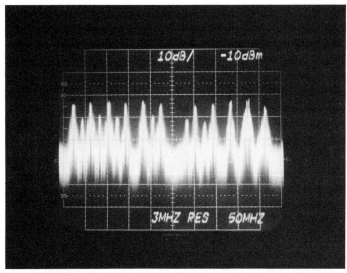

6-16 Horizontally and vertically polarized transponders are barely separated by 6 dB amplitudes. This always means interference.

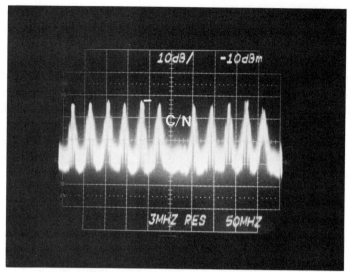

6-17   Use your polarity controls for best V/H transponder separation.

We are, indeed, very close to relative perfection! True, we can spread these transponder signals out considerably at 20 MHz or less per division, but you'd see very little more than some extra noise and possibly additional modulation detail. Were there interference, however, you would certainly work with the analyzer's controls and discover as much information, including frequency, as possible so that trapping or passband filters might take care of the problem.

Otherwise, one of National A.D.L.'s or California Amplifier's TI resistant feedhorns might help considerably. Trapping is always a last resort because it often affects adjacent transponders and even other satellites. For TV/radio 300-ohm twinlead, which was lousy at best, quarter wave and half wave traps often did help. But you're working in gigahertz instead of megahertz now, and trapping here is tricky as any north woods electronic guru will tell you. If at all possible, do not trap. Further, for best reflector results into the feedhorn, always be sure the face of your feed and the center of the antenna are in exact parallel.

Interference and faults

To avoid interference conditions as much as possible, each ground or raised site should be azimuth and elevation checked with either an amplified standard gain feedhorn or, preferably, a site survey antenna and electronics on the very spot the new installation is planned. In this way, almost all interference can either be avoided or at least anticipated and possibly dealt with prior to earth station erection. Additionally, signal gains may be measured and any antenna or mount corrections instituted prior to final equipment placement and test. Often installers neglect such precautions and receive many a headache and time loss for their oversight. When working with microwave technology always play it safe; one careless move can mean outright disaster!

Satellite earth terminals do not "see" interference unless it enters the feedhorn; therefore, several feet or even an inch or two in the intended mounting area may readily solve your problem before you even have to struggle.

In the newer television receivers, by the way, black level thresholds instead of traditional crt brightness keep these sets cut off until either noise or picture is visible. Therefore, when working with satellite downlinks and their receivers, a blank screen doesn't mean spacecraft absence, it just means no signal is being received. If your spectrum analyzer shows you're tuned to a satellite, the 18–24 V LNB supplies are obviously working, even with the satellite receiver turned off, so your problem could be the cables between the two receivers. If the satellite receiver is on, and your analyzer now shows nothing, just like the TV, then your LNB amplifier/converters are probably not working and, for some reason, your receiver dc output to these LNBs has vanished. Now you have the task of finding an open or short affecting the LNB supply, which could either originate in the receiver or the cable itself. The LNBs are more likely to open than short, therefore we suggest cable as the culprit first, especially its F-connector couplings. Recall, however, that "wicking" can result in signal loss but allow the dc supply to continue operating.

Signal faults are somewhat more elusive because few are outright failures. Look again at the "bottom" noise in Fig. 6-17. If this moves up into the transponders, you receive a "snowy" picture, similar to TV, with shaky figures and misty-appearing images. And when signal levels fall from –40 dBm to –35 dBm or less, just such symptoms occur with somewhat sickening regularity. Unfortunately, some of the lesser, underpowered spacecraft can present such an image, especially if your terrestrial equipment isn't the best. Unless you're fortunate enough to own and use a spectrum analyzer, your only hope in analyzing the problem is to check with someone who does possess a first-class earth terminal—and, unfortunately, there aren't many of these, so you'll have to suffer the consequences. A satellite system installed for $2,000 for even C band simply won't make the grade unless it is placed in the best signal area of the country; but even then it won't last very long due to a flimsy reflector, half-vast electronics, and a "linear" mount that won't handle Ku. Add another $1,000 or $1,500, however, and you can own a very good product with excellent longevity, especially if the antenna is fiberglass or solid metal and the mount offers double count and horizon-to-horizon sweep.

Polarities are becoming extremely important now that more transponders are operating and the Federal Communications Commission is requiring horizontal or vertical emissions in specific instances among adjacent satellites. Satellite magazines such as ORBIT are rendering a considerable service by printing H or V polarities and typical transponder transmissions on a very handy C and Ku reference card that's easily removable and very handy for both installer and customer. It's highly advisable to check your own receiver against this listing to be sure the polarity indicators are correct, otherwise you'll be missing a great deal of programming and actually operating an incorrect receiver. A Ku band example is illustrated in Fig. 6-18. Here, we're receiving a very fair video on Ku at − 42 dBm, but the on-screen display claims transponder 17 has vertical polarity, and it does not. This discrepancy needs to be corrected immediately! At Ku, your transponder fine tuning must also be very effective because the wide bandpass of most of these transponders is many MHz wider than the 40 MHz set aside for C band. Ku can easily vary between 54 and 72 MHz for channels carrying video and consumer receiver IFs seldom extend beyond 140 MHz, and passbands of 27 MHz before detection. True, you literally can't see video luminance beyond the NTSC limits of 4.2 MHz, but satellite images on Ku, when reproduced through TV baseband monitors, appear in superior detail to broadcast transmissions. And although this is certainly due in part to terrestrial interference, TV antennas and cabling, the satellite has a clear field with no obstacles other than space loss and inclement weather at Ku. C band, of course, is not really affected, and the stronger Ku satellites will only experience a 4 dB loss in a deluge.

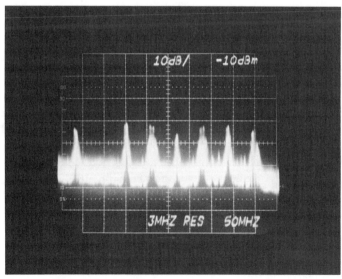

6-18   G.E.-Americom's K2 responds well at − 42 dBm and a C/N of 13 dB.

Polar-mounted Ku antenna

As promised earlier in the chapter, if we made any real progress with a small-aperture Ku band antenna (Fig. 6-19) it would be described and characteristics noted. This has now been done with a 1.2-meter reflector having an rms curvature accuracy of 0.025 inches, a focal distance over diameter (f/D) of 0.333, fabricated entirely of electro galvanized perforated steel.

A new unit from the Winegard Co., this antenna was originally designed for European applications but now becomes available for U.S. distribution once overseas orders have been completed, possibly in both aluminum and steel versions. Shipped in a sturdy cardboard box, it weighs only 73 pounds, including wooden crating support and strapping. Once unpacked, it's easily mounted by a signal individual.

As I have previously cautioned, Ku band is considerably different from C band in that it has higher power and wider bandwidth, but its three times higher frequency and tiny access spectrum, which is 75 percent less than C band, makes positioning, fine tuning, and often polarities rather difficult. While you can use linear actuators with reasonable results for C band, only horizon-to-horizon mounts with enclosed motors and gears appear to stroke the necessary 1/4 degree general target for Ku. Actually, such mounts should have reed counters positioned near the magnet wheels so that dual counts approximating 0.133 degrees can occur. G.E.-Americom's K1 and K2 satellites are easy to access, with their 45 W/transponder and 54 MHz bandspread, but GSTAR 2 and some of the others with but 20 W/transponders require better than average equipment for good video reception (Figs. 6-20, 6-21). Therefore in dealing with Ku, we have found that minimum satellite video reception requires at least a 27 MHz passband, and an expansion to 30 MHz wouldn't hurt.

But a super reflector and wideband receiver are only part of the necessary Ku ingredients. You need good feedhorns, exceptional low-noise block downconverters, a reliable and completely adjustable roof mount, superior downlead cabling, and extremely careful north-south polarity adjustment, exact declination for your particular area, and expert tracking of the various satellites always positioned above the equator. In short, the very best earth terminal gear for Ku is an absolute must, in addition to arc tracking with a decent spectrum analyzer such as the Tektronix Model 2710, which I described in some detail in a previous chapter.

Don't be discouraged, however, more instruments are appearing on the market every month, and we fully expect basic analyzers in the $3,000 to $5,000 or less range to be available possibly by the time this book is published. Considerable effort is now underway to meet that goal, although there will be limitations on such instruments as sensitivity, overall dynamic range, time/frequency base stability, and internal sweep characteristics. But limitations or not, Ku and also the even higher DBS K

6-19 Winegard's brand-new 1.2-meter antenna with 0.030 curvature accuracy is specifically designed for Ku. Our tests are continuing.

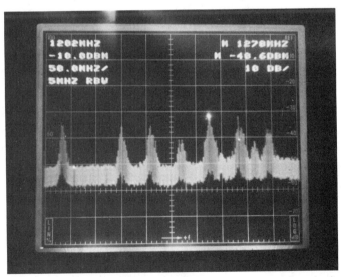

6-20 Strong satellite SATCOM K2 is easy to access, but don't set up on this one.

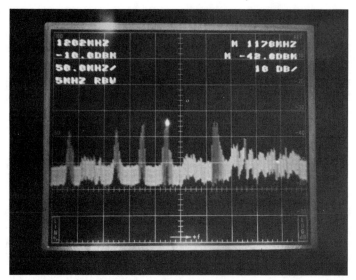

6-21 SBS 4 or GSTAR 2 are better setup picks, then K1 and K2 are tracked nicely.

band to come, will certainly require very precise setups and azimuth tracking for any polar mount arrangement to be successful. So put away a few nickels now for some real goodies tomorrow.

As the photo in Fig. 6-19 indicates, this 1.2-meter reflector is not a toy, nor can it be derived from chicken wire and 1 × 2s in the back yard. Molds are very expensive to achieve such curvature accuracy and must be sufficiently durable for literally thousands of pressings to pay for their existence and make a reasonable profit. However, between European and American usage, the little Ku radiator should do very well for its good manufacturer.

You will also want to closely inspect the simple mount, which is no more than three pieces of pipe, two of which measure some 24 inches in length and 2 inches in diameter. The 3.5-inch king post is pivoted on its center stand and can be adjusted for exact perpendicularity with respect to the earth, if you use an angle finder calibrated in at least 1/2 degrees. Spirit levels, unfortunately, are not accurate enough. Roof fasteners can be either lag bolts or J hooks; just be positive you can locate the roof rafters (joists), install them in the center, and then liberally seal with roofing cement to prevent leaks. The king post and Accu-Trak mounts also accommodate 6-foot antennas with no problems.

You should also remember that heavy rain and snow conditions affect the weaker Ku banders up to 10 dB and the heavy hitters to 4 dB. So don't make overly liberal ''perfect signal'' promises too freely: clear-sky guarantees are your best insurance. And do not be misled by the additional 9 to

10 dB Ku gain that some antenna manufacturers emphasize. Space loss at 11 GHz becomes 206 dB rather than 196 at C band, and bad weather takes another bite out of the supposedly additional signal.

Further, you will need precise positioning, good transponder fine tuning, mono and stereo audio capability, and even incremental polarity rotation for reasonable results. Nonetheless, with a good, wideband receiver having a low noise figure and equal feed and downconverter quality, Ku band pictures are remarkably good.

If you would like to review what a worthwhile Ku spectrum looks like, the transponders in Fig. 6-20 tell the tale, and our springtime sky was completely overcast and dribbling rain, to boot! Ku has certainly arrived and is as lusty as the flowers in May. Be forewarned, however, that all transponders decidedly do not carry video, there is considerable business communications scrambling, and many of the Ku spacecraft are not continuously transmitting, especially SBS (Satellite Business Systems), so they're sometimes hard to identify.

Here in the east, we begin with Satcom K2 and work west. But do not setup on K2; you could be on its broad sidebands and this will knock the rest of the azimuth arc silly. GSTAR II would be a good one for starters.

Finally, just as a reminder, Table 6-3 lists U.S. Ku satellites presently in orbit. Surprised at the numbers? Now add Canada's Aniks and one or two more from other countries, and you have a very representative group indeed. Also recall that Ku belongs to the Fixed Satellite Service and is positively not DBS.

Table 6-3. Ku satellites in orbit today

Satellite	Orbit location (degrees, west longitude)	Transponders (bandwidth, MHz)	Notes
ASC-1	128	6/72	hybrid
GSTAR III	125	16/54	
SBS V	123	10/43	
SPACENET I	120	6/72	hybrid
GSTAR II	105	16/54	
GSTAR I	103	16/54	
SBS I	99	10/43	
SBS II	97	10/43	
SBS III	95	10/43	
SBS IV	91	10/43	
SPACENET III-R	87	6/72	hybrid
SATCOM Ku I	85	16/54	
SATCOM Ku II	81	16/54	
SPACENET II	69	6/72	hybrid

Antenna lifts

Since many readers might be working singly, it's nice to know there are ways to shimmy up a king post with a 300-pound parabola and survive—all with a little planning and the touch of a forefinger and thumb. Perusing J.C. Whitney's auto catalog, a special Superwinch electric lift was advertised for under $150 that was guaranteed to snatch 1,000 pounds at a 90-degree angle with no sweat and just 80 amperes from a 12 V battery as the motivator (Fig. 6-22).

6-22 Lifting a heavy antenna to its mount with SuperWinch clamped to the king post. For this 12 V system, power is supplied directly by a car battery.

It stands to reason that if such a hoist could be attached to a newly installed king post, there'd be no trouble in handling a 300 to 500 pound satellite antenna if all other general conditions were met, such as a sturdy antenna attachment and a steadying line (nautical term for *rope*) topside (at the peak), in addition to mounting brackets for the electric motor.

A trip to a large auto supply store secured the 4-inch truck exhaust brackets and 3/8-inch u-bolts. Then a local welder took but a few minutes to tack the brackets to our motor frame. Finally, we considered that a set of cable strain relief rollers might contribute to the process, and so these were purchased from a local distributor.

As the illustration shows, all were mounted on a king post in readiness to either lower or raise an old or new antenna from the ground to its intended mount. Observe, however, that a nonmetal auto tow rope and a pipe bar fitted with end caps are supported by mounting brackets on the rear of the antenna, and all lifting and lowering takes place using this pipe with cable hoist secured to its center. The additional rope from topside steadies the reflector on its way up or down and can easily be pulley-attached to your truck's radiator support panel near the battery that will supply all 80 amperes for motor lift.

Thereafter, it's only a matter of a little skill and some confidence to become comfortable with this extremely handy arrangement. The manufacturer is Superwinch of Putnam, CT, maker of both ac and dc electric winches as well as the Fairlead 1560 set of rollers. My little winch is the EX1, which includes the up/down switch and its fairly long positive and negative wire conductors.

All you have to do now is to make the lift and cable attachments, mount the winch securely on its king post, connect the battery leads and hoist or lower away. Just take it easy for the first several times so that the action becomes routine. It saves a broken back every time and makes it possible for one-man installers to operate just about anywhere they wish. Observe one word of warning: Although the winch has a certain amount of holding power once current is removed, don't count on it supporting heavy weights without some sort of locking action such as a bolt or other similar restraint.

Enjoy your new acquisition but don't overdo!

Tech notes

While signal analysis is usually sufficient to overcome a majority of local problems, there are times when simple and even complex adjustments are needed to make certain systems and subsystems operate as designed. True, engineers should not overdesign when less exotic stages or their multiples will do. But when a piece of equipment is initially blocked out, some "super networks" are bound to creep in due either to lack of experience or sometimes justifiable ego.

R.L. Drake's Model 2450

Superior sensitivity and threshold extension highlight this unit's outstanding characteristics, which include discrete and matrixed stereo sound, a 140 MHz second IF passband, efficient satellite location tuning, rapid channel scan, and two methods of programming (one for satellites only and the other for specific channel video/audio), azimuth location, and an electronic log number assigned for individual transponders and their orbit locations.

In the Miamisburg, Ohio engineering offices, however, the old idea that sync had to be LC-stripped from video in discrete stages and sync adjustments with potentiometers were needed to keep integrated circuits honest conjured up a considerable vertical/horizontal sync network that hasn't even been seen in television receivers for more than 10 years. True, the design works, but with time and temperature aging, there will certainly have to be adjustments. That's what this tech note is all about.

The problems are twofold: The Sync Regenerator under the front panel must first be stabilized, and then oscillator coil L102 under the modulator board has to be very carefully tuned ("twiddled") for steady picture sync. You may or may not have to touch up horizontal hold potentiometer R218 in extreme cases of misalignment.

For this operation, the modulator and its supporting pc board requires removal from the chassis. Located on the left rear of the 2450 receiver, two securing nuts on the chassis' back frees the Sanshin modulator, which has a long circuit connect lead so that it can be conveniently placed on the bench behind the chassis. Other than the two nuts there are no other disconnections. Place the receiver in its setup mode.

With all signal inputs removed from the receiver, the front panel sync regenerator potentiometer is adjusted from counterclockwise toward clockwise to firmly lock in the on-screen display. Then a satellite input is connected to the receiver and adjustable L102 is located (which is marked K102 on the parts location diagram and L102 on the schematic). This coil is almost centered in front of IC U105, which was generally obscured by the modulator board, even though there is an entry hole available which may or may not permit diddle stick entry.

Having the modulator out of the way, simply connect a high-impedance digital voltmeter to the rear end of capacitor (pin 23 of U105) and tune L102 for approximately 2.45 to 2.5 volts. This should take care of wandering horizontal sync and keep the on-screen display in evidence at the same time. If there are still slight jitters, gingerly adjust horizontal hold R218, and then recheck L102 for good measure. With this accomplished, your difficulties will probably vanish into very good pictures and delightful sound. You may now either move into the program or operate modes for satellite selection or general use.

7

Sound from baseband to broadcast

THERE ARE MULTITUDES OF SELF-APPOINTED EXPERTS ON AUDIO. The only problem is they all hear differently and few know enough about instrumentation to verify either praise or condemnation. This chapter will try to avoid either extreme and deliver results based solely on test analysis. In this way, equivalent results can be verified and contentious situations avoided. However, having been a fair trumpet-playing musician in years past, there is reasonable foundation for quality sound recognition and the establishment of test procedures to substantiate. In a single chapter, of course, we can't cover the entire subject in exhaustive depth, but a general overview and specific circuit examinations should be of considerable aid to those whose audio interests may extend at least to the stirrup, anvil, and auditory canals. Conversely, for those avid rocksters and Army-Navy military who've had 60 dB amplifiers and cannon bangs blow cotton from their sensitive ears, we'll simply have to describe the high frequency ranges which they no longer recognize. Above 10 kHz, unfortunately, these categories are blessed if they hear a scratchy tweet. If you can recognize one of the older television receiver flyback transformer squeals at 15,734 Hz, then your audible senses are better than normal. If not, telephone frequencies at 3 kHz max may suit you exactly, and at less than 30 Hz you're fairly lucky if interesting tones are even available below normal speaker ranges, which often extend no lower than 50 Hz, if that.

Should you really want to check audibles in a purely practical way without sophisticated numbers, buy a pair of good earphones, plug them into a worthwhile radio receiver, connect a reliable and calibrated sinewave generator to the radio (at baseband) and twirl the dial. Without external noise present you may hear a mite more, but the results are probably repeatable at comfortable volumes. If you have to substantially increase volume as frequencies increase, you're decidedly in trouble. In this age of no-tune "music," youngsters are particularly vulnerable to loud and raucous sounds masquerading as professional orchestrations. Always check their hearing! My own, for instance, having been serenaded by 3″/50 or 5″/38 dual-purpose Navy shipboard weapons, ranges from a soft 22 Hz flutter to an 8 kHz whine. My wife, who's seven years younger and an artist, hears up to 12 kHz and is much better at high frequencies than those that are low. Wind instruments blowing a driving musical rendition in five-part harmony are her special anathema—something today's auto-synthesizers may well understand since even two-part harmony to them is probably a single mother's blessed event.

Historically

When one speaks of radio, they're considerably more than just a few thousand AM-FM stations scattered across the globe. You have aeronautical, amateur, cellular, citizens band (remember CB?), government, land mobile, maritime, radio astronomy, space communications (including satellites), ship-to-shore, underwater, and many lesser types that generally combine under these headings. Nonetheless, the main interest lies in the commercial/consumer category, which indeed occupies spectrum space from 0.535 MHz to 1.605 MHz for amplitude modulation (AM) and 88 to 108 MHz for frequency modulation (FM). Strictly speaking, radio wavelengths extend between 10 kilohertz to 3,000 gigahertz and are divided into 8 bands from very low (VLF) to SHF and EHF, which are super-high and extremely high frequencies.

In a vacuum (or outer space), light travels at the rate of 186,282 miles/second, or 299,792 kilometers/second, which is the speed all electromagnetic fields advance. Visible light appears between some 750 and 390 nanometers, with the longest being red and the shortest violet. Frequencies may be converted to periodic wavelengths by the simple equation:

$$\lambda = \text{speed of light/frequency (in feet or meters)}$$
$$\lambda = 9.84 \times 10^8/f \text{ (feet)}$$
$$\lambda = 3 \times 10^8/f \text{ (meters)}$$

At sea level, however,

$$\lambda = 1.1 \times 10^3/f \text{ (feet)}$$

which is a very considerable difference from propagations in vacuum.

Historically, Italian Guglielmo Marconi produced the first wireless telegraph in 1895 and American physicist Reginal Fessenden demonstrated the first voice transmissions in 1900. Then, in 1904, English engineer John Fleming invented a vacuum tube that would detect radio signals (a diode) and Lee De Forest added a grid to a tube in 1904 for controlled amplification. So this is how radio actually began. Radio broadcasting in the U.S., however, did not commence until 1920 (amplitude modulation only), and it was not until the 1930s that Major Edwin Armstrong evolved frequency modulation for high signal-to-noise ratios from medium-strength radiations. Today in the U.S. alone we have 4,966 AM and 4,251 commercial and 1,414 noncommercial FM stations.

Each method has its singular advantages, however, with distance and low frequency for AM and clarity and fidelity for FM. But AM is characteristically noisy, and FM, being almost line-of-sight, must use considerable power to be heard other than locally and exhibits annoying capture kickouts among weaker signal areas, especially in auto radios. Now that both are stereophonic, the larger cities usually offer a choice of at least one hi-fi AM and a baker's dozen of FM stereophonic emissions. Many foreign countries are following suit, especially since Motorola's C-QUAM now seems to be the accepted AM stereo format. Meanwhile, the National Association of Broadcasters and associates are making concerted efforts to improve AM radio and will probably have some significant advances to announce during 1990 or early in 1991. At the same time, BTSC-dbx TV stereo broadcasting has also improved, and MTS TV receivers, especially those with digital-processed sound, are an auditory delight with adequate signal-to-noise (S/N) from local transmitters. They are even beginning to rival discrete and multiplex satellite stereo from 22.3 kilomiles out in space—believe it or not!

So in examining sound, we're really considering standard amplitude modulation, multichannel stereo sound, frequency modulation, and the two satellite wideband stereo modes. Simulcasting, one FM and one AM/FM channel, is not included since this mode is now a rarity and will probably be largely discontinued for audio. Not so in video, however, because expanded bandwidths resulting from compression and expansion are now probable for high-definition television, with standard NTSC programming on one channel, and expanded/compressed (companded) information on another. Audio for HDTV has not been decided upon at this writing, but it's sure to be digital and could become the best sound medium of all if permitted adequate passbands.

With this relatively brief background as foundation, let's launch into some of the various systems, show a few available block diagrams and schematics, and apply instrumentation to certain circuits where appropriate. Regular AM modulation might not be exactly exciting, but AM stereo should rock you awake in reasonable short order, especially Motorola's C-QUAM.

Amplitude modulation

Amplitude modulation is nothing more than varying the width of a radio-frequency signal usually with voice, speech, video or facsimile information. But here the process is limited to AM radio.

By authority of the Federal Communications Commission, AM radio is allocated 107 channels of 10 kHz each covering the spectrum between 535 kHz and 1605 kHz, with subsequent expansion to 1705 kHz before 1991. It's usually illustrated as a sine wave alternating between positive and negative values (Fig. 7-1) with varying degrees of compressed or expanded modulation, all with respect to time. If the RF carrier operates above and below a center zero or dc reference, the resulting measurements are termed peak-to-peak (p-p) and modulation is measured between 0 and 100 percent. Should the carrier operate between 0 and some negative or positive value, measurements are related in terms of peak (p)—both terms ultimately relating to root mean square.

Now to equate p-p and p with an equivalent (heating) value of ac and dc called root-mean square (rms), you need to divide p-p by 2.828 and p by 1.414 to arrive at a similar dc value. For instance, 120 rms volts of ac would register 339.36 Vac (p-p) on the face of your oscilloscope. Just don't try this measurement unless your scope is "floating;" that is, there must be no ground connection since the case of the oscilloscope is ac return. Any such measurement should really be made with a good isolation transformer between the scope and *all* ac power. And even then, you had best take every imaginable precaution to avoid joining either the winged angels or the forked tailed coal dust twins, unless you aren't choosy.

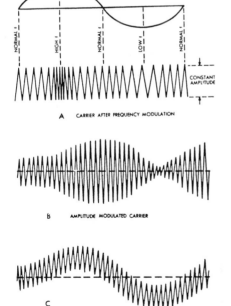

7-1 Frequency and amplitude modulation generated by a single sine wave.

RF carriers are all measured in terms of dBW or dBm (dBW + 30 = dBm). But modulation here consists of percentages because it operates only on carrier amplitudes. And if these low-frequency signals happen to pick up extraneous information or if poor signal-to-noise conditions develop, you will have undesirable effects in the detected information.

Of course there could be no broadcasts without antennas that convert electromagnetic energy into electrical signal current. This current produces a magnetic field (H) and the charge across or along the antenna results in an electric field (E), the two fields being 90 degrees out of phase with one another. Normal AM transmissions occur during the day resulting from surface, direct and reflected wave components, the latter two traveling in relatively straight lines and are exposed to ionosphere reflection called the D layer some 25 to 50 miles above earth. At night, however, this D layer disappears, low frequency transmissions are not absorbed and sky waves cover much greater distances and often garble local radio emissions clearly heard during the day.

Furthermore, AM is always susceptible and vulnerable to low-frequency waves emanating from power lines, lawn mowers, nonresistor auto spark plugs, sputtering light bulbs, power tools, some electric motors, and almost anything else in the hertz-kilohertz spectrum that sparks and rotates. In amplitude modulation, good grounds and some "hash" filtering are often essential. Conversely, when full ground waves blend, daytime distances over reasonable terrain are excellent and C/N passably low.

AM broadcasting has already been improved by the addition of AM stereo. It will be further rejuvenated through ongoing programs already in progress by the National Association of Broadcasters. Our regular NTSC (National Television Systems Committee) television video portion is also amplitude modulation, but that will be discussed elsewhere. So, too, will any other AM segments that don't belong in this radio examination.

Monophonic sound

The dictionary definition of monophonic describes a single strain of music without harmony or accompaniment. Strictly speaking, this is accurate, but we do have plenty of harmony in mono recordings. It all originates from a single source, the microphone. So, to split bowstrings, an orchestra with accompaniment and harmony can deliver sounds to a single pickup device but there is no dual-channel or separation system we have all come to know as stereophonic. Therefore, monophonic it is until we complete this section of the chapter.

Let's look at a few waveshapes to analyze and prove our points, along with some interesting measurements you might want to remember. Figure 7-2 shows a uniform but simple sine wave on top and a modulated sine wave below. Oscilloscope settings are 2 μs/div at an amplitude of 0.5 V/div. This is approximately 90 percent of somewhat sloppy modulation at approximately 382 kHz. Nonetheless, the modulation is adequate to the

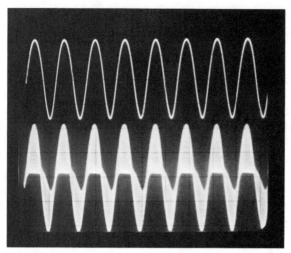

7-2 Modulated (bottom) and unmodulated (top) sine
waves as seen via a Hameg HM 604 oscilloscope.

occasion if a 1 kHz modulation frequency suffices. Most generators, like
the B&K-Precision 2005 unit we're using has both a 1 kHz internal fixed
modulation and an input for more if external modulation is needed. I think
it is required because a range of modulating frequencies should be illustrated rather than some arbitrary number that's been "standard" for decades or years. Fortunately, this instrument accepts modulation between 50
Hz and 20 kHz. Just remember to keep your incoming "intelligence" at
half or less of the RF frequency at all times for acceptable carrier-to-
intelligence action.

Since we have a fair signal generator and a very good intermediate frequency HM604 oscilloscope, the next thing you might want to know would be
the passband of the 60 MHz oscilloscope. Be careful here, however, because
you need a leveled output across the frequency range to positively establish
the 3 dB down point of the scope. Fortunately, B&K anticipated this requirement and installed a frequency monitor output that drives an electronic
counter or permits a worthwhile check on percentage of modulation.

Roughly, 0.7 of the original amplitude is the −3 dB bandwidth point.
Therefore fill four divisions of the graticule with the initial waveform and
work up until the 3 dB point is reached (Fig. 7-3). It seems the scope had
adequate passband, but the signal generator is, itself, 3 dB down at 23.4
MHz. It's a little difficult to evaluate 60 MHz oscilloscopes under those
conditions. Sure there are better generators, but do you want to write a
check for a thousand or so dollars? Or can you make do with this one? If
you know your instrument limitations, you can accomplish a great deal
with relatively little.

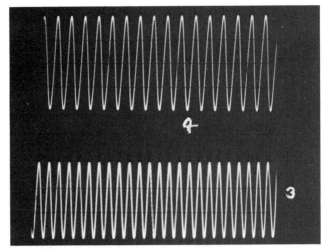

7-3 To check passbands of instruments or analog systems, establish a 4:3 ratio on the graticule. The -3 dB point lies at three divisions.

Scope tricks

There are a couple of little tricks you should know when using oscilloscopes. If you'd like to translate peak or peak-to-peak into decibels—current and voltage, that is:

$$\text{dB(analog)} = 20 \log \text{ p-p readout}$$

For instance:

$$\text{dB} = 20 \log 4 \text{ volts} = 12.04 \text{ dB}$$

Beware when using logs, however, for 0 dB is a gain of 1, whether current/voltage or power ratios. And below 0, you'll only read negative numbers, and they represent a loss. Power translations are 10 log times power ratio (P_2/P_1). These helpful tidbits can make electronics life easier, especially if there's no spectrum analyzer. Now, if you'd like to translate time into frequency, we can also solve that, too. And here you would have a crude spectrum display with only oscilloscope accuracy, which, at best, is little more than 3 percent (Fig. 7-4).

We already know that frequency is the inverse of time, and time is the *x* portion of your oscilloscope's graticule. But readouts are seldom within the comfortable limits of a single graticule division. Therefore, you have to compensate. Let's take an interesting example:

$$T = 1/f \text{ and } f = 1/T$$

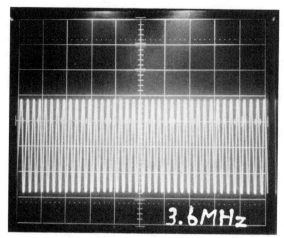

7-4   Translate time base into frequency for spectrum count.

Conveniently, the time base of the oscilloscope is set at 1 μs, which amounts to 10^{-6}. As nearly as we can measure, there are 3.8 oscillations in each horizontal graticule division. You could expand this to several divisions and count the oscillations for greater accuracy, but if your scope isn't precisely calibrated, the inaccuracy will be that much greater. So let's look at how this time-to-frequency translation works out.

$$f = 3.8/1 \times 10^{-6} = 3.8 \times 10^6 \text{ or } 3.8 \text{ MHz}$$

This isn't too bad for both the signal generator and scope errors because a fairly accurate frequency counter reads 3.598 MHz after a short warmup. Conversely, if you were counting the cycles in, say, three divisions, the equation would read

$$f = 11.5/3 \times 1 \times 10^{-6} = 3.83 \text{ MHz}$$

Therefore, for gross measurements, a single division will do equally as well as a half dozen because low-cost oscilloscope inaccuracies tend to exaggerate over half graticule to full scale. This is also a satisfactory means of calibrating your oscilloscope's time base with minimal equipment, and in this instance you don't need a constant amplitude or dial-accurate sine-wave source, just a calibrated electronic counter and recognizeable sine or square waves. By using only one division we missed the counter readout by 200 kHz, but that's only 5 percent. So the discrepancy isn't that bad at all. Read the foregoing over several times to fix these several simple equations firmly in memory, then continue. For henceforth, the going does, indeed, become a little more difficult, accompanied by considerably better technical equipment and somewhat more intensive explanations.

Spectrum analysis

First, let's look at this 3.6 MHz sine wave (Fig. 7-5) with a Tektronix 7L5 spectrum analyzer and see what happens. At 10 dB/division (taken from the top), you count backwards, so that the continuous wave signal appearing actually measures approximately – 20 dBm. The dot above it registers exactly 3600 kHz, or 3.6 MHz. That confirms the counter readout, shows a good waveform without harmonics, and an S/N ratio of 35 dB (taking into account any obvious constraints) and the 4 dB noise floor, which is really 38 – 33, and that's how we arrive at the 5 dB difference. Were this either a video or satellite carrier, then entirely different constraints would apply— Topics covered later in detail. The 3 dB resolution bandwidth (10 dB/30 kHz) is exactly 30 kHz as indicated by the analyzer's bottom graticule readout.

Now we're working up to a worthwhile analysis of such analog information, but we have to return to baseband because the audio spectrum is between 20 Hz and 20 kHz, even though only the vary sharpest ears can hear beyond 15 kHz, and some of that might be imagination. So let's look at the audio output of a good table recorder radio, a Casio CP-750, and see what the earphone port responses represent.

A stereo/audio generator with RF external modulation is to be used for both carrier and sound tracking. Since we're dealing with only voltage, spectrum analyzer outputs are set for dBV or dBmV. If you'd like to convert dBm at 50 ohms to dBmV at 75 ohms, it can be done easily:

$$dBmV = 54.5 + dBm$$

Note: dBV/dBW = dBmV/dBm + 30

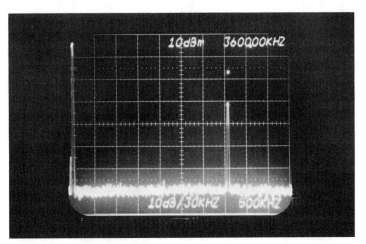

7-5 A spectrum analyzer display of the 3.6 MHz waveform (above) at a resolution bandwidth of 30 kHz.

Other than introducing external modulation into the stereo generator between 2 kHz and 20 kHz, there's nothing more to the proceedings than tuning the radio to the generator's RF frequency of 100 MHz. You must, however, have securely shielded and grounded cables between the earphone radio plug-in and your analyzer or oscilloscope. Otherwise readings will be considerably degraded and just plain wrong. On the other hand, a microphone in front of the receiver's speakers would be somewhat more realistic than the earphone jack, which does produce some excellent read-outs. But only use a very good directional microphone or you're in trouble all over again.

Figure 7-6 does illustrate a broad frequency response from about 1 kHz to 18 kHz, but a 35 dB drop along the way would indicate more than considerable fall-off at high frequencies. Some of this, however, could depend largely on settings of the receiver's three equalizers, which do have an effect on audible response. Adjusted to center position, these equalizers show the low-to-high frequency drop to be just over 20 dB, (Fig. 7-7) rather than the 35 dB illustrated in the preceding figure. And with 75 used preemphasis added, the drop is only 10 dB. Be careful, therefore, of all radios with compensating adjustments because they might not all offer the perfect spectrum analyzer display. Remember, you hear logarithmically and not linearly. Additionally, attempting this same type of frequency with an AM signal generator is just about as disastrous as the toboggan appearing in Fig. 7-6, especially if you use an external antenna that's not especially suited for AM emissions.

Let's combine signal-to-noise (S/N) and total harmonic distortion (THD) in a single display (Fig. 7-8) and read some encouraging FM num-

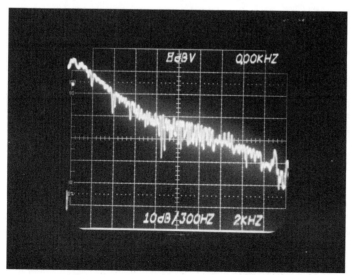

7-6   A great 18 kHz frequency response, but at a 35 dB drop, some might not hear it.

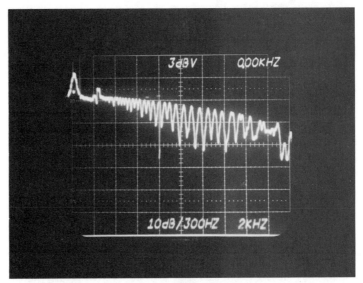

7-7 With all equalizers centered and the 75 μs source engaged, the frequency drop is only 10 dB rather than 35 dB.

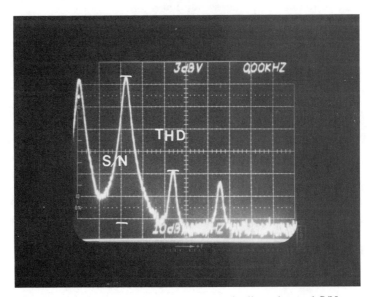

7-8 You can easily combine total harmonic distortion and S/N on one display.

bers. Here, preemphasis is not engaged, and you see the results exactly as they appear: approximately 62 dB for S/N and a dB figure of 42 for THD, which translates to about 2 percent distortion including the 3rd harmonic both figures being excellent! A distortion translation chart is shown in Table 7-1:

Table 7-1. S/N ratio versus THD

Ratio (dB)	THD (%)
20	10.00
22	7.94
26	5.01
31	2.87
40	1.00

The first analog measurement on signal-to-noise (S/N) involves the entire signal-generating and processing setup. Consequently, it is probably not a true reading because the spectrum readout is actually a modulation of the 1 MHz carrier at 1.4 kHz with a resolution of 100 Hz. Furthermore, the actual noise floor, which is 10 dB apparent from the bottom of the graticule, might actually be 5 dB. Therefore, this particular peak detection could easily be off a few dB, but it does show a relative S/N that is useful in judging the product from input to output. As illustrated in Fig. 7-8, the gross S/N measures 62 dB, but a correction factor of 8 dB is required due to analyzer processing. Therefore:

$$S/N_{actual} = S/N_{apparent} - 8\,dB = 54\,dB$$

Frequency modulation

FM, electronics of a different sort, depends on signal deviation rather than straightforward carrier compression and expansion. Expressed very simply, the carrier amplitude remains constant while carrier frequency is varied. When broadcast, FM carrier frequency is described as the center or resting frequency. But when modulated, the carrier contracts and expands according to its frequency of modulation. Such changes on either side of the center/resting frequency identify as frequency deviation. Frequency deviations of 75 kHz are equivalent to 100 percent AM. FM sidebands, therefore, develop both from the modulating frequency and subsequent deviation on the carrier. This, then, establishes an important term called the modulation index (m_F).

$$m_f = \frac{\text{maximum frequency deviation}}{\text{maximum signal frequency}}$$

It's worthwhile knowing that when the modulation index is well above unity, sideband bandwidth will approximately double the frequency deviation and will be little affected by the modulating frequency.

Since few if any of us have FM-only generators, we'll use the L (left) signal of a stereo generator as an example of an output voltage into an oscilloscope (Fig. 7-9). Sideband-pair deviation isn't evident here, nor is

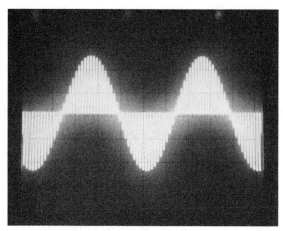

7-9 A shapely left baseband output from a stereo generator into an oscilloscope.

the 19 kHz stereo pilot signal on. But this should offer an idea of what to expect with an FM generator as signal swings above and below dc as it moves through several cycles.

With modulation introduced, sideband component amplitudes vary with the modulation index and frequency. In the Bessel technique, carrier amplitudes null, and all energy transmits in the sidebands. A chart of bessel nulls and the Bessel function itself is illustrated in Fig. 7-10. This is a differential equation solution used to determine the bandwidth of an FM emission. As you see, Bessel functions appear as damped ringing or descending-amplitude sine waves. In calculations, they are often written $J_1(M)$, $J_2(M)$, $J_3(M)$, $J_4(M)$. etc., with subscripts defining each function order.

Bessel nulls are readily found by using the null chart and dividing the modulating index into the maximum peak deviating frequency of 75 kHz. If we wanted to establish the fourth null position, then

$$f = 75 \text{ kHz}/11.7915 = 6.360 \text{ kHz}$$

which is most assuredly within the FM audio passband. But you'd better have a good electronic counter handy to monitor the audio generator. The frequency, as you can see, extends to four places and could be a little difficult to precisely set. Start with generator amplitude at zero and gradually increase the output until the carrier nulls, then continue the output for a second null, which indicates exactly 100 percent modulation.

The Bessel checkout is great for transmitters but doesn't do much for the homebody radio because all you'll see at the output is the modulating tone, normally 1 kHz. But to verify that the generator is really operating, our Tektronix 7L12 shows an excellent spectrum at a passband of 10 kHz/ division and a resolution bandwidth of 3 kHz, the center frequency of this

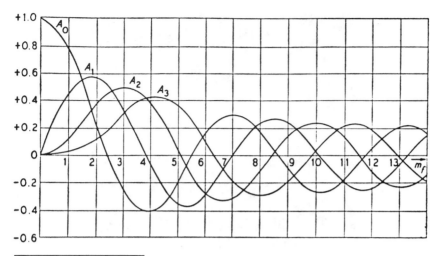

dB DIFFERENCE	ADD TO HIGHER LEVEL
Same (OdB)	3.01
1 dB	2.54
2	2.13
3	1.76
4	1.46
5	1.19
6	.97
7	.79
8	.64
9	.51

RATIO in dB	% of READING	RATIO in dB	% of READING
20. (40:60)	10% (1% .1%)	30 (50.70)	3.16% (.31, .031%)
21	8.9	31	2.87
22	7.94	32	2.51
23	7.08	33	2.24
24	6.31	34	2.00
25	5.62	35	1.78
26	5.01	36	1.59
27	4.47	37	1.41
28	3.98	38	1.26
29	3.55	39	1.12

7-10   Bessel functions and tables aid in harmonic distortion measurements.

display being 50 kHz (Fig. 7-11). However, all you'll hear at the output of this radio, if it's working and in good condition, is a nice, pure 1 kHz tone. Try this same waveform on an oscilloscope and you'll see only the 1 kHz sine wave. Once again, there's no substitute for a spectrum analyzer, except two of them.

Stereophonic sound

Now we come to the meat of the chapter, the result probably being easier on both of us. Monophonic came along at the turn of the century and its principles are so steeped in history that it's difficult to bring present day

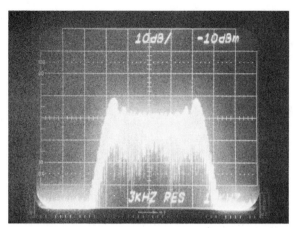

7-11 A 100 MHz center carrier at 10 kHz/div. The FM wave spans 40 kHz with more than adequate information.

developments up to date, primarily because it is so intertwined with stereo. A single IC radio often becomes the rule rather than the exception, and mono testing (other than pure signal tracing) some think is a worthless, nonpaying chore. With stereo, however, there are a considerable number of possibilities, most or all of which can be explored as this portion of the chapter continues.

Here, we'll try to cover the three types of stereo currently heard on terrestrial broadcasting, leaving discrete and matrix stereo for the satellite explanation that must await its own particular chapter. This is because satellite electronics are quite different and interdependent prior to audio takeoff following the final IF. Detection electronics are also unique, and we like to think the excellent end results are, too, although digital audio processing in top-of-the-line television receivers and some video cassette and camcorders have improved considerably in the past couple of years.

Actually the three broadcast systems have a number of circuit similarities especially the L(left) + R(right) monophonic portion and the L − R stereo channel, although multichannel sound (BTSC-dbx, a Zenith invention) AM/FM stereo radio transmit mono in FM, while the major AM stereo by Motorola developed system is all AM. A general block diagram (Fig. 7-12) illustrates an AM/FM arrangement, including the usual 75 μs preemphasis, the summing of the two stereo channels, the modulator, filters, and a final RF output. The receiver displays a discriminator following the IFs, phase comparator, voltage-controlled oscillator, bandpass filter, demodulator with pilot detector, the L − R decoder matrix and the two deemphasis outputs for L and R speakers. The B&K-Precision Model 2007 FM stereo signal generator we're using actually simulates a broadcast transmitter, beginning with a 304 kHz internal oscillator, a 1 kHz oscillator for modulation, subcarrier, amplifiers, a metering circuit, and a

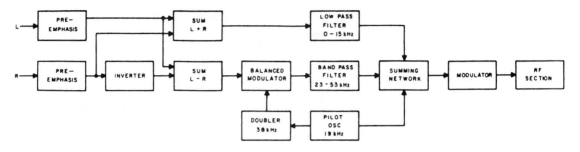

FM Stereo Modulation Scheme, Transmitter Block Diagram

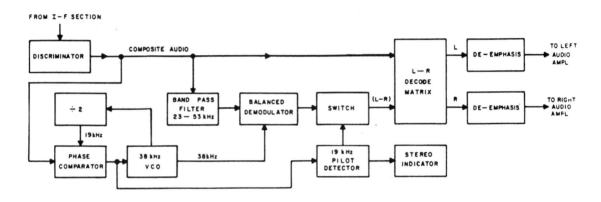

FM Stereo Demodulation Scheme, Receiver Block Diagram

7-12 A fairly typical stereo transmit-receive block diagram illustrates a general FM system. B&K-Precision

separate oscillator for the FM carrier. The 304 kHz oscillator is divided down so that it furnishes both the 38 kHz subcarrier frequency as well as the 19 kHz pilot. Selectable 85 and 98 MHz bands are tunable within ±2 MHz. The radio under test operates either on baseband or RF, as selected by the tester.

Just to interject the explanation and relieve a little prose boredom, I made an oscilloscope photo showing stereo separation between the two L and R outputs (Fig. 7-13). The top trace is channel one at 0.5 V/div with the lower channel at 100 V/div. As you can see, the lower channel amplitude occupies 1.7 volts, while the upper channel measures only 120 mV. Take the usual E_2/E_1 ratio and its log times 20 and you have the actual channel (some say stereo) separation:

$$\text{channel separation} = 20 \log 1.7 \text{ V}/120 \text{ mV} = 23 \text{ dB}$$

And that's not bad at all for a "boom box" portable radio.

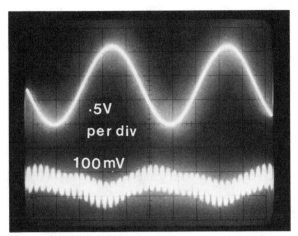

7-13 Left and right channel comparisons for stereo separation. At 23 dB, this one's very adequate.

But here's the interesting part, this radio had NO external speaker outputs. Therefore it was necessary to purchase a small stereo speaker plug, make up a couple of shielded leads and plug them into the oscilloscope. This is obviously more accurate than using a microphone since there's better coupling (more amplitude) and less noise. Apparently these stereo earphone jacks deliver pretty good response and may even be superior to speaker ranges and losses, especially when a microphone has to pick up the air pulsations and translate them again into electrical signals. We'll know more as the examination proceeds.

In the meantime, if you are able to work between ICs and signal trace in some of any of these analog stereo systems, a solid state signal injector-tracer can stand you in good stead, picking up dropouts or information loss between or among IFs, detectors, and audio amplifiers. Use RF with modulation if possible and see where inputs either fade or reduce to nothing. Should this sort of defect appear, consider the particular IC apparently delivering problems, trace signals on either side, and you might have already found your culprit. Unfortunately, oscilloscopes and voltmeters don't add a great deal to in-circuit checking unless there are catastrophic failures. The prime reason is you usually have no waveforms and few, if any, dc voltages. Power supply outputs and ac ripple, naturally, are good meter/scope checks, especially with good dc scope amplifiers. You switch to ac for ripple and noise, of course.

Radio stereo

Let's consider radio first because that's been our prime concern all along. Then we'll proceed to the exotics, with multichannel sound bringing up the rear. For straightforward continuity, let's look at Motorola's recent C-QUAM stereo system, especially a pair of new integrated circuits that are said to deliver wonders. These are for car radios because AM stereo table radios at the moment are almost nonexistent.

C-QUAM proved its own design mastery after the Federal Communications Commission declared an "open market" for all systems, refusing to sanction any single one. Consequently, the entire concept was delayed a number of years while consumer and commercial interests settled down and approved a leading technology. Now, however, most automotive manufacturers are at least offering AM stereo as an option, and top-of-the-line vehicles often have both AM stereo and FM stereo as standard equipment. It shouldn't be long before home table radios are also available in this important communications medium, certainly by 1991.

C-QUAM stands for Compatible Quadrature Amplitude Modulation, and Motorola claims its system is comparable to TV's I and Q color combination in carrier-suppressed modulation that eventually combines with luminance to produce a color picture. Initially, a carrier generator excites two carriers in 90-degree quadrature that are modulated by left and right audio signals, producing double sideband amplitude modulation. These two sets of sidebands in quadrature are combined by summing for transmission. In the receiver, envelope detectors demodulate linearly, reproducing dual channel stereo and amplifying for speaker or earphone output. In an operating radio, you can expect a carrier level modulator, quadrature phase detector for PLL, a VCO supplying a phase detector, 45-degree phase shifters and two balanced modulators which are actually synchronous detectors for right and left outputs.

When QUAM is initially generated, the QUAM signal subsequently passes through a limiter and is then remodulated with $1 + L + R$. Thereafter, $L + R$ and $L - R$ are processed separately, along with the stereo pilot, and these are the signals that are summed, with audio modulation then applied to the AM transmitter. Usually, C-QUAM features both in-phase and quadrature detectors, although such information may be decoded by "a number of methods," according to sources other than Motorola. As you can see, this is another $L + R$ and $L - R$ stereo system, complete with pilot exciter, filters, and double sidebands.

On a spectrum analyzer, the simulated carrier (center) and its two sidebands appear as in Fig. 7-14. While there is no phase information apparent, you can consider these as "I" sidebands for purposes of explanation. These are the in-phase components. The phi (ϕ) components reach the transmitter as RF, phase-modulated information that actually replaces the transmitter's crystal oscillator. And it's sideband phasing that influences interactions with the carrier that result in waveform amplitude additions or subtractions.

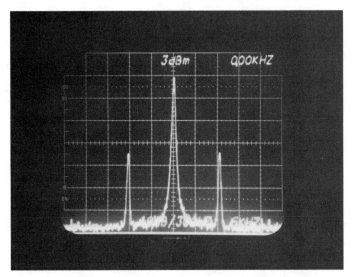

7-14 A simulated AM carrier (center) and its two apparent sidebands. The center frequency, of course, is not 0 kHz, but a
ready reference.

Since the ϕ sidebands appear much as FM emissions, linear amplification is no problem. Conversely, I sidebands do need this sort of expansion
but can be cleanly removed from the transmission by good limiting.

You may wonder, then, how receiver interference is avoided. An envelope detector, Motorola says, won't demodulate "perfect" phase modulation sidebands and a phase detector won't operate on "perfect" amplitude
modulation. This is why I and ϕ signals must be divided in any AM stereo
system.

During *encoding*, L + R and L – R modulate a pair of balanced modulators whose RF inputs are 90 degrees out of phase. A divide-by-4 Johnson
counter does the phase shifting and also inserts the RF carrier into the I
and Q modulators (Fig. 7-15). These signals are summed and then limited
to strip undesirable AM, leaving only ϕ modulated sidebands. The result
continues on to the transmitter's RF input as a slightly phase-shifted quadrature modulation on carrier. Nonstereo L + R passes directly from the
encoder to the transmitter's normal audio input. When *decoded*, the
"almost" QUAM information is converted to full QUAM and then a true
quadrature detector demodulates the stereo L – R (Fig. 7-16). At the
same time, both an envelope and I detector extract the L + R portion of
the transmission. They are compared, and the resulting difference then
gain-modulates the two I and Q detectors. When there is no stereo, envelope and I and Q see the same input, there is no error generated. there's no

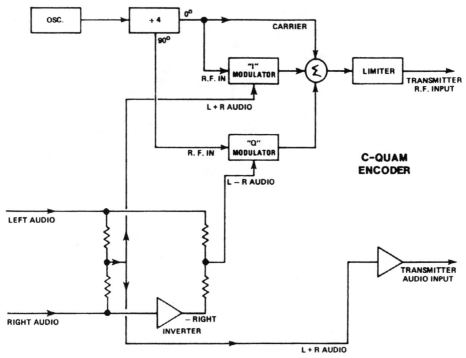

7-15 Basic C-QUAM encoder. Motorola, Inc.

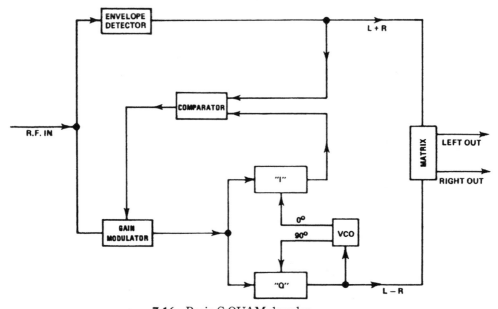

7-16 Basic C-QUAM decoder. Motorola, Inc.

gain modulation and signals continue unchanged. Finally, I and Q information are matrixed to L and R output information.

Unfortunately, I have no AM stereo-generating equipment and therefore cannot illustrate special waveshape information. There is doubt, however, that the basic format isn't a great deal different than other forms of L + R and L − R stereo except that this system is AM/PM rather than AM/FM in both FM stereo and BTSC-dbx multichannel sound (MTS), which I describe in the succeeding paragraphs.

New AM stereo radios

Not that I necessarily carry the torch for Motorola, but who else is a major innovator and provider of AM stereo? Target Tuning is already producing a single frequency operating C-QUAM portable receiver and three new integrated circuits by Motorola, the MC13022, MC13023, and MC13024, will make fully tunable versions in portables and home receivers available very shortly. A description of each follows:

The MC13024 will probably appear in personal radios before this book is published and therefore should have a lead description because FM/AM auto stereo is already well established. A functional block diagram appears in Fig. 7-17 illustrating the complete makeup of a fully tunable C-QUAM receiver contained on a single 24-pin monolithic IC. It includes a high-performance C-QUAM decoder and AM tuner, pilot tone

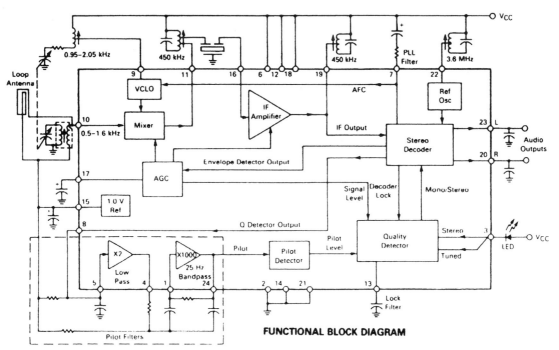

7-17   A self-contained tunable AM stereo radio on a single MC 13024 IC. Motorola, Inc.

detector, wide dynamic range mixer, highly accurate and fast-locking VCLO, only 5 mA of current drain, and will operate on power supplies from 1.8 to 8 Vdc. Its reference oscillator operates at 3.6 MHz, and a divide-by-eight circuit phase-locks to the IFs by varying the voltage-controlled local oscillator (VCLO), generating a built-in automatic frequency control (AFC) and permitting customer fine frequency adjustments without vernier fine tuning. All mixed information then passes through two 450 kHz stages of IF and on to the stereo decoder. Here, the phase-locked loop designed for L − R detection also controls the VCLO, always placing the processed signal in the center of the IF passband.

As previously described, the stereo decoder has both analog divider (I) and a synchronous Q detector with comparator, delivering a Q output that is the stereo L − R.

Internal detector transition from analog to digital is supplied by the motion sensor, the overpilot detector, pilot threshold detector, and pilot crossing detector. Initial action occurs when the zero detector switches at V_{reg} upon a change of 2 mV, turning on a 25 Hz clock for the digital integrator and quality detector. This quality detector is a shift register sensing inputs from the lock, overvoltage, threshold and excess I detectors plus the motion sensor, deciding if the transmitter is generating stereo based on receipt of a 25 Hz pilot tone from the Q detector output.

Tuning control has a dual-window detector consisting of a wide (outside) and narrow (inside) detector, allowing switching from mono to stereo operations. Outside window detector limits reduce to ± 2 kHz when the RF signal becomes too weak to actuate automatic gain control (AGC). Thereafter, the radio tunes like an ordinary receiver. For stereo, the local oscillator has to be within the narrow window detector range, the tuned indicator lamp lights, the pilot tone detector is enabled and a search is underway for the pilot frequency and, subsequently, the stereo mode. The LED lights slightly upon center-frequency tuning but brightly when the pilot frequency is detected. Automatic gain control developed in the stereo decoder maintains necessary operating levels in the mixer, quality detector, and IF amplifier. AFC is reserved for the VCLO.

The heavy hitters

Mainstay ICs for Motorola, however, are the recent MC13022—an advanced medium-voltage stereo decoder—and the new MC13023, which is the receiver front end and tuner stabilizer. The latter is a 16-pin IC for manual and electronically tuned AM stereo radios, and the MC13022 can be used as a decoder in home, portable, and automotive C-QUAM radios.

Let's talk about the tuner first and then follow with decoder information as furnished by Motorola from both Phoenix, AZ, and Schaumburg, IL, the respective and respected integrated circuit and C-QUAM design centers. Individual ICs are described first, then joined together as a tuner-decoder unit.

The manually tuned MC13023 includes a mixer, 450 kHz IFs, a divide-by-four circuit, VCO, discriminator, control logic, varactor control and outputs to the tuning control, varactor tuning, and tuning indicator (Fig. 7-18). The electronic tuner uses much the same general components, but emphasizes wideband AGC for the tuner, an external RF amplifier in addition to an outboard frequency synthesizer.

AGC, however, comes from the companion MC13022 and a shunt attenuator preceding the second IF. Coupling wideband AGC to the first RF filter keeps the mixer and/or varactor from overloading under strong signal reception. The voltage-controlled local oscillator (VCLO) operates at four times the local oscillator frequency, ensuring low noise and good mixer isolation. On a small-signal loop antenna, RF AGC is probably unnecessary, but varying signal conditions welcome IF ranges of some 85 dB and a dynamic circuit to control them. The MC13023's dynamic range, however, is 75 dB between 1.47 microvolts and 8 millivolts. Usually wideband radio AGC is not necessary except in automobile receivers.

In one manual mode, the tuner stabilizer operates with the VCLO frequency determined by the discriminator and the radio hand-tunes like any other radio. In the other, the VCLO is controlled from the loop driver voltage in the MC13022, the IFs are center tuned, microphonics eliminated, and the RF frequencies can be tuned without disturbing the IFs.

A discriminator in the manual mode continuously checks the delta (change) frequency between the local oscillator (tuned loop) and LO with stabilizer in the tuning mode. More than average mistuning trips the tun-

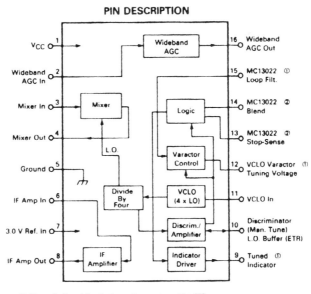

① Manually Tuned Application only — not used for ETR
② Manually Tuned Application only — disabled by 100K Ohm to 3.0 V for ETR

7-18 A pinout of the MC 13023 identifies inputs and outputs and many internal connections. Motorola, Inc.

ing sensor and the MC13022 reverts to the tuning mode. Discriminator bandwidth is some seven times the tuned window bandwidth, or ± 42 kHz.

Varactor control and logic for blend and stop-sense take their excitation from the discriminator amplifier. When a new channel is tuned, the out-of-window detector pulls down the stop-sense circuit and also reduces audio bandwidth to 2 kHz, reducing noise. At the same time, the MC13022 blends audio from stereo to mono and below 0.7 volt the pilot detector stops. Once the MC13022 locks, however, the VCLO centers on the local oscillator frequency from the discriminator, the stop-sense line is released, the tuning lamp lights, and the MC13022 AFC's the VCLO for center IF frequency. In electronically tuned receivers, except for the four times oscillator frequency and divider, the MC13023 operates about the same as most standard AM receivers. Nonetheless, improvements such a degenerated mixer, a better varactor circuit for the first RF coil has been designed, and a light-dependent resistor (LDR) situated before the RF amplifier is considerably more linear and has better dynamic range than ordinary diodes or transistors.

The MC13022 advanced AM stereo decoder is a 28-pin monolithic IC that requires between 4 and 10 volts dc supply at a typical current drain of 18 mA. It features an IF amplifier with two-speed AGC, 10 kHz notch post detection filters allowing adjustable auto audio bandwidth, noise reduction, cochannel discrimination, signal-strength indicators, signal-strength-controlled IF bandwidth, and a noise-immune pilot detector. A general basic block diagram appears in Fig. 7-19.

BASIC ELEMENTS OF THE SYSTEM

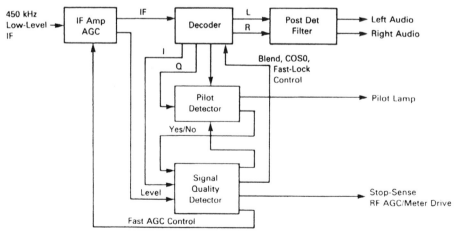

7-19   A block diagram of the MC 13022 28-pin advanced AM stereo decoder.

The envelope detector (L + R) portion consists of a buffer, a limiter and multiplier, with inputs from the IF/AGC block and a matrix control AGC circuit. Next to it is the QUAM detector with a pair of multipliers, and then the Q detector with its multiplier and quadrature demodulators. The envelope detector actually contributes less than 1 percent distortion at 100 percent modulation.

However, the actual decoding begins with the C-QUAM to QUAM converter and the QUAM detector. QUAM signals require that the I multiplier form a $1 + L + R$ output and the Q multiplier an $L - R$. With syntheses and C-QUAM, the I term equals $1 + L + R$. Also by comparing it with the envelope detector, the Q-multiplier output becomes $L - R$. When QUAM conversion is slightly altered, the I detector output can change from $1 + L + R$ to $1 + L + R \times \cos\phi$ and the Q detector's product from $L - R$ to $L - R \times \cos\phi$. And this, then, results in QUAM detection.

With full demodulation accomplished, the PLL loop driver locks to $L - R$ for best stereo operation and balanced current needs to flow in the loop driver circuit, maintaining maximum channel separation and low distortion. Input signals for the fast lock and pilot tone circuits derive from the Q drive circuit. The RF AGC meter drive and stop-sense functions operate continuously as level detection and blend circuits deliver inputs into OR and AND gates and a switch called the *stop/sense circuit*, which allows or disallows decoder action based on incoming signal quality. The decoder fast-lock system can lock onto a valid station and deliver a stop/sense signal in less than 50 ms. Once this occurs, the blend circuit with its $\cos\phi$ and blend translater optimize the decoder to handle changing signal inputs.

For stereo operation, the pilot tone detector manages within narrow lockup limits to reduce false acquisitions and permits the MC13022 to detect stereo transmissions just above incoming interference. Finally, there is a system control circuit that actually manages the decoder function. Sensing voltage on the blend circuit capacitor and its discharge levels can trigger the stop/sense, enable adaptive pilot detection, add lock current drive, and deliver fast stereo release. Other outputs are fast AGC, stop/sense, and blend. Hundredths of a volt determine some of these operations, therefore problems in system control of all the foregoing operations could very well depend on this highly effective circuit and its voltage-level sensing.

The foregoing should give you a reasonable idea of Motorola's C-QUAM excellent AM stereo development, and to offer an idea of its effectiveness throughout the U.S., circled areas of signal radiation by the various AM stereo stations in the "lower 48" are shown in Fig. 7-20, as supplied by Motorola. Foreign countries that have adopted C-QUAM as a broadcast standard or are testing it for adoption include: Canada, Australia, South Africa, Venezuela, Brazil, China, R.O.C., Puerto Rico, Ecuador, Spain, Chile, Thailand, and Japan.

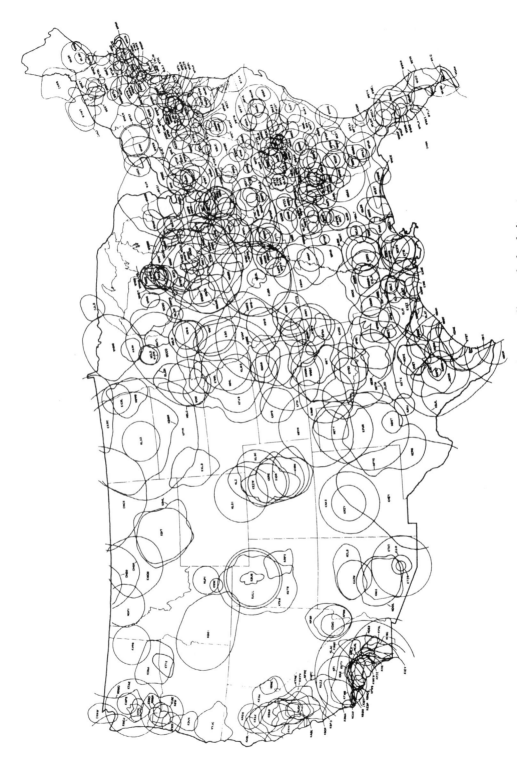

7-20 C-QUAM coverage in the U.S. Tune in when traveling and check it out.

BTSC-dbx

BTSC-dbx is also called MTS, which stands for multichannel (broadcast) sound. Approved by the Federal Communications Commission on March 29, 1984, the system, designed and submitted by Zenith and dbx, Inc., has slowly expanded across the U.S. until approximately half the television broadcast stations on the air today and all the networks are carriers. The dbx contribution helps quiet buzz and noise that would be apparent without such processing in addition to whistles and hiss.

Another L + R and L − R system, the main portion is frequency modulated while the stereo portion is amplitude modulated with double sideband suppressed carrier. The Federal Communications Commission did not expressly give its blessing to the Zenith proposal, but they whipped up a rather sneaky strategem whereby no one but Zenith could qualify. It specified that those using the 15,734 Hz pilot subcarrier had to both transmit and receive the BTSC-dbx system. Thus there wasn't a contest and Zenith won with no further competition.

Figure 7-21 nicely illustrates the several modes of MTS from full stereo plus second audio program (SAP), to stereo only, then monophonic plus SAP, and finally spacing entirely used/reserved for only professional channels. Note that all auxiliary channels above the L + R main channel, including stereo, are multiples of the 15,734 Hz horizontal sync frequency. This is why each segment above f_h (horizontal frequency) is marked $2f_h$, $3f_h$, etc.; the final being $6.5f_h$, amounting to 102.3 1 Hz. With the exception of the L − R stereo channel, all others are FM modulated with deviation of 10 kHz for SAP and 3 kHz for the remainder. The mono L + R still occupies 25 kHz, while L − R was boosted to 50 kHz, so that maximum allowed deviation for the system amounts to 75 kHz, with stereo separation of 20 dB or better suggested as being adequate.

The dbx part of MTS has complementary encoder/decoder operations for transmit and receive, with compression and expansion undertaken on a 2:1:2 basis, with preemphasis at about 1 kHz. Low-pass filters in the encoder remove any undesirable signal components, signal levels are kept above noise with no over-modulation. Levelers in the receive expander track only the compressed information, with clipping operating only on small transients, allowing little if any signal attenuation. Over its entire range the expander actually mirrors the compressor, restoring signals to their original form.

That should provide a working background for ensuring information that will not go "live" with some of the newer advances in MTS, using current operating systems. This is especially important at this time due to the gradual entry of digital TV sound processing that makes a tremendous difference in overall audio quality. How much? You could probably measure it with even analog MTS equipment on one digital and one analog major brand receiver(s) of current manufacture. The channel separation and probably harmonic distortion figures should certainly differ consider-

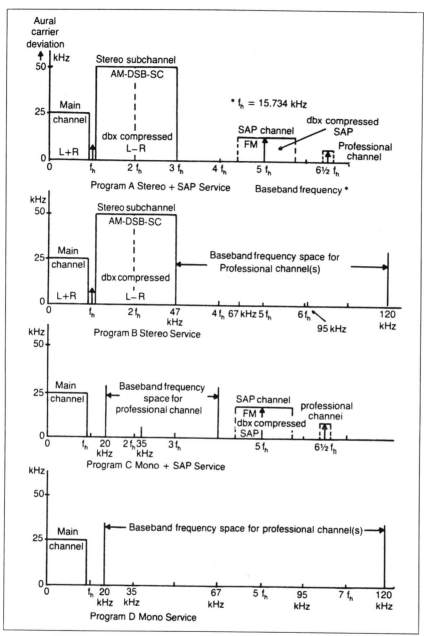

7-21 The various modes of FCC-approved multichannel sound. Zenith Electronics

ably, and audio frequency response should be substantially improved over standard MTS analog.

Equipment to be used in this test consists of B&K-Precision's 2009 MTS TV stereo generator. This lower-cost instrument generates "soft" modulation at 300 Hz, 1 kHz, and 8 kHz, each of which simulates the dbx levels of encoding, and these signals can also be injected directly into both audio and stereo decoder circuits. A full schematic of the equipment is shown (with permission) in Fig. 7-22. Other test gear involved are the Tektronix 7L5 spectrum analyzer with 7613 mainframe (power supply and crt), and Hameg's excellent dual-trace HM604 oscilloscope that can signal-lock on anything and invert both channels, too. We'll investigate the analog receiver first and then compare results with the digital audio read-out in Table 7-1.

In the stereo separation test, both waveforms were jumpy and the stereo separation amounted to

$$20 \log 3/.8 = 20 \log 3.75 = 11.483 \text{ dB}$$

Along with raggedy waveforms, this just isn't really satisfactory and the circuits here need realignment and/or repair. Even though the receiver is almost four years old, separation needs to be at or above 12 dB or more for worthwhile stereo reproduction (Fig. 7-23). For the SAP examination, an L − R generator input is used plus modulation.

The broad rectangle that almost fills the screen and the SAP on light indicates from a crt standpoint all's well. But from an oscilloscope angle (Fig. 7-24), there seems to be extra low frequency noise in one channel and the solid portions of the two displays are unequal in amplitude. Very fortunately, the generator has several outputs such as a 4.5 MHz intercarrier that may be modulated with mono, stereo or SAP, which can be injected into any aural carrier circuit; a composite signal for the stereo decoder with switching for right, left, pilot, and SAP outputs; a standard video IF peaked at 45.75 for injection into the appropriate portion of the intermediate frequency amplifiers; and dbx companding can be typically adjusted at the FM detector output with a 300 Hz L + R signal at 100 percent deviation, a test already built in that is exactly 12 dB below full deviation, according to most manufacturers specifications. External modulation, by the way, can also furnish 300 Hz signal of 6 volts p-p for 100 percent deviation.

Finally, signal-to-noise and total harmonic distortion (Fig. 7-25) are always of more than passing interest because these two, along with stereo separation, directly illustrate the quality of your TV stereo system, good or bad. As always, S/N is measured from the tip of the fundamental to the center of noise (on this analyzer) less 8 dB for analyzer processing, while THD evaluates from the fundamental tip to the tip of the second harmonic, and also the third if it isn't at least 6 dB lower than the second. Here we'll be generous. Therefore,

$$\text{S/N} = 45 \text{ dB} - 8 = 37 \text{ dB}$$

for only fair audio, at best, and

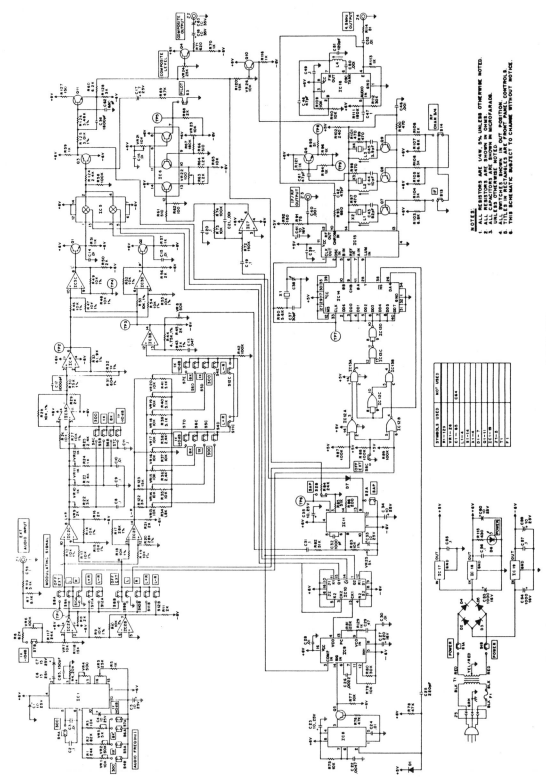

7-22 Schematic of B&K-Precision's low-cost M 2009 MTS TV stereo generator. B&K-Precision

Table 7-2. Comparison of MTS analog and digital readouts

Test	Analog	Digital	Frequency
Stereo separation	11.48 dB	17.62 dB	1 kHz, 8 kHz
Harmonic distortion	3.16%	4.70%	1 kHz
Signal to noise	37.0 dB	40.0 dB	1 kHz, 8kHz
SAP	SAP lamp responds		1 kHz

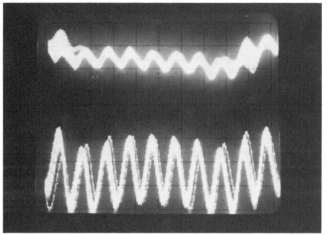

7-23 Analog waveforms and stereo separation displays.

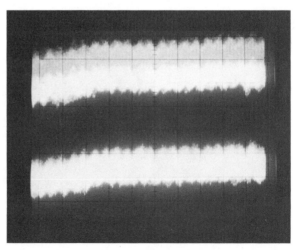

7-24 SAP display shows more low-frequency noise in the upper waveform, which isn't normal.

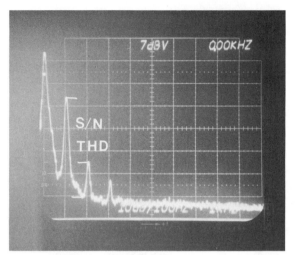

7-25   S/N and THD signals.

THD = 30 dB, which, using the chart, converts to 3.16 percent

(which isn't so hot)

Now let's examine the digital receiver in exactly the same way, show the waveforms, and tabulate the results. In this instance, however, the receiver is a new SF2795W Zenith digital receiver with good volume and crisp audio reproduction.

Digital stereo separation was initially a disappointment until I learned that bass, treble, and balance controls all had an effect, in addition to frequency. At 1 kHz, separation was poor, but at 8 kHz with controls properly

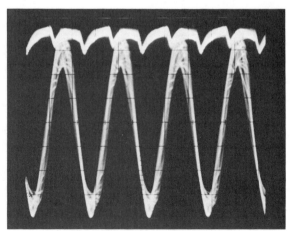

7-26   Stereo separation wasn't outstanding at 1 kHz, but at 8 kHz, ratios improved from 5 to 7.6 percent.

adjusted, stereo separation amounted to 7.6:1. By applying the usual 20 log 7.6 equation on Fig. 7-26, the difference amounted to a delectable 17.62 dB. So the moral of this story is to set your controls properly the first time, and then take a reading. It's also wise to examine the entire frequency range with external modulation to discover a true reading. Some of these equipments will fool you, especially those with operator-controlled frequency adjustments or equalizers. Otherwise you'll be seriously misled. Do you really want higher frequencies peaked in one way or the other? Certainly they'll be more audible to the listener who usually requires a boost of one description or another. True, you can't learn everything with this oscilloscope method of stereo separation, but between it and your generator, a great deal can be resolved.

Here we used the L channel only, but a quick check of the right channel should be undertaken also to see if amplitudes and waveshapes are the same. This will be proven in Fig. 7-27 where the SAP input is applied through quiet channel No. 3. With scope amplifiers adjusted similarly, as they were in the example above, you can observe similar amplitudes and

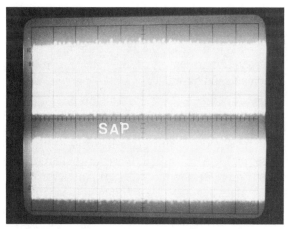

7-27 Good waveform appearance and nearly equal amplitudes illustrate effectiveness of SAP generator and digital receiver.

the nice evenness of both waveforms with very little external noise (top trace) apparent.

The final waveform in the audio series, Fig. 7-28, once again illustrates both signal-to-noise and total harmonic distortion. A much-improved 48 dB S/N is apparent, and with the analyzer correction factor,

$$\text{digital S/N} = 48 \text{ dB} - 8 = 40 \text{ dB}$$

and that's quite acceptable for television sound.

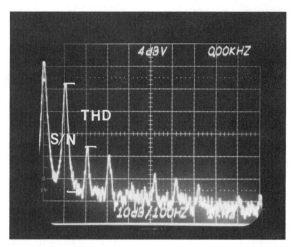

7-28   S/N and THD combine in a single spectrum display at 1 kHz/div.

To see how THD fares, unfortunately, there's a third harmonic that must be added also, even though it is only 4 dB. From the tables, this requires subtracting 1.46 dB from the 28 dB difference between the fundamental and the second harmonic, or 26.54 dB. So from the tables, and being generous, you would have to assign a 4.7 percent THD at 1 kHz, like it or not!

The resultant comparison of the two receivers was not exactly what I expected, but in stereo separation and S/N, the digital set was certainly better, but not quite as good on harmonic distortion, although excellent on second audio program (SAP). Digital, however, is here to stay, and I suspect these ratios and measurements will certainly improve as engineering understands more of its ongoing tasks. Video in these improved-definition receivers is absolutely outstanding compared to only a couple of years past, with much more to come in the fairly near future. So hang in there for the coming of the mid 1990s. Better video and audio are absolutely on the way.

Digital stereo

If you think MTS analog stereo is the berries, wait until you experience digital multichannel-processed sound, followed by satellite discrete and multiplexed stereo: the MTS digital is good; the satellite digital is remarkable! Unfortunately I don't have the very latest information on special digital stereo, but I do have ITT's Intermetall forerunner, which should agree fairly closely with the TV versions of today except, possibly, that the two-chip format of 1985 – 1986 could graduate to a single unit with a few improvements.

Digital TV audio was not bad in 1989, but it has become remarkable in 1990. No longer do you need a pair of huge baffles with special woofers, tweeters, and midrange sound gear; you simply need a 27-inch or larger receiver with its surprisingly excellent sound. We're speaking especially of Zenith's Digital System 3 Color TV offering in the SF and SG series, particularly the SF3191H receiver/monitor with its picture-in-picture, 30 on-screen menus, auto channel search, premium stereo sound and Dolby Surround Sound decoding, plus a nice, resonant oak cabinet.

The ITT system consists of two complex ICs, and ADC 2300 U and the APU 2400 U. The first is an audio analog-to-digital converter, and the second an audio processor unit. Somewhat abbreviated descriptions of both with illustrative diagrams follow.

ADC 2300 U

The ADC 2300 U consists of a pair of PDM pulse density modulators (Fig. 7-29). Three analog switches, an IM bus circuit, a L – R AM detector, SAP detector and SAP amplifier, FM demodulator, and a muting circuit.

Inputs into this IC include the complete MPX-demodulated sound, left

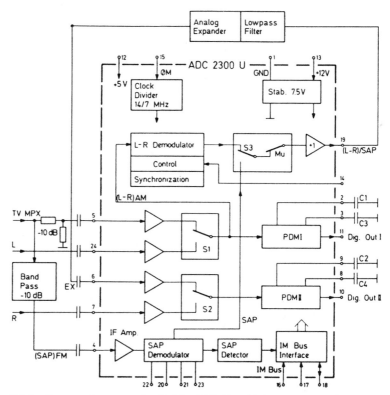

7-29 One good reason why digitized MTS audio is so very good over terrestrial broadcasts. ITT Semiconductors

and right signals and the second audio program abbreviated SAP. All except SAP are buffer amplified, reaching switches S1 and S2, where they can be switched from composite (including external input) to L or R which are local audio sources. S1 and S2 direct such information to a pair of pulse-density modulators, which are sigma delta modulators with feedback loops to furnish pulse trains having densities proportion to those of their analog inputs. Sampling rates are given as 7.1 MHz.

S1 also supplies the stereo L – R AM signal to the L – R demodulator, which is controlled by pilot excitation from the APU 2400. Switch S3 may then either supply stereo information or SAP from the demodulators to a buffer that passes these signals through both a low-pass filter and analog expander back to the EX input of S2 when stereo is detected.

APU 2400 U

Inputs from the pulse-density modulators enter the APU 2400 U via decimation filters that develop two 16-bit (wide) audio streams converted from parallel to serial format to the data RAM (random access memory) at a sampling rate of approximately 31 kHz. There is also 15,734 Hz pilot stereo frequency information from channel 1 passing through the decimation filters, part of which goes to a waveform coder and part to the pilot detector after pilot filtering and on to the IM bus interface. Here, IM bus information is transferred to the RAM. Meanwhile, the waveform coder doubles the pilot frequency to 31 kHz whenever there are stereo transmissions for L – R detection (Fig. 7-30).

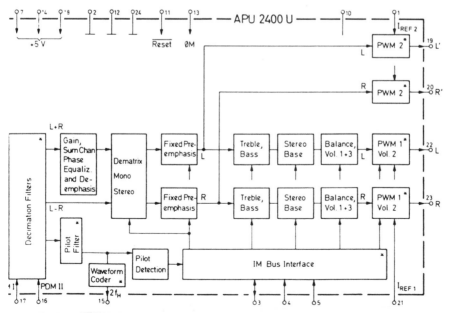

7-30   A second reason digital MTS audio is outstanding.   ITT Semiconductors

In the monophonic L + R channel, you see a variable 6 dB sum channel to equalize gain of the external expander; a sum channel equalizer for phase response equality for stereo separation; and a 75 μs sum channel deemphasis. Both L + R and L − R then enter the dematrix mono stereo block controlled by RAM and IM bus. Right and left channels next undergo fixed preemphasis to equalize low-pass output filters.

Outputs from these two filters in the form of L and R information proceed directly to pulse-width modulators No. 2, or to pulse-width modulators 1 via the dual bass, treble, and balance controls. Separate filters adjust treble and bass, along with treble and bass boosting at less than full volume where it would not be possible. Volume (2) analog adjustments have been added in PWM 1 to maintain a high signal-to-noise ratio at low levels or volumes.

8
Master antenna systems

MUCH LIKE CATV CABLE, MASTER ANTENNA SYSTEMS (MAT) AREN'T usually easy to either set up or maintain because there are amplifiers, cable runs, innumerable connections (drops), connectors, adverse weather conditions, and just plain ornery customers. But the magnitude of these multiple installations is considerably less on the home front compared to CATV, and we'll try and keep most of the procedures as simple as possible.

As for the satellite master antenna system (SMATV), you're very much limited here since there can be only one prime control in operation at one time, and all other connected satellite receivers must submit to its jurisdiction, other than accessing transponders on a given satellite. Actually, this is a positioner control condition rather than that of the receiver, but skew, programming, and block downconverter operating voltages do eminate from the receive portion and not the positioner. So, really, there are dual considerations in the satellite situation that are not paralleled in the more simple MATV. But, as indicated, MATV installations may have hundreds of outlets rather than just a few shared by a single antenna. Further, there are relatively few SMATV community setups owing to signal levels, satisfactory equipment, charges and local congeniality. Two families of avid viewers on the same antenna, for example, wouldn't be on speaking terms in 24 hours if each wanted a different satellite. But the TV group may tune any channel the antenna can access, provided there is enough amplification to supply decent signals.

The big trick in any MATV system is suitable amplification without excess noise. All this boils down to adequate signal-to-noise (S/N) voltages eminating from a specific head end that are "clean" enough to tolerate a number of taps, additional amplification, and reasonable signal response at the downstream (lower) end. You must also be certain there is sufficient isolation among the taps or drops to avoid undesirable feedback on the main signal line. All this, of course, includes initial signal power assumptions followed by drop calculations that confirm adequacy of the entire system with signal levels of ample dimensions for the job, with just a few dBs left over for sagging (slumping) amplifiers and possibly wicking (wet absorbing) cables. He who designs any system that offers only bare essentials soon redesigns in considerable discomfort and elevated costs. In simplistic TV language this would be a "call back." And call backs have been known to absorb more capital than even the original installation. So all calculations, amplifiers, branches and "nodes" should at least be double-checked before either system installation or final delivery. "A step in time," to quote an old saying, "saves nine." Once the installation is completed, a signal level measurement at each outlet, preferably with RF or baseband, whichever is used, will ensure adequacy. The minimum instrument here could be a field-strength meter, but a spectrum analyzer would be much more accurate for both signals and any latent-developing interference. At baseband, even an oscilloscope might be suitable for frequencies in the low megahertz and kilohertz. There, a function generator or video generator could substitute for the head end as wiring was secured in place. Good function generators, too, have ramp sweepers, and limited bandwidths could easily be examined. Pulse and burst functions are also available on these same generators, simulating data or even computer talk, and would immediately "snuff out" any ringing or feedback among the lines that might be promptly filtered or damped by adequate terminations. For if voltage standing-wave ratio (SWRs) are allowed to accumulate, poor signals and low power results throughout the system. In any transmission line, VSWR is always your chief opponent next to an absolute open or short. You cannot be too careful! And if one glitch is caught during installation, think of all the grief that's been avoided.

Should the worst occur and final checkout reveals problems, you might have to beg, borrow, or steal a time-domain reflectometer (TDB) to find the source or sources. In long cable runs or multiple taps, such an instrument is invaluable because it can pinpoint difficulties, often within inches, so there's no aimless hunt. Should this extreme become necessary, be sure to find a TDR with printout so difficulties are firmly recorded for present and future reference. In addition to opens, shorts, and discontinuities, unusual inductance and capacities are all traceable to their source with this equipment. Unfortunately, however, TDRs are not cheap and do require some fairly educated interpretations. Therefore, avoid this "last resort" if at all possible.

That should be sufficient introduction to set the tone for the remainder of the chapter, so let's get on with the various systems and how one goes about designing and evaluating them.

Head end

Head end is the signal processing plant (Fig. 8-1) that absorbs electromagnetic energy or voltage from cable, satellite, recordings, studios, and broadcasters, usually demodulating their RF signals and then remodulating them on selected carriers suitable for local reception. All this often requires highly directional antennas, excellent amplifying equipment, massive runs of cable, and even large-to-huge reflectors for satellite signals, especially those on low-powered C band spacecraft launched in the 10 years past. Fortunately, such reflectors are usually on fixed AZ/EL mounts, and once installed are supposed to remain in position "forever," depending on local wind forces and the usual concrete foundations. You might remember that a 12-foot antenna has 1.5 times the wind load of a 10-footer. Further, after approximately 30 mph, virtually all satellite parabolic antennas appear solid to any wind, regardless of their "holey" or smooth construction. And while C-banders can tolerate almost 1 degree of "slop" in azimuth and possibly elevation, Ku signals only allow $1/4$ degree tolerance and are often several dBs more temperamental in heavy rain or snow, especially the 20 W/

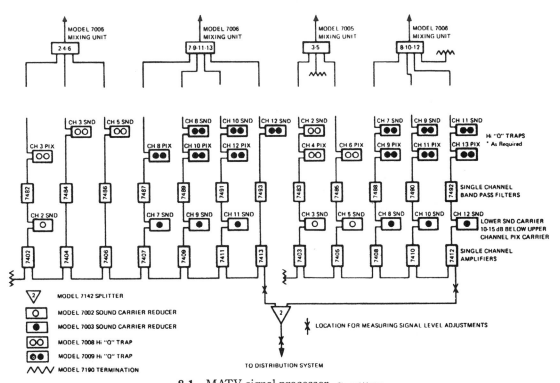

8-1 MATV signal processor. Channel Master

transponder variety such as the SBS group. Therefore, with multiple transmissions coming in and out of the head end, there are many electronic and mechanical segments that require attention.

Multichannel sound, for instance, can be a headache but settop converters often consist of unstable and band-limited components, and FM random noise power density is 8 dB greater at the 5H SAP second audio programming subcarrier than the 2H carrier. Split sound demodulators are also taboo because these same settop converters can load synchronous noise on both sound and picture carriers due to their noisy local oscillators. The better CATV systems, of course, can avoid most of these problems, provided they balance their trunk amplifiers often enough to avoid undue interference and inevitable nonlinearities. With ultimate conversion to fiberoptics and improved home converters, many of these problems will pass into history for the CATV operators but at advanced rates for the consumer. Unfortunately, sophisticated electronics aren't cheap. Interest rates on capital investment aren't 1 percent either.

CATV's head end is actually the originator of RF signal distribution and one- or two-way information to television owners who subscribe to the service for a monthly fee, which usually increases at asynchronous intervals. Many channels are in the clear but others are routinely scrambled and some are pay-per-view.

In the head end are mixers and modulators, downconverters, signal conditioning, scrambling, bandpass and bandstop filters, taped and local studio programming, as well as pilot carriers for controlled AGC (automatic gain control). And some head ends also possess microwave carriers for reception or transmission to or from distant sites. All this requires a fairly extensive business, programming, and technical staff to keep the station operating satisfactorily, particularly field maintenance personnel assigned to trunk and customer drop operations. For once video and audio or data are ready for distribution, it is remodulated and channeled over trunk cable lines, distribution cables, and then subscriber "drops" directly into the home or business. Because of normal attenuation, amplifiers and possibly filters are required at various intervals to maintain signals and levels at or near original values. And because of wide temperature variations, amplifiers must be automatically gain controlled, with a high frequency pilot doing the job on the gain control detector and a low-frequency pilot manipulating the slope detector.

I trust your system isn't as complex as CATV, but this information should supply some insight into what an extensive master antenna distribution system could approximate. With all this in mind, let's return to the head-end proper and see what's involved in the way of a modest MATV you may have to calculate and engineer. This process isn't especially difficult, but it is certainly tedious and you don't want to make mistakes. Just be sure to begin with enough drive and finish with sufficient signal to fully satisfy the final display. In between, you'll probably struggle, to a certain extent, with intermediate conditions requiring considerable care and some ingenuity. First and foremost, however, use at least RG6/U cable and only the best connectors. In this way many VSWR difficulties will have already been avoided, plus the misery of external pickup, especially cochannel.

Basic calculations

Let's look at several equations initially and the useful relationship between dBm (dBs with respect to 1 mW) and dBmV (which is the equivalent with respect to 1 mV).

$$1 \text{ W} = 1,000 \text{ mW and } 1 \text{ dBW} = 30 \text{ dBmW}$$
$$0 \text{ dBmV} = -48.75 \text{ dBmW}$$
$$\text{dBmV (75 ohms)} = \text{dBm (50 ohms)} + 54.47 \text{ dB}$$
$$\text{dBmW (75 ohms)} = \text{dBmV (75 ohms)} + 48.75 \text{ dB}$$
$$\text{dBm (75 ohms)} = \text{dBm (50 ohms)} + 5.72 \text{ dB}$$

and in terms of logarithms

$$\text{dBmV} = 20 \log_{10} \text{ rms (in mV)}$$
$$\text{dBm} = 10 \log_{10} \text{ rms (in mW)}$$

Except for a little arithmetic, these equations and Fig. 8-2 should see you through most, if not all calculations; remembering from time to time that dBmW applies to power (10 log) and dBmV to voltage (20 log). Then you take 10 or 20 log of the ratio of voltage/current or power for the answer (P_2/P_1 or E_2/E_1). Almost any of the $20 calculators can do this little exercise easily and considerably more accurately than you could longhand. When dealing with power, we often leave the "W" off dBmW because the watt portion is normally understood. Should P_2 or E_2 be less than P_1 or E_1, then enter a minus sign in front of the voltage or power ratio and the answer will appear as a loss rather than a gain. In some calculators such as T.I.'s model 36, logs of numbers less than 1 automatically generate a negative loss sign in the answer. This makes logs that much easier and allows straightforward calculations without the usual juggling. The TI-36, by the way, will handle all simple video/audio and satellite calculations rapidly and with functions to spare, and teach you some mathematics too.

MATV antennas are usually either broadband or channelized and should be erected at maximum height with maximum S/N ratios. Where feed sources eminate from divergent locations, individual channels might have to be separately received (or grouped) and amplified. But if all signals are received from some central source, the broadband radiator will normally handle the load if there is no undue interference and C/N ratios are adequate. Usually if off-the-air signals measure levels as much as +20 dBmV or −28.75 dBm and a C/N of better than 40 plus. Then you're in pretty good shape and no preamplifier is needed, nor is any conversion necessary unless you wish to rechannel some or all of the signals. UHF channels, however, should be downconverted to VHF because high losses and balancing problems could probably develop. If VHF channels are especially strong, then it might be wise to translate their signals to other VHF outputs to avoid direct pickup from same channel broadcasts resulting in a companion signal appearing microseconds later, called a *secondary image* or *ghost*. Weak over-the-air emissions many miles away might well require preamplifiers that should be first carefully examined for low noise, adequate gain, and excellent S/N. First rate TV studio quality video requires 54 dB S/N wherever you might be. Therefore, remember that in MATV or broadcast work with AM video modulation:

$$S/N = C/N + 5 \text{ dB (splitting the 4 to 6 dB difference)}$$

Consequently, you'll need a C/N of around 50 dB to produce the needed results and signal levels certainly better than -40 dBm.

Head-end units are all well advertised, so select those required on the basis of manufacturer's specifications and recommendations from knowledgeable sources in the industry. Most of these units have been around for some time.

Going downstream

Here is where your series of calculations begins and will continue until the last connection or drop line has been mated with someone's television set. But first be sure amplified signal strengths will be greater than distributed losses when under full load and maximum modulation.

In small distribution systems, you will have splitters whose losses vary between 3 and 7 dB if they're passive (without amplification). Then you have to include cable loss, insertion loss, and isolation loss. Ordinarily, RG6/U cable such as that manufactured by Comm/Scope with 67-percent shielding is sufficient, but longer runs may require even lower loss conductors, in addition to extra amplification. However, when totaling all distribution losses, the isolation loss of the final tap-off is used. If, for instance, there was a 30 dB line signal and a 20 dB isolation tap-off provided the final signal split, then $30 - 20 = 10$ dB would still be available, and 20 dB would be identified as the isolation loss.

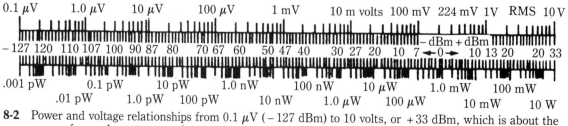

8-2 Power and voltage relationships from 0.1 μV (-127 dBm) to 10 volts, or $+33$ dBm, which is about the range of a good spectrum analyzer.

The 20 dB dropped between line and receiver, however, has no real effect on the overall downstream signal because its insertion loss is only about 0.3 to 1.5 dB. But a 12 dB isolation would amount to a 0.9 dB insertion loss because the isolation is considerably less, in other words, a greater load. So be both careful and accurate! You should also know that in MATV the 0 (zero) level equals 1 millivolt (mV) or 1,000 microvolts (μV), and measurement at 0 dBmV is that figure. Most television receivers, by the way, operate at this signal strength, which is the same as -48.75 dBm, but carrier signals of -40 dBm are preferred, which amounts to just over 2 mV. An additional 9 dBmV won't hurt at all and certainly affords better-than-average video.

At this juncture, I'd like to convert some dBmV carrier reference to dBmW since we're examining certain signals in terms of power, and dBmV applies strictly to voltage. Also be reminded that all oscilloscope displays appear on graticules as peak-to-peak, and they often have to be reduced to rms (the root-mean-square definition of ac voltage equality with dc). That is, ac $= EI_{max}/2 =$ power heating across equivalent resistance to a similar direct effect in dc. Therefore, divide p-p displays by 2.828 for a true rms value, or peak displays by 1.414. These, then, become the effective ac values for alternating current now fully equivalent to direct current. So:

$$p\text{-}p\ ac\ rms = (E_{max} \times I_{max})/2 = 2.828$$

The setup

Now we're ready to calculate a small MATV system that you can use verbatim if your drops are nearly similar, and this exercise, with few changes, should serve as a classic example for even larger MATV endeavors just by varying some signal inputs and possibly adding another amplifier or so. But don't attempt further amplification with only a small voltage remaining since you'll amplify noise probably more than the actual carrier and its modulation. Recall also that dBs add and subtract, not divide and multiply.

Let's try an up-scale 100-foot, two-story home requiring a strong RF video loop that can support several carriers of equal intensity and can accommodate at least five tap-offs. Were only four required, we could further simplify the entire process with new four-way amplifiers from Jerrold/Cometic, which are modestly priced and deliver gains of approximately 3 dB to each port for the Mod. 414, or gains of at least 18 dB for Mod. 480, which also has a variable 10 dB gain control, an FM trap and flat response within $\pm$ 2 dB. Both amplifiers cover the range between 50 and 890 MHz, inclusive. Noise figures for the two are approximately 6 dB. Channel Master also makes a good four-way amplifier, but its range extends to only 300 MHz, which is strictly VHF and midband/superband CATV channels. TDP's 4-way couplers extend the frequencies to over 800 MHz with variable gain.

Returning to the five – tap-off MATV system, to make this project a little more interesting, we'll use both an amplifier and splitter at the head end
so that an additional five outlets can be offered for other purposes, if so
designed (Fig. 8-3). All tap-offs, then, can simply be doubled and the same
outputs at each wall plate are identical. And since a somewhat similar system was originated by Channel Master, we'll use their equipment in system
calculations. The splitter, of course, must have identical outputs for each of
the two trunks. And for cable, we'll substitute Comm/Scope's RG6/U 5730
all-weather and sun-resistant cabling with losses of only 6.14 dB per hundred feet at 900 MHz, with calculations only for worst case losses.

Let's begin with Fig. 8-3 and see how the various losses tally.

Cable loss	6.0 dB
Splitter loss	3.5 dB
Insertion loss at 0.8 dB/tap	4.0 dB
Final isolation loss	14.0 dB
	27.5 dB

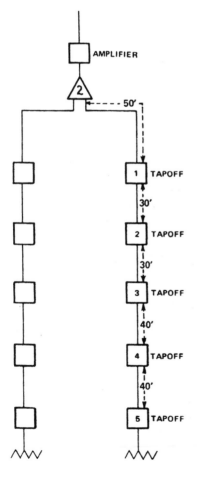

8-3   A simple MATV
system with splitter and
amplifier and an option
for five additional
outputs, if needed.
Channel Master

Total system loss becomes 27.5 dB, which must be compensated for with amplification. We'll also add an additional few dB for extra protection since more than a 30 dB amplifier could be required. If, however, all incoming signals are more than considerable, you could, conceivably, choose a smaller, say 30 dB, less expensive amplifier to do the job. But you will certainly be safe with 50 dB Model 7354 UHF/VHF/FM unit that also has 10 dB input attenuators, tilt compensation, FM rejection switch and an FM tuneable notch filter. As for power, 200 mA at 120 Vdc does the trick easily. Suggested retail of $552, however, is a bit rough, and you may want to compromise on VHF only, or a 30-watt unit for U/V/FM, Model 7335B at a suggested retail of $205. All depends on customer pocket depths and desires. But at any rate, you will want about 1.6 millivolts, or − 43 dBm. And with an adjustable 10 dB control in the amplifier, you should be able to deliver all the signal needed for even antique TVs.

Now for the sake of calculations, say the customer has $250 and not $500, so we'll attempt to go with the 30 dB unit, allowing only a dB or two for aging and other possible problems such as leaky connectors or out-of-tolerance taps or drops. Here, cable loss between amplifier and splitter is negligible, so it will not be included since we have a dB or so to work with in the very low loss cable anyway.

$$
\begin{array}{r}
30.0 \text{ dB} \\
- 3.5 \text{ dB splitter loss} \\
\hline
26.5 \text{ dB}
\end{array}
$$

So 26.5 dB will reach both splitter branches. Now each cable segment will approximate 20 feet, or a 1.0 dB loss per segment. So the first tap-off has a 1 dB cable loss plus 0.8 insertion loss. Therefore,

$$
\begin{array}{r}
26.2 \\
- 1.8 \\
\hline
24.6
\end{array}
$$

This, subtracted from the 23 dB isolator, leaves 1.4 dB for the first receiver, which is more than sufficient.

Tap No. 2, however, can't support a 23 dB isolator because of additional cable and insertion losses subtracted from the signal remaining. There, we'll drop to a 17 dB isolator. Therefore, 24.4 less 1 dB cable and 0.8 dB insertion loss equals 22.6 dB.

$$
\begin{array}{r}
22.6 \\
- 17.0 \\
\hline
5.6 \text{ dBmV}
\end{array}
$$

which is considerable signal for tap-off No. 2. Tap-off No. 3 now sees another 1.8 dB loss subtracted from 22.6, or 20.8 dB. Therefore, we can use another 17 dB tap-off and still have 3.8 dB into the TV. Once again the 1 dB plus the insertion loss of 0.8 dB is subtracted from 22.6 dB, leaving 20.8 dB. So the 17 dB isolation tap-off is still good because

$$\begin{array}{r} 20.8 \\ -17 \\ \hline 3.8 \text{ dB} \end{array}$$

Tap-off No. 4 must again take into account cable and insertion loss, and so our 20.8 dB figure now reduces to 19 dB.

$$\begin{array}{r} 19 \text{ dB} \\ -17 \text{ dB} \\ \hline 2 \text{ dB} \end{array}$$

This is a more than adequate signal for the receiver. No. 5 tap-off goes through the process once more, leaving but 17.2 dB for the isolator.

$$\begin{array}{r} 17.2 \text{ dB} \\ -17 \quad \text{ dB} \\ \hline 0.2 \text{ dB} \end{array}$$

This is just a little light but is still over 1000 microvolts, which the book says is sufficient. If not, then you'll have to use a lesser-value isolator and drop the voltage accordingly. So we actually wind up not with 0 dBmV but 0.2 dBmV, which is all to the good, with more than adequate signal for everyone.

One cheerfully admits to simplifying this exercise somewhat by averaging out the isolator insertion losses and also the 20-foot cable segments and limiting their numbers to five. Were values and isolators varied and the several cable lengths not uniform, then you'd have a little more complexity calculating the tenths of a dB here and there to complete the various drops. But the system calculations are there regardless, and all you have to do now is select the specific isolators, make the connections and enjoy the view. For convenience and simplicity, you might want to consider Channel Master's variable isolation wall tap-offs that can be adjusted from 12 to 25 dB at insertion losses between 0.3 and 1.5 dB, all of which are ac/dc passive. Models are 7313 and 7513. A newer and less expensive 7324/7524 wall flush-mount using standard electrical boxes is also available with variable 12, 17, and 23 dB isolation values, but with insertion losses ranging between 0.5 to 1.5 dB. It depends on what you want to pay and how much loss is tolerable. This is why we averaged the various losses in the previous example.

As stated, a second trunk with identical components may also be connected, delivering a total of 10 connections, all driven by an equivalent amplifier. Were you to use a three- or four-way passive splitter, however, the RF and power losses could prove more than most home-type amplifiers could handle. In a dual system you only have to deal with the final isolation loss, the minimal insertion losses and cable attenuation which, in a quick calculation would amount to 27.5 dB plus 24 dB, or a total of almost 52 dB, which would certainly call for the 50 dB amplifier and possibly then some. Therefore, calculate all needed amplification and losses very carefully before quoting a firm price; then double and triple check results for accuracy. A small mistake here could amount to big bucks.

And by the way, if you were only running a single trunk and don't need the 3.5 dB splitter loss, drive the trunk directly and leave the splitter in the box. Under such circumstances you could probably add some more isolation, offering both better gain and pictures. As you can see, there are a number of ways to solve these small problems, it just takes a little effort and practice. But don't fail to use the best available components. One callback could cost more than the selling price of the original system. And do be careful matching one manufacturer's amplifier, isolators, and splitters with those of another. A mixed bag could run into real problems, and we would suggest working with one source rather than several. Above all, don't fail to terminate the trunk in its characteristic resistance or impedance. This, of course, would approximate 75 ohms.

If some impedance value disturbs you, simply take a 250-ohm potentiometer or thereabouts, put a signal on the line and determine the exact impedance when you reach 50 percent of the waveform's value. A measurement between the arm and end of the variable resistance will supply the answer.

Modulator

The term "modulator" suggests you plan for additional baseband source(s) from cameras, FM/AM tuners, VCRs, microphone, or even satellite inputs. Channel Master's 7632-7643 series handles such inputs nicely and will output modulated video/audio on any VHF 2 through 13 channel with low spurious beats, good adjacent channel rejection and a high maximum output level of +50 dBmV with S/N ratio of 50 dB minimum. Frequency response is 30 Hz to 4.2 MHz visual and 50 Hz to 15 kHz audible. Suggested list price: $505. So this rack-mount audio/video modulator isn't precisely cheap, but certainly effective. There are also level controls for suitable audio/video outputs for minimum distortion and maximum delivery. Nonadjacent channels can also be combined on the output without external joiners and offers a diplexed output; but only, we might add, on VHF channels.

By now it should have become apparent that signal transmissions over multiport liners aren't that simple. It takes planning, analysis, electronic competence, and a fair knowledge of available equipment to successfully undertake and complete the job. On the other hand, once a few systems have been characterized and installed, much of the surrounding reticence and mystery will have evaporated. Obviously no two systems are precisely alike, but then no two people or animals are either. So a considered approach, good execution, and final QC tests should make everyone happy.

Checkout time

I prefer to use a spectrum analyzer, but even a field strength meter with an oscilloscope/video output could at least offer an indication of a few fields of signal that shouldn't be loaded with low amplitudes, channel smear, noise, or peculiar sync. As a prime example, let's put a charge voltage into a Sadelco FS-3D VU signal level meter, operating it on ac input via a wall-plug power source and see what the oscilloscope readout is all about (Fig. 8-4). What you see are almost three full fields of video and sync sandwiched in between horrendous peaks of ac ripple that are almost 4.5 volts tall. How do you know this is ac? Because it repetitively occurs about the 60 Hz rate, which is the sine wave of your 120 V U.S. power source. In the lower portion of the waveform, all sync tips are regular and the video doesn't seem to be loaded with noise, but that's hard to tell. On the FS (field strength) meter, we can read 27.5 dBmV. And that's all the information available from two $1,000 (approximately) instruments.

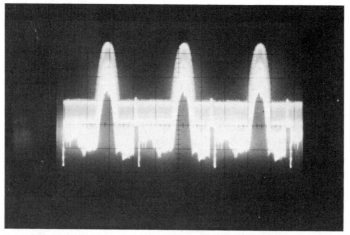

8-4 Voltage of channel 4 as seen through a field-strength meter with oscilloscope output. Large positive peaks are ac hum.

Now let's investigate this same channel 4 waveform directly on a spectrum analyzer and see what a dynamic check reveals (Fig. 8-5). First, the left top readout shows center frequency at 67.28 MHz (the channel 4 video carrier), 0 dBm attenuation, 2 MHz/div frequency setting, and a resolution bandwidth of 500 kHz. In the upper right (first picture) you see the marker frequency readout at 67.52 MHz with its level at −21.5 dBm, and the graticule set at 10 dB/division. In the lower picture, the left column of numbers remains the same, but the right column is programmed for C/N of 24.5 dB at a bandwidth of 4 MHz. Both pictures also show good color subcarrier suppression and audio about 10 dB below the video carrier, all with very little noise or spurious interference. Now which one would you take? (Oh, you don't have a spectrum analyzer? Want some straightforward advice? Get one!)

Let's now correlate the two readings. The FSM tells you only the envelope detection (quasipeak) properties of the ac information and registers 27.5 dBmV on its wide-faced meter. Now the analyzer showed −21.1 dBmW as its true peak readout. So if you recall the 48.75 dB difference, simply add the two:

$$27.5 + 21.5 = 49 \text{ dB}$$

Is this close enough for good instrument calibration? You can bet your bundle on that one. But do you turn down the analyzer? Can you?

Preparation X-X

All the modulators, amplifiers, splitters, cables and everything else matters little if your head-end site and its receiving antennas don't supply

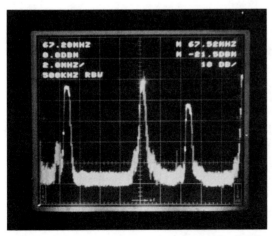 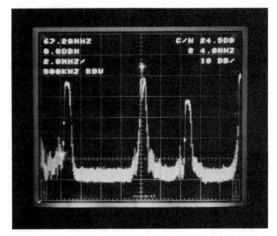

8-5 Push-button readouts of peak amplitude, frequency, and power levels, with carrier-to-noise in the lower photo.

trouble-free signals. In these days of 4 and 6 GHz microwave Ma Bell terrestrial communications, government land and sea chatter, and plain old ordinary two-way radio can all affect your precious reception at the right time (for them) and the wrong way (for you). Harmonics and spurious transmissions can play havoc with reception anywhere if they approach your fundamental incoming carriers and their modulation. But unlike narrow aperture satellite feedhorns, television antennas are considerably more broadbanded and do, indeed, often invite undesirable interference and/or intelligence. This requires some special measures not often encountered in home or small business reception. Usually an FM bandreject filter or a high-pass filter can cure most radio or auto-lawn-mower interference with just a slight loss of signal and little more. But the CATV or MATV folks need every bit of clean signal possible coupled with the avoidance of any signal-deteriorating notch or bandstop filters wherever placed. This is done with limited beamwidth radiators, especially single-channel Yagis, selectively placed on some higher elevation such as a building or mast. And with -40 dBm or better incoming signal level, noise-free, full-definition luminance and chroma should appear on all subscriber screens. This is why TV broadcasters always seek the highest metropolitan area point in their local townships. And translator and MATV systems should do the same if their electromagnetic information comes by air.

Knowing that but a few feet can make the difference in either MATV of SMATV installations, site surveys before permanent installations are absolutely necessary for maximum interference-free signals. It's easy enough to twirl a TV antenna around and move it from place to place seeking best results. But trying this with a large satellite antenna could be more than a problem. Therefore, a standard gain feedhorn coupled to a block downconverter with cabling to a spectrum analyzer will often suffice. After all, you are looking for interference that's within 10 or 15 dB of the C- or Ku-band transmission signal in amplitude and virtually on the transponder's carrier and its modulation frequency.

So activities on the head end rooftop or a special tower do become a trifle tricky, regardless of the MHz or GHz frequencies (Fig. 8-6) you want to receive (Table 8-1). But all this rigamarole decidedly pays off when antennas are mounted and locked in position for their final placement. If no further adjustments or trappings are required, then you've done your job correctly and signals can commence flowing into headquarters without further adjustment.

One further comment on the standard gain feedhorn technique is that the good ones have a gain of only 15 dB compared with 30 to 40 dB for good parabolic antennas, so you are at some slight disadvantage. But if you will establish accurate elevation angles for each of the satellites you intend to use, and then sweep the azimuth on a stable tripod, any severe

8-6   Typical 2.4- and 3-meter TVRO satellite installations. Note concrete platforms for extra stability. The accurate prodelin fiberglass reflectors are self-cleaning.

Table 8-1. Frequency band designations from 3 MHz to 300 GHz

Designation	Frequency Bands
HF	3MHz –30MHz
VHF	30MHz – 300MHz
UHF	300MHz – 1GHz
L	1GHz – 2GHz
S	2GHz – 4GHz
C	4GHz – 8GHz
X	8GHz – 12GHz
Ku	12GHz – 18GHz
K	18GHz – 27GHz
Ka	27GHz – 40GHz
Millimeter	40GHz – 300GHz

interference in the 4 to 6 GHz bands should appear since it is fairly high in amplitude. Now if hostiles are at least 15 dB below signal level, then they should NOT be a problem. Remember, satellite interference must enter the feedhorn or it is no signal threat. Stray energy a few feet left/right or up/down makes no difference. It's what the amplifiers and receiver read that's the fault. And if you are able to do the site survey with a reflector, set it up exactly as you would the ultimate antenna and either work from the intended AZ/EL or polar mount position, tracking the entire or appropriate portion of the azimuthal arc, making sure to add declination corrections in the number of degrees required.

Television antennas may be slightly oriented (turned) to avoid interference, but satellite signals come from 22.3 kilomiles in the heavens, are geosynchronously locked to a 0.5 to 1 degree west longitude position, and you must tune them, not vice versa. Additionally, your mount (Fig. 8-6) must face exactly north and south or you'll never track the azimuth arc above the Equator at all. This is especially critical for polar mounts that swing some 140 degrees between east and west. Such would be horizon-to-horizon (H/H) mounts and not the 80 degree "linears" with their poor resolution and sticking actuator arms.

Satellite antennas are indeed tricky and you had best set up with a decent spectrum analyzer (not a spectrum display) for accurate azimuth access regardless of mounting characteristics; and this especially applies to Ku band where, once again, you are reminded that access requires better than 1/4-degree accuracy.

SMATV

SMATV stands for satellite master antenna television or even "private cable," according to Blonder-Tongue Laboratories. And while television antennas and microwave transmission paths should usually be installed at rooftop level or higher, satellite antennas often fare better on the ground where natural shielding is available, microwave paths do not interfere, and equipment servicing is simple. Once positioning and lack of terrestrial interference (TI) has been determined, transponder amplitudes from particular spacecraft(s) have to be measured for effective reception and transmission. Ordinary amplifiers boost noise as well as sound and picture, so incoming intelligence must be pretty clean to begin with because this is usually a commercial undertaking and not a relatively inexpensive consumer system where losses here and there can be forgiven. This means that antenna diameters have to be carefully calculated for maximum/ minimum gain and coupled with the best block downconverters available. Here, a 1 dB noise figure for Ku is not now unusual, nor is a 30 degree LNB for C band.

In such an undertaking, you must be able to specify the intended system, the anticipated programming, scrambling devices, any additional services such as health, fire, or burglar alarms, the needed settop converters, union or nonunion labor requirements, technical personnel to operate the installation, security, safety precautions, insurance, and financing.

You must then comply with FCC regulations on any "must carry" programming, and even plan to pay for rebroadcast services if the National Association of Broadcasters has its way. UHF channels then should usually be converted to VHF and vice versa to prevent any cochannel interference. Heterodyne channel processors work well here, or it might be necessary to use individual amplifiers and converters with respective filtering, all the while remembering that balanced outputs, level controls and frequency stability are highly important. There are also modulators and receivers with fixed or selectable frequencies, head-end combiners, computerized subscriber programming, and then the inevitable cabling or point-to-point microwaving that transfers such signals to the eventual user. Each SMATV supplier offers variations on many of the equipments referenced, so we won't name names in this one because of both complexity and costs (obviously they're not cheap).

Combining MATV and SMATV

One hears lots of inquiries concerning combining MATV and SMATV. There are plenty of MATV systems but not too many combinations—only wishes and some legitimate requests for the combination. Now a simple one- or two-signal source would become multiple, with probably additional off-the-air programming as well as specific satellite reception and one or more reflectors. Down- or up-conversions become the order of the day to avoid interference, auxiliary services must be considered, vacant channels cannot be arbitrarily filled with data, shopping, or allied services due to cochannel beat, as well as sporadic pay-per-view and outright scrambling. Aural and visual carriers must be balanced at about a 6 dB differential, the aural carrier lower in amplitude but 4.5 MHz above the video carrier in frequency.

Now, plus the usual filters, amplifiers, tilt padders, etc., the satellite portion will need power dividers, block downconverters, low loss cabling, a first class feedhorn, and exact orientation and overall installation. Then there's the diplexing loop instead of conventional signal combiners for efficiency and good output levels, followed by the inevitable system impedance and signal matching for adequate reception. Wideband, better-shielded cable might have to be installed to carry wider band programming, as well as certain filtering for antique television receivers. And any system that's already saturated with subscribers could require an even greater headend output, extra trunk amplifiers, and less leaky drops. How about +60 dBmV headend output for starters?

In short, you will have to replan your MATV system, taking into account the many contingencies, and then ask for assistance from some of the SMAT/MATV manufacturers and specialists around the country who know even more problems, have the required gear, and can direct you toward the straight path of success. Already, however, you're probably well aware this is no simple undertaking if multiple services are rendered, so ask, plan, and execute whatever your financial abilities dictate. Some of these combinations could be more than risky, especially if extensive MATV updates are required.

A basic calculation

Let's say you wanted to use sports-oriented Satcom F-4 and were situated somewhere near the center of the United States, the best of the signal areas. Each satellite, as you do or should know has a footprint, a group of concentric circles indicating its terrestrial signal levels called EIRP, or effective isotropic radiated power expressed in terms of dBW (watts). This one's center contour is listed as 38 dBW. And let's say you'd like to "get by" with a 3-meter (10 foot) antenna but pay a few bucks more for a good quality feedhorn (C and Ku band, just to make sure), suitable block down-converters with very low noise and gains of approximately 60, a cable run of no more than 100 feet, and a – 60 dBm to – 20 dBm receiver with a 6.5 dB threshold. Sound pretty good? We'll see. In fact, we'll try and duplicate these conditions within 10 dB, using a 100 degree LNB and an older feedhorn that may be just a little noisier than preferred. A transponder spectral display will shortly tell the tale. In the meantime, however, let's see if a 10-footer will really do the job.

First you know that space loss for C band amounts to a loss of 196 dB, or 206 dB for Ku. From this you can eventually calculate the carrier-to-system temperature and use a quick approximation for $T\,°K$ (the Kelvin temperature of the antenna).

$$T\,°K = 14 + 180/e$$

with e being the angle of elevation specified at 20 degrees (Table 8-2) for temp/noise figure comparisons). Therefore,

$$T\,°K = 14 + 9 \text{ or } 23\,°K$$

, Knowing antenna temperature and having gain specified at 39.5 dBi (referenced to an isotropic antenna):

G/T = 39.5/23 °K (converting temperature to dB = 10 log 23, or 13.62 dB)
G/T = 39.5 – 13.62 = 25.88 dB/°K

So far, so good, but the G/T is the actual gain over temperature of the system, so another somewhat longer equation will have to be solved before we can look at C/N (carrier-to-noise) and then finally signal-to-noise (S/N). However, this is a long and involved equation, and the receiver and feed amount to virtually nothing in the calculations. Therefore,

G/T system = 39.5 – 14.8 = 24.7 dB/ °K
10 log 30 °K = 14.8 dG (feedhorn)

Carrier-to-system temperature (C/T) can easily be established for C band:

**Table 8-2. Kelvin (T° K)
temperatures equal specified noise figures.**

T °K	NF dB	T °K	NF dB	T °K	NF dB
10	.148	175	2.056	340	3.378
15	.220	180	2.103	345	3.412
20	.291	185	2.149	350	3.446
25	.360	190	2.194	355	3.480
30	.429	195	2.239	360	3.513
35	.496	200	2.284	365	3.547
40	.563	205	2.328	370	3.580
45	.628	210	2.372	375	3.613
50	.693	215	2.415	380	3.645
55	.757	220	2.458	385	3.678
60	.819	225	2.501	390	3.710
65	.881	230	2.543	395	3.742
70	.942	235	2.584	400	3.773
75	1.002	240	2.626	405	3.805
80	1.061	245	2.666	410	3.836
85	1.120	250	2.707	415	3.867
90	1.177	255	2.747	420	3.897
95	1.234	260	2.787	425	3.928
100	1.291	265	2.826	430	3.958
105	1.346	270	2.865	435	3.988
110	1.401	275	2.904	440	4.018
115	1.455	280	2.942	445	4.048
120	1.508	285	2.980	450	4.077
125	1.561	290	3.018	455	4.107
130	1.613	295	3.055	460	4.136
135	1.665	300	3.092	465	4.165
140	1.716	305	3.129	470	4.193
145	1.766	310	3.165	475	4.222
150	1.816	315	3.201	480	4.250
155	1.865	320	3.237	485	4.278
160	1.913	325	3.273	490	4.306
165	1.962	330	3.308	495	4.334
170	2.009	335	3.343	500	4.362

$$C/T = EIRP - L_P + G/T \text{ (system)} = 39.5 - 196 + 24.7 = -131.8 \text{ dB}$$

Now we can move on to the most important statistics of carrier and signal-to-noise, which will determine if we can really use a 10-foot reflector, by using Boltzmann's constant of 228.6 and converting a 36 MHz standard C band bandwidth to logarithms.

$$C/N = 131.8 + 228.6 - 10 \log 36 \times 10^6$$
$$C/N = 131.8 + 228.6 - 75.6 = -207.4 + 228.6 = 21.2 \text{ dB}$$

Or for a consumer receiver with a 27 MHz bandwidth, the figure would be:

$$C/N = 131.8 + 228.6 - 74.3, \text{ or } 22.5 \text{ dB}$$

And note how a 3 MHz decrease in bandwidth increased C/N by more than a dB. Now you can easily determine if your signal-to-noise for either commercial or consumer receiver is sufficient.

S/N commercial = C/N + 37.5 dB = 21.2 + 37.5 = 58.7 dB
S/N consumer = C/N + 37.5 = 22.5 + 37.2 ≅ 60 dB

So you're well within the 56 dB S/N studio limit for satellites in both instances, but you'll lose a little resolution and definition with the 27 MHz bandwidth when using a consumer sat. receiver.

Be forewarned, however, that noisy block downconverters, high noise receivers (18 to 20 dB), and poor rms curvature accuracy antennas exceeding 0.030/inch will negate much of this analysis and put your installation on the road to ruin. Above all, watch out for cheap, sloppy mesh reflectors. Some perforateds you can work with providing their curvatures are suitable, but the best we've ever used are the Prodelin fiberglass group. They're heavy, require considerable assembly time, and need to be carefully mounted. But their accuracies are excellent, they do not sun damage or blow away in a big wind. And when mated with an AJAK 180 mount and counterbalance, the results are excellent.

Proof of the pudding

We promised a few paragraphs back that we would tune in Satcom F-4 and show a spectrum display across 500 MHz of its transponders in action in addition to a carrier-to-noise measurement. In Fig. 8-7, this has been accomplished, with a C/N readout of 19.1 dB as shown on the graticule of Tektronix' microprocessor-controlled 2710 spectrum analyzer. Referring back to the C/N measurements at 36 MHz and 27 MHz: they're 21.2 and 22.5 dB respectively. Don't you think they would have been precise if our block downconverter had been 50 degrees or less, just as it was calculated? Proof of the pudding is always in the actual measurement; provided, of course, you have a decent antenna, downconverter, a good coaxial feeder line, receiver, and analyzer.

This also illustrates the absolute value to the installer of C/N measurements before attempting sales and/or service. If you know specific satellite measurements with certain equipment, then there's little element of chance and usually positive satisfaction. Unfortunately, too, many guess and make a mess! No one eats high on the hog that way.

In the photo, do observe that not all these transponders are precisely the same amplitude but, in this instance, all are video modulated. When carrying voice or data, this much amplitude is not required. Transponder levels will be considerably reduced at least several dB or more. Note also that the transponder on which the C/N measurement was made, displayed an excellent level of – 35 dBm, well above the "approaching – 40 dBm" requirement we have set as a standard level for both broadcast AM and satellite

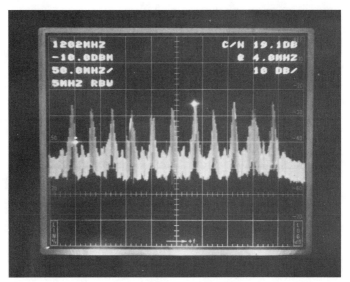

8-7 A direct measurement of transponders on Satcom F-4 fully support text calculations.

FM carriers. Finally, the 19.9 dB C/N added to 37.5 dB amounts to 57.4 dB, which is still studio quality for satellite measurements.

Troubleshooting

There are a few prime topics concerning troubleshooting that you should be aware of that sort of combine ordinary TV installations, satellite operations, and MATV/SMATV in a single bundle. Television cabling, terminations, connectors, antenna amplification, etc., you should already know to a certain extent. Maximum signal reception, some interference rejection, and quality cabling may be unfamiliar but can be learned with just a little practice. Let's use as little trapping as possible in these installations, relying instead on bandpass or passband units to remove most faults. This is particularly true when dealing with satellite reception from the block downconverter to the receiver. When you trap one transponder you can possibly affect others and even an entire satellite if you aren't careful. So trap interference only with considerable caution. And in all cabling and amplifiers, keep return losses as high as possible to prevent excessive VSWR.

Once within the distribution system, overload distortion and cross modulation is possible if you don't watch your carrier levels and amplitudes. When overloaded, amplifiers draw considerably more current, reduce signal output and become nonlinear. Pictures then darken, either/or vertical/horizontal sync is sometimes lost under worst conditions, often accompanied by audio buzz, and unrecognizable video, almost simulates some forms of scrambling, especially the out-of-sync condition. If your amplifiers had been operating satisfactorily in the past and the input signals haven't increased, you then have a repair job on your hands requiring immediate attention.

Cross modulation is somewhat more subtle and a bit more difficult to diagnose and locate because two or more channels or carriers will beat against one another and superimpose one image over the weaker one, leaving the latter in the background. Not surprisingly, it's the stronger signal that causes the interference and might not necessarily appear "on the interfering channel," according to Channel Master. Video or FM modulation on carrier is usually the culprit.

There is also adjacent channel interference, which is just plain strong signal override, and finally cochannel interference is an interfering channel from the antenna's rear of the same frequency and superimposed so that one appears possibly above or on top of the other. Adjacent channels are those next to one another without guardband separation.

Finally, secondary images can become a serious problem because this is actually the same signal delayed by a few microseconds. Usually they are reflections off of buildings, surrounding hills or even water. There are both leading and trailing ghosts. Leading ghosts result from direct, unshielded cable pickup before the antenna and lead-in have time to route signals to the receiver. The story moral is don't use twinlead or cheap coax, and do have a continuous positive common between antenna/amplifier and receiver.

As usual, the solution to most problems remains as antenna orientation or substitution for a narrow beamwidth, higher powered Yagi, trapping where necessary, and a new or improved set of amplifiers. Only in raw overload will you immediately recognize your problem since some of the other conditions tend to overlap and often confuse. Variable gain amplifiers also help, AGC adjustments might lessen signal drive, copper screen shielding (if you're desperate), and finally rejecting the problem channel altogether and use another.

Most of these difficulties can be overcome fairly readily, but conditions peculiar to your SMAT of MAT location always must be considered first. Unfortunately, there is no one solution that clears all interference. But past experience does help.

To prove a point, take a look at the photo in Fig. 8-8. Note the broad stripes across the suit of the individual shown. Can you guess why? It is the lower third harmonic of an interfering signal that can couple into your MATV system at any time if conditions are right. This is why high-pass, low-pass and bandpass filters are used to contain reception within their appointed spectrum. Had these bars been very fine in appearance, the interference would be above the fundamental video carrier. It's only a basic example of what can happen when stray carriers with or without modulation cross your path. Don't just try to shoot the offender; experiment a little and turn it away. Most interference can be subdued fairly easily with a little thought and effort. By the way, had the spurious signal in Fig. 8-8 been of the identical carrier frequency and strong enough, it would have blacked out the original figure completely.

I hope this chapter has proved useful in your understanding of MATV/SMATV. It isn't the first time layouts have been devised and systems investigated, but I do hope it's a somewhat different approach with some new and timely information. If you'd like to experiment with some self-induced problems, find a signal generator, a splitter, some video-signal source such as a VCR, and put the two analog voltages into a TV receiver. You'd be surprised how much can be duplicated on screen with this simple setup. The learning curve should become linear in no time!

In closing, Tables 8-3 and 8-4 are from Channel Master's valuable book of MATV systems, which contains a wealth of information on all of these MATV topics.

This entire chapter has been an interesting study for me and, I hope, for you too. Some of the painful details were omitted, but careful reading should offer sufficient guidelines for useful applications. The satellite numbers just illustrate what a little extra time and ingenuity can produce if you're willing to work just a little harder to understand and solve a reasonable problem.

8-8 Broad diagonal stripes indicate interference below that of the TV carrier; here, it is a third harmonic.

Table 8-3. dBmV/microvolt equalities

dBmV	uV	dBmV	uV	dBmV	uV
− 40	10	0	1,000	40	100,000
− 39	11	1	1,100	41	110,000
− 38	13	2	1,300	42	130,000
− 37	14	3	1,400	43	140,000
− 36	16	4	1,600	44	160,000
− 35	18	5	1,800	45	180,000
− 34	20	6	2,000	46	200,000
− 33	22	7	2,200	47	220,000
− 32	25	8	2,500	48	250,000
− 31	28	9	2,800	49	280,000
− 30	32	10	3,200	50	320,000
− 29	36	11	3,600	51	360,000
− 28	40	12	4,000	52	400,000
− 27	45	13	4,500	53	450,000
− 26	50	14	5,000	54	500,000
− 25	56	15	5,600	55	560,000
− 24	63	16	6,300	56	630,000
− 23	70	17	7,000	57	700,000
− 22	80	18	8,000	58	800,000
− 21	90	19	9,000	59	900,000
− 20	100	20	10,000	60	1.0 volt
− 19	110	21	11,000	61	1.1
− 18	130	22	13,000	62	1.3
− 17	140	23	14,000	63	1.4
− 16	160	24	16,000	64	1.6
− 15	180	25	18,000	65	1.8
− 14	200	26	20,000	66	2.0
− 13	220	27	22,000	67	2.2
− 12	250	28	25,000	68	2.5
− 11	280	29	28,000	69	2.8
− 10	320	30	32,000	70	3.2
− 9	360	31	36,000	71	3.6
− 8	400	32	40,000	72	4.0
− 7	450	33	45,000	73	4.5
− 6	500	34	50,000	74	5.0
− 5	560	35	56,000	75	5.6
− 4	630	36	63,000	76	6.3
− 3	700	37	70,000	77	7.0
− 2	800	38	80,000	78	8.0
− 1	900	39	90,000	79	9.0
− 0	1,000	40	100,000	80	10.0

Table 8-4. Return loss VSWR listing

RETURN LOSS/VSWR CHART

Return loss	VSWR	Match ratio	Reflection coefficient	Percentage reflection
2 dB	8.71	1.26 : 1	.79	79%
4 dB	4.42	1.59 : 1	.63	63%
6 dB	3.01	1.99 : 1	.50	50%
8 dB	2.32	2.52 : 1	.40	40%
10 dB	1.92	3.16 : 1	.32	32%
12 dB	1.67	3.98 : 1	.25	25%
14 dB	1.50	5.01 : 1	.20	20%
16 dB	1.37	6.31 : 1	.16	16%
18 dB	1.28	7.94 : 1	.13	13%
20 dB	1.22	10.0 : 1	.10	10%
22 dB	1.17	12.6 : 1	.079	7.9%
24 dB	1.13	15.9 : 1	.063	6.3%

Return loss	VSWR	Match ratio	Reflection coefficient	Percentage reflection
26 dB	1.11	19.9 : 1	.050	5.0%
28 dB	1.08	25.1 : 1	.040	4.0%
30 dB	1.07	31.6 : 1	.032	3.2%
32 dB	1.05	39.8 : 1	.025	2.5%
34 dB	1.04	50.1 : 1	.020	2.0%
36 dB	1.032	63.1 : 1	.016	1.6%
38 dB	1.026	79.4 : 1	.013	1.3%
40 dB	1.020	100 : 1	.010	1.0%
46 dB	1.010	199 : 1	.005	0.5%
50 dB	1.006	316 : 1	.003	0.3%
54 dB	1.004	501 : 1	.002	0.2%
60 dB	1.002	1000 : 1	.001	0.1%

9

The new TV
on the block

STILL IN SHORT PANTS BUT GROWING, THE MAJESTIC TELEVISION LINE formally debuted in February 1990, is now distributed across the U.S. by Majestic Industries, Inc., with main offices at 8220 Wellmoor Court, Savage, MD 20763. The company reaches nationwide via its branches in many other states.

A well-known brand in monochrome days, Majestic faded with the advent of color and it's probably been about 30 years since the original product graced our market. There is no comparison however, between today's Majestic and the oldie, nor do the distribution sources have any connection. So it's a totally new ball game with well-defined stakes and a solid background.

Mostly cabinet-chassis mated by Wells Gardner Electronics in Chicago, Majestic's roots spring from one of America's best-known quality TV manufacturers, who operates both under its own brand name as well as supplying private-label distributors. Beyond that, I cannot say more, but open up a Majestic cabinet and you'll recognize the parent immediately by its modular, home-serviceable chassis, distinctive wiring and excellent pictures. Many of these models have both comb filters and audio/video jack packs for baseband exits and insertions, thus making most units monitors as well as television receivers, although baseband derives only from identical inputs and not the receiver itself.

Microprocessor-controlled, all-tuning, and on-screen displays are executed digitally in multicolors with precision. Multichannel sound (BTSC-dbx) fully digitized is also included for the audio buffs, and better than average speakers project it. Picture tubes for this series are all made by Rauland of the usual shadow mask vertical stripe construction with black surround material between the RGB stripes. Cabinets, except the floor models, are fabricated of plastic. Normally traditional, decor is not flashy and should go with most any home or office interior, and good signal sensitivity means good operation on cable, broadcast, and satellite reception. In this regard, we understand the Japanese are now working on dual down-convertion for their TV receivers, with the first oscillator-converter set at 965.25 MHz and cable identification to 1 GHz. If so, this probably will carry over to U.S. types fairly shortly because it might eventually permit direct satellite block-downconverter tuning, along with the usual terrestrial CATV and off-the-air signals. In addition, this could possibly lift some or all of the FCC-imposed "taboos" on UHF channel usage—a really big leap forward in TV technology, if and when it becomes a reality. But unless this frequency is increased or our 950 to 1450 block frequencies are decreased, a combination of the two technologies could still be several years more in development. And we still don't know if TV IFs of 27 MHz could be engineered at any reasonable cost without running the price of the receiver skyward beyond reason.

Features

The new M32 Majestic chassis has almost 20 first-class features, comes in 11 table and console models, and includes tube sizes from 20 to 27 inches. There's also a multipurpose remote control included that will operate cable decoders, VCRs, or television receivers in the Majestic line or other brands because it is fully programmable to actually learn the other systems, what's really meant is storing remote commands in readout memory for recall and execution.

The M32 series has a nine-function audio/video jack pack that permits a single U/V/Cable input, audio/video inputs and outputs, and variable right and left audio output for externally switched speakers. There is also automatic channel programming and channel search, digital audio processing, comb filter, MTS multichannel sound, on-screen displays, parental control, 178-channel electronic tuning, programmable video and audio functions, a black matrix picture tube and automatic cathode-ray tube tracking to maintain accurate gray scale if and when picture tube cathode drives vary. It even has a sleep timer that's programmable in 15-minute segments over a total of 2 hours. And the remote multipurpose programmer operates receiver volume whether in TV CATV or VCR control, all virtually copied directly from the initial specification sheet which, we hope, is an absolute symbol of total conservative veracity.

Near the end of the chapter is an electronic analysis of this new receiver based on its parent manufacturer, which should provide some agreeable surprises compared with many of its contemporaries still cluttering the market. And although not a high-tech receiver in the sense of all 1s and 0s following the video detector, it does have digitally processed sound combined with BTSC-dbx broadcast stereo, a dc-efficient switch mode power supply, and programmable audio, video, and sleep functions for individual customer adjustments via the remote control.

Functionally, the M32 chassis has three exchangeable modules. One is for the sweep and switch mode power supply (Fig. 9-1) and the other two are for video plus audio (Fig. 9-2). Control source is a single 52-pin microprocessor, supported by additional ICs in the IFs, etc., in addition to tuners, control keyboards, IR detector, audio processors, and mini- or maxi-jack packs with fixed and variable outputs plus loop through connections. Depending on specific features, there are some 10 ICs and a scattering of discrete transistors and diodes, mostly in the sweep and power output circuits, with high voltage and focus voltages developed in the secondary of the flyback transformer. ICs, transistors, and diodes are all hard wired, which means they are soldered to the printed circuit boards.

For all chassis, there is a single pc board set with appropriate components added for the more deluxe versions or larger tube sizes. Power supplies and sweep subsystems are tailored to accommodate crts and the several drive requirements. Either of the modules are replaceable under available parts exchange programs that the manufacturer supplies directly for a set fee, which reduces hunt-and-peck servicing times considerably.

Other assemblies on these modules include the U/V/CATV tuner, remote amplifier, stereo or mono keyboard, digital or mono amplifier detector/processors, jack packs and high voltage. The remote control is another accessory that will command the television receiver, video cassette recorder, and/or cable television. In addition, the operator's guide has a broad list of operator codes for a number of other TV brands permitting their remote, programmable functions also.

The chassis offers two types of on-screen menus, one for the consumer and the other for servicers, primarily in the shop, when and if required. When menu, channel down and volume down keyboard keys are simultaneously depressed, there appears the original factory setup menu routine for each receiver prior to shipping. Obviously not for the set owner, this mode will probably rarely be used even by shop technicians unless parts require changes. The initial customer adjustment menu for chroma and luma functions, time and auto channel search, inputs, and audio should suffice more than adequately for preset or custom picture and sound conditions desired by any receiver owner. Main module changes may or may not require parameter resettings, but changing the microprocessor might, depending on prior programming or testing. Chroma and luma ICs or digital sound should bear replacement without disturbing any programming at all, and certainly sync, sweep and high voltage circuits should be totally immune from special adjustments other than those specified on the pc boards, but not in software.

The foregoing just about wraps up the general features discussion, leading us directly into main circuit analysis, much of which has been provided by the original manufacturer and technical engineering staff. We'll try and interpret and interpolate as the discussion proceeds with, we hope,

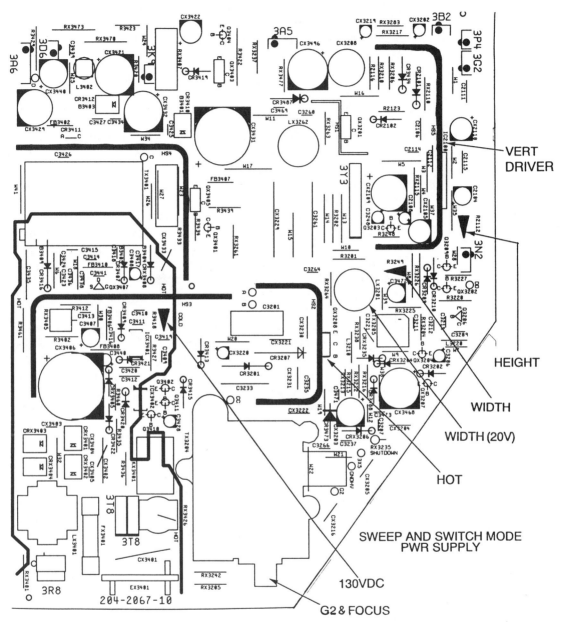

9-1   Sweep and switch mode receiver module and the power supply various adjustments.   Majestic Industries

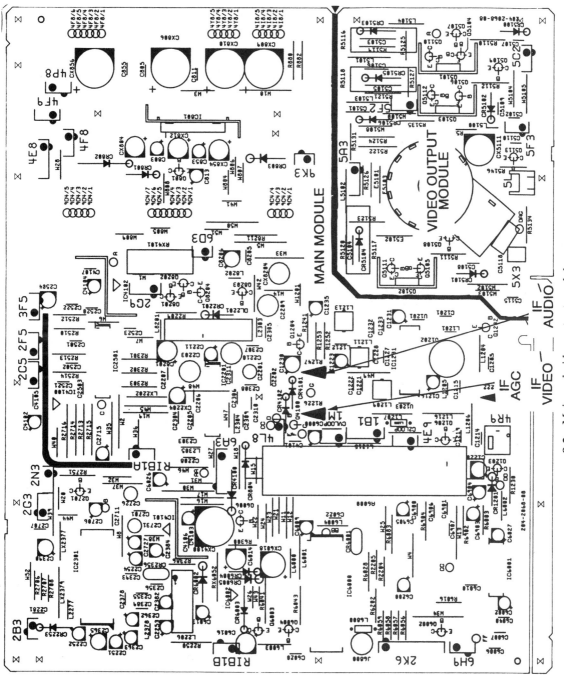

9-2 Main and video output modules. Majestic Industries

an educated projection of how and why this receiver operates as well as it does.

Before theory occurs, however, when programming broadcast channels in the auto function, be sure the input selection reads B-CAST (for broadcast), AFT (for automatic tuning) and BAND for B-CAST (again). Then when the entire auto-programming has ceased—there's CATV tuning, too—program input back to B-CAST for full channel selection. Otherwise, you'll probably remain on CATV or something else, and only access the usual VHF channels.

Power supplies

Always a prime topic in any sophisticated electronic equipment, these receivers have advanced switch mode supplies operating directly from the 120 Vac line (Fig. 9-3), with the same open-ended diode bridge configuration called a universal input because it can be powered by any of the world's nominal power mains from 100 to 240 V if suitable components are used. This one, of course, is designed for U.S. drives at 60 Hz and operates on alternate half cycles, producing 150 volts dc for the primary of power transformer TX3401.

When current is initially drawn, diode CRX3405 rectifies the turn-on spike providing a "kick start" dc voltage for ICX3401. Once oscillations begin in the timing RC network connected to IC pins 3 and 4, a 12 V square wave from pin 6 is further shaped in the gate of switching MOSFET QX3407, the bridge rectifier is now conducting and +150 V flows from its output to the resistive ladder network and terminal No. 1 of TX3401. Blocked by back biased diode CR3416, dc continues to flow from TX3401 terminals 1 to 3 and from there to the drain of QX3407.

MOSFET QX3407 will then conduct into the timing RC networks between its drain and source setting up a much more precisely timed repetition rate from the primary of TX3401. Feedback from the drain of QX3407 to pin 3 of ICX3401 helps sustain the IC's repetition rate which can be altered by potentiometer R3418 connected to pin 4 through R3419M and C3411 by varying the dc potential delivered by half-wave rectifier CRX3408 via R3417M. By this time, CR3407 is also supplying dc to pin 7 of ICX3401 and "kick on" diode CRX3405 is back biased and out of the circuit.

As voltages from the drain of QX3407 swing positive and toward "hot" common, the secondary of TX3401 is modulated, and its output delivers half-wave rectified and filtered potentials of 130 and 16 Vdc. The 130 V output may be adjusted by R3418 and the repetition rate of QX3407, which sets the 16 V power source at the same time. A third power source is also developed across output terminals 15 and 17, which is half-wave rectified by CR3412, RC filtered and connected to cold chassis

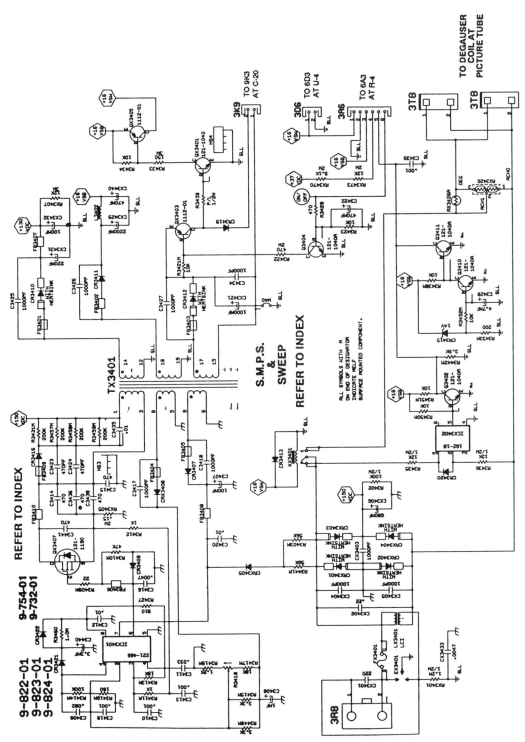

9-3 Schematic of the main, highly regulated switch-mode power supply and chassis isolation in the secondary of TX3401. Majestic Industries

common by W40. This source is both positive back bias for pnp transistor QX3403 as well as the power potential collected for Q3404.

Beyond R3429 in the base circuit of Q3404, you will see an on/off (switch) symbol developed from Q6006 (not illustrated) via a grounding signal instituted by the IC6000 control microprocessor on the main board upon operator command. When this 4.75-volt pulse arrives at the base of Q3404, npn Q3404 conducts, pulling the base of QX3404 toward ground, current then flows from CR3412 through the emitter-collector of QX3404 and on to the base of QX3401 and thence to QX3405, which then closes degaussing relay KX3401, causing the crt to be degaussed in milliseconds along with low power delivered to the sweep circuits and audio. Once fly-back transformer TX3204 is functional and the +37-volt source becomes operational, degaussing has been completed and the entire receiver can now deliver its full potential.

In addition to the kick voltage generated at the top of the diode bridge, a half-wave portion of ac also travels down through R3435 to pin 1 of ICX 3402, a 60 Hz generator and Q3402 amplifier for the microprocessor. As long as the +16 VSB potential supplied by TX3401 in its secondary remains, zener CR3415 conducts, biasing Q3410 on and pulling the base of Q3411 negative so the Q3411 is off. Should +16 VSB's potential reduce below 14 Vdc, however, Q3410 cuts off, the base of Q3411 rises positive and shunts 60 Hz oscillations directly to ground, removing their input to the microprocessor.

The tuner

Not being able to visually inspect this tuner's components from the schematic, assume it has the usual varactor tuning and inductor shunt diodes common to almost all of today's electronic tuners. This one, however, is somewhat more complex since it is said to access 178 U/V/CATV channels. Therefore, it must switch to low band, then high band for VHF and high band/super band for cable, followed by UHF. Switching voltages are listed at 12 volts, Nominal B+ is 5 V, varactor tuning 0.8 to 29 V, and automatic gain control (AGC) can vary between 1 and 8 volts. Having no tuner diagram, this would suggest direct replacement rather than even minor repairs. In such complex front ends, even component layouts are highly important for quality operation and substitute transistors should never be used. Simply remove the old tuner and replace with a new or reworked one from the manufacturer. Long gone are the days when a couple of resistors restored an old tube RF amplifier to a semblance of operation and a few squirts of tuner lube took care of both switch and barrel tuner contacts. Today most tuner repairs are either factory undertakings or products of specialty shops. Seldom do even the large service centers maintain specific sections for these difficult front ends. Fortunately, they're relatively easy to check, and a substitute tuner plugged into the video IF jack can quickly determine states of either good or bad. Switching from mode to another, however, requires a good voltmeter—digital preferred, including autoranging.

This tuner control diagram does not show an input for automatic fine tuning, although there is one for automatic gain control (AGC). However, since we know one is available, it probably enters the tuner elsewhere operating when required. In these tuners, a phase-locked loop system and AFT maintain correct frequency on either side of center tuning up to a variation of ± 1 MHz.

IFs and video detection

Carrier frequencies are accessed by the tuner and beat with a local oscillator and mixer, producing video and audio frequencies separated by a constant 4.5 MHz contained within a passband extending from approximately 39.75 MHz to 47.25 MHz, which are the respective adjacent video and adjacent sound traps. Audio and video IF "carriers" then appear at 41.25 MHz and 47.75 MHz, fully defining their 4.5 MHz separation after passing through the accoustical wave filter (SAW) and its preamplifier.

Video IF is detected directly, but audio is nominally "reduced" to a 4.5 MHz intercarrier signal before being phase detected since its transmission medium is frequency modulation rather than video's amplitude modulation, exactly opposite to systems in France called SECAM. Germany's PAL translates to phase alternating line denoting color phase rotation every other line, ostensibly to cancel different phase errors.

Instead of an ineffective germanium half-wave diode detection of yore, video is now synchronously detected, often with a 45.75 MHz designated frequency as the switcher and the usual composite information being supplied to its IC amplifiers. As you might note, the only video IF adjustment in the entire 30-pin IC belongs to the L1211 inductor in the tank circuit of its oscillator, making this IF easily "aligned" with only monochrome multiburst extending from 0.5 to 4.2 MHz since you're actually only looking for maximum bandpass through the IF anyway. Both color and sound are later detected separately according to their separate characteristics: audio by phase involving frequencies between approximately 30 Hz and 15 kHz; and chroma between about 2 and 4.08 MHz, which is then recombined with luminance to form composite analog information for the cathode ray tube.

Other potentiometer adjustments outboard of IC1201 (Fig. 9-4) are for composite video, AFC, audio level, AGC RF, and a second LC arrangement for the 4.5 MHz sound detector. The TAC portion below the IF is proprietary to the manufacturer and designed for specific cable systems using his scrambling coders/decoders. Observe that this IC is powered by +9 V instead of 12 or 16 V, which are evident elsewhere. The source derives from an additional regulator in the right hand lower corner of the

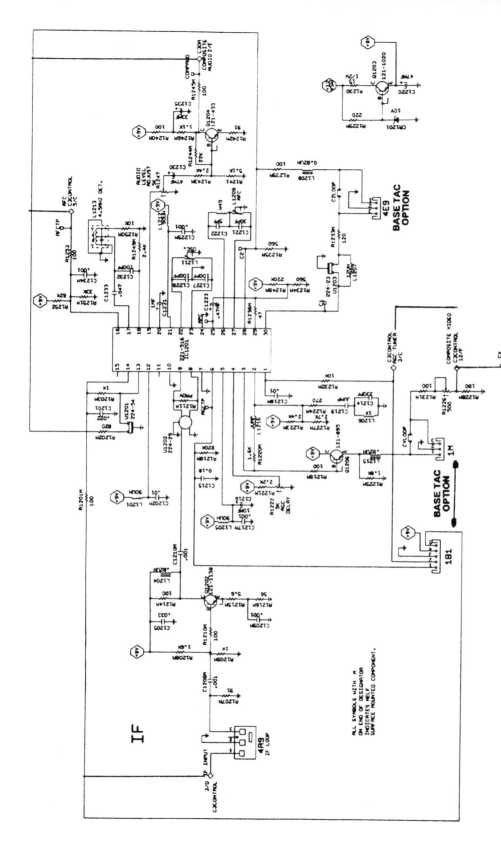

9-4 Video IF, AGC, AFC and audio detector. BASE TAC option is not included in the M32 chassis. Majestic Industries

diagram and originates with a 12 V supply located elsewhere. Q1203 is a simple regulator with zener base bias of 10 volts. Limited current through its cathode resistor for the zener maintains the Q1203 base voltage, and an additional 0.7 V drop through its base-emitter junction delivers approximately 9 volts dc. Any additional noise the zener might add is capacitor-filtered at sensitive IC inputs.

In summary, this single 30-pin analog IC demodulates video, detects 4.5 MHz intercarrier audio by the frequency difference between audio and video carriers, develops automatic fine tuning and automatic gain control as dc correction voltages—a very good testimonial to considerable advances in IC technology over the past several years, especially the mixing of several frequencies across a common substrate.

After intercarrier detection, audio is actually demodulated by quadrature phase action and exits this IC at pin 19. APC automatic phase control and the video demod actually use the same demodulator, with the APC RC filter appearing at pin 25, while video equalization occurs at pins 2 and 3.

Internally

Inside the IC, a commercial M51365SP device, the block diagram appears as illustrated in Fig. 9-5. This shows the various detectors, amplifiers, limiters, AGC, as well as the usual outboard components required to make this IC operate. Entry into this IC1201 passes through a stabilized SAW filter in balanced input through pins 8 and 9 to a pair of 40 dB gain amplifiers with no dc feedback. This dual amplifier permits up to a 110 dBu input having maximum AGC speed control between 50 and 60 dBu. AGC, of course, is developed following the video detector and returns with filtering through pin 30 to the lock detector, BNC, and finally to the IF AGC. This is a dual amplifier that also connects to the RF (delayed) AGC internally with level set potentiometer visible at pin 4. Having pin 28 designated threshold, max clamping voltage is set near 100 IRE, or white level.

APC is a phase comparator that delivers corrective voltages corresponding to phase differences between the IF and voltage-controlled oscillator (VCO) via the +45-degree phase shifter. APC output becomes 0 when the B-phase angle is +90 degrees out of phase with the IF, but APC output current goes positive when the phase angle lags. As current converts to voltage, it is low pass filtered so that the VCO is controlled and the lock detector latches as phase error becomes inversely proportional to loop gain.

With the IF signal locked, the switched video detector with its two current generators strips away the 45.75 MHz IF envelope, leaving a linear 4 MHz video baseband signal for further luma/chroma processing. APC and the video detector use double balance multipliers.

On the schematic, pin 11 has no connection, but on this diagram, 41.25 MHz sound is shown entering the IC and its sound IF detector with a beat difference between audio and video of 4.5 MHz. This intercarrier frequency

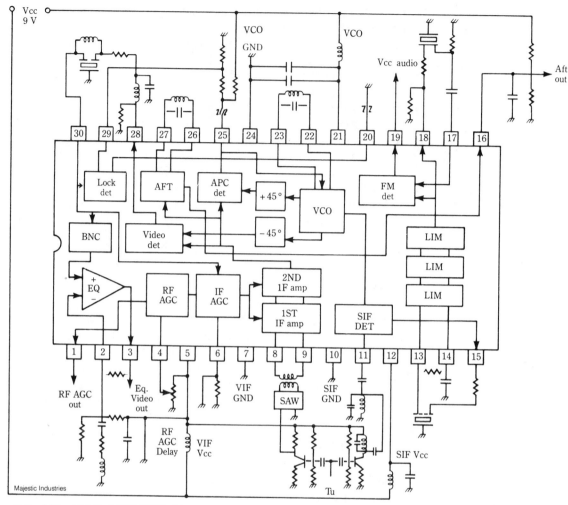

9-5 Mitsubishi's M513655P video IF, detector, sound, AGC, and AFC does it all with good results.

subsequently passes through a triple limiter into the FM detector and its tank circuit at pins 17 and 18 probably for quadrature FM demodulation, even though the spec sheet calls this RLC unit a *discriminator*.

With a relatively small amount of information available, the foregoing should at least make this complex IF, AFT, AGC, SIF integrated circuit reasonably understandable. For troubleshooting, there are a couple of test points indicated, as well as some voltage sources, but a 30-pin extender will certainly be required if you need to check at least the prime outputs and dc operating voltages since multiple jacks/plugs are often a tight fit for even miniature oscilloscope and meter probes.

Tuning system control

This description involves operations of the 52-pin IC6000 and its IC6001 nonvolatile random-access memory (RAM) (see schematic). In total, the microcontroller responds to 26 digital commands beginning with 00001 and ending with 10010, representing preferred channel down and CCU halt, respectively, all responding to five-bit color TV codes and two six-bit factory codes. Functions begin with the on (power) key, continue in a negative scan system, and end with the adjust down key. The factory menu and CCU halt do not have actual keys, but are accessed by alternates.

In channel tuning, broadcast (B'CAST) and CATV, channels 2 through 13 are identical and other CATV channels are synthesized from 00 to 134. From 0 to 13, CATV channels must be tuned within 54 ms. Scan tuning steps at two channels per second. As for audio, either stereo or monophonic selection is available and the stereo subsystem functions through the IM bus, with volume selectable in 64 steps, bass and treble in 9 steps, and balance in 19 steps. In mono audio, a pulse-width modulated signal integrates for analog control voltage which also has 64 steps.

Upon power on/off, the receiver blanks and mutes for 750 ms so that the last channel tuned and all other customer settings are recalled or, in the event of a power failure, this will be displayed on the crt. Upon turn-off, the receiver blanks and mutes for approximately 1 second, switched power is removed, and any power failure condition results in complete shutdown and remains so until 60 Hz signals are again available from the power supply.

Once operational, stereo sound levels adjust at five levels/second, with a maximum of 64 steps that can be muted as desired, but it will unmute if a new setting's programmed for another level change.

Menu

There are both main menus and as many as five adjustments to each in indicated colors as the various selections appear. A secondary menu for the factory and technicians is not obvious and must be accessed by simultaneously engaging the menu, adjust, and prefer red channel up keys. There is also a customer-operated source menu for antenna, cable, and VCR hookups that must be carefully selected for B'CAST, AFC, and correct BAND off-the-air programming. If these three are not in sequence, auto-programming will go only to channel 13 and keep repeating because the microprocessor must know your inputs (antenna), broadcast band, and have an active automatic fine tuning (AFC) in operation. Thereafter, weak or undesirable channels might be individually set via the favorite channel programming mode to be stored in permanent memory unless manually erased.

The remainder of the programming information is contained in the operator's manual and you can read it there. Unfortunately, we don't even have a block diagram of how the microprocessor operates and it will simply be necessary to follow various signal leads in and out of the 52-pin CMOS device if you are circuit tracing. Otherwise, any control function that is not operating a particular subsystem has to be tested electronically to determine if difficulties are in the processor or the affected device. Menu-selection parameters can be increased or decreased by rocker arm adjust key on the remote control.

Remote-control-only functions include mute, 0 to 9 direct entries, and flashback. Should it become necessary to recall the factory menu, you may then adjust display position, jack pack structure, color sentry levels, and self demo. During any time the factory menu is requested, keyboard keys that are normally unused for menu selection serve as command channels. Each cycles some in/out (I/O) unit subservient to the microcontroller and are essential for both factory and problem sets diagnosis.

The color sentry and video filter are two important functions that should be stressed because their meaning might not be entirely clear in the operator instructions. The color sentry is simply an automatic, factory-programmed feature that varies color, picture, and hue (tint) conditions based on room lighting. When this set is active, however, the three chroma controls are fixed and cannot be adjusted. For those with color preferences, it's recommended that custom adjustments prevail. The video filter affects both sharpness and picture content. When engaged, it can selectively modify auto picture adjustments depending on picture content and moderately ragged edge scene transitions, but still permitting certain small detail emphasis to be sharpness adjusted.

All other controls are reasonably self-explanatory in the operator's handbook and require nothing further here. Nonetheless, you should know that the microcomputer receives current once the receiver is connected to the power mains. If the receiver is disconnected or there is a power failure, the microcomputer is reset and will begin a channel search beginning with the lowest programmed channel and sound resumes at any nonmuted level prior to power loss. Sound, however, is always muted for 0.7 second during turn-on. Phase-locked-loop tuning accuracy is synthesized at ±45 kHz of the local oscillator's prime frequencies. Any direct entry channel number responds within 2 seconds after operator command. Programmed channels operate at 2 per second and skipped channels are passed over at some 67 per ms. Fine-tuning arrangements are not included with this microprocessor, but sound is muted between channel changes for approximately 260 ms. During scan periods, audio is muted continuously. Should you set the sleep timer, the on-screen display will flash and continue for 5 seconds. With the sleep timer programmed, any time remaining can be visible up to 90 minutes. Upon turn-off, the timer will flash 1 minute prior to receive shutdown. The time can be extended, however, by depressing the sleep timer key or retarded by either activating the on/off switch or repeatedly engaging the sleep timer key until the display reads zero.

Video processor

The video processor is a 42-pin proprietary device that processes both video and chroma with some sync tossed in (Fig. 9-6). Here we'll have to primarily work from the main schematic and base a number of assumptions on integrated circuits of the past. This 42-pin IC, however, seems to have a considerable number of innovations that deserve more than casual attention because its processes combine the light-sensitive photo cell, luminance information, chroma demodulation, flyback pulses, synch processing, automatic brightness limiting, and RGB color outputs. All this means that 2 MHz of wideband chroma must be detected and combined with luminance for red, blue, and green outputs, horizontal and vertical sync adequately separated and correctly counted, coordinated blanking, regeneration of the color 3.579545 MHz chroma subcarrier with crystal accuracy, and quadrature phase detection, color detection occurring between pins 9 and 12. There is also an automatic chroma phase control filter at pin 11, demodulator input at pin 3, luminance input at pin 1, and photo cell input at pin 2.

Since luminance has already been detected, this more rapidly moving information must be delayed by L2206 before it can successfully combine with chroma for the RGB outputs. At pin 4 you see ACC, which stands for automatic chroma control. In the past this has depended on the amplitude of burst on the back porch of the horizontal sync pulse, and probably still does because there is obviously incoming sync at pin 17 and horizontal output activity at pin 28, as well as vertical sync output at pin 31. Automatic brightness limiter (ABL) at pin 38 should be fairly obvious, while ident at pin 34 appears to refer to audio, and is probably mono/stereo identification, which the microprocessor would have already signalled to IC2301. Lumas L and C at pins 40 and 41 are subject to some sort of RLC network which could be resonant at a high frequency, but the inductor is damped by R2267, making it a series phase shifter and filter.

RGB outputs and blanking proceed to buffer IC2501 for both microprocessor control as well as transmission to the final video output panel on the cathode-ray tube for RGB into the crt, technical setup, and RGB sampling. The 2B3 connection is simply an input from the flyback transformer for the automatic brightness limiter control on IC2301. This is the most uniform chroma demodulation I've observed in a television receiver and is very apparent in either gated rainbow or NTSC color bar patterns.

Crt socket and electronics

Also called the "video output," this group of circuits are actually on the main chassis rather than on the crt socket, which is simply an attachment

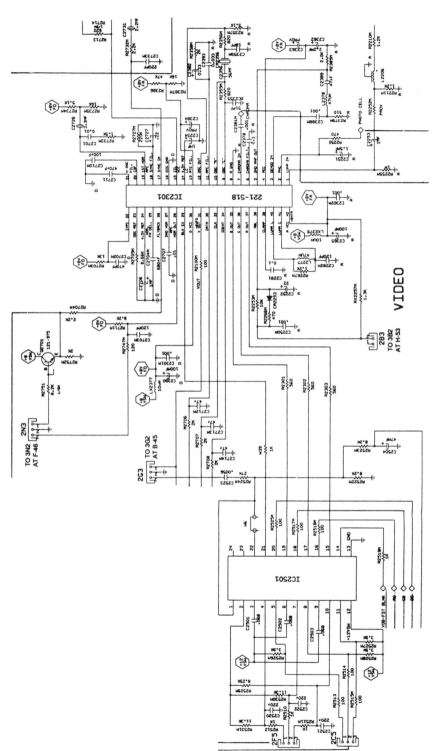

9-6 The video/sync/chroma processor and its IC2501 buffer and output. Majestic Industries

(Fig. 9-7). They consist of RGB drivers and amplifiers, a few zener and guide diodes and dual-voltage supplies from both the 12 V SW and 215 V sources. And in the lower center of the schematic, you will find the 5L jumper terminal for initial setup. Normally, terminals 1 and 2 are connected, providing a path to ground for transistors Q5104 through Q5106. These are the lower portion of stacked transistors Q5101 through Q5103. Together they are driven by their respective red, blue, and green (RGB) sources from video processor IC2301. But when 5L terminals 2 and 3 are connected, 12 volts flow to the emitter of Q5113 as well as the emitters of Q5104, 5 and 6, shutting these transistors down so that only low-level single RGB horizontal bars are visible on the crt. Drivers Q5107 through Q5109 remain conducting during this period, as does Q5113 because its base voltage is only about 6 volts due to the two resistive voltage dividers and its emitter is virtually at almost a full 12 V potential from 12 V SW.

Under normal operating conditions, final RGB amplifiers Q5110-Q5112 supply the three red, blue, and green picture tube cathodes with mixed luminance and chroma potential while their collectors furnish red, green, and blue sample voltages for balancing crt gun regulation via 390 kΩ load resistors. Zeners CR5103, 4 and 5 deliver adequate clamping and biasing between emitter and base for the three final amplifiers during normal and abnormal operations. Spark gaps are also strategically placed wherever necessary to conduct any crt cathode arching to ground. The three 560 pF capacitors shunting the three zeners are obviously filters and may also aid in crt turnoff transient reduction, even though their values are rather small. Connections from sweep and main modules reach the crt through pins 9 and 7, respectively.

Sweep circuits

Fortunately, sweep and power supplies are on the same module, so you can refer both to Fig. 9-1 as well as Fig. 9-8 for layout and schematic information. Besides vertical sync countdown and processor IC2100, this portion of the schematic contains all the horizontal drivers and shutdown circuits as well as the flyback transformer and its built-in high-voltage rectifiers and focus adjustment.

Usually, vertical sync is derived in television receivers from horizontal repetition rates and then digitally counted down to the standard 59.94 Hz prevalent in NTSC color systems of today. Under routine conditions, countdown from 15,734 Hz is nothing more than a digital divide-by 262.496 for field and frame rates. Occasionally, however, a few counts or even an entire field fails to trigger the vertical processor and the count must be extended for an additional number of digits that either pick up the correct count or begin a new field so that vertical sync is not lost and viewing continues uninterrupted. There are some divider resistors and filter/

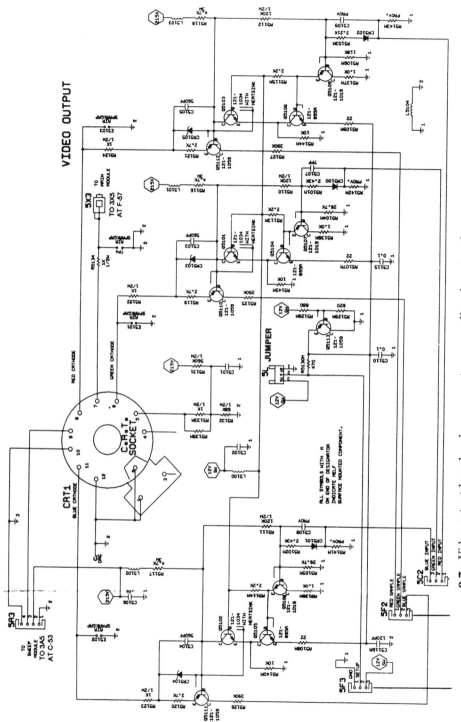

9-7 Video output board and components surrounding the crt socket.   Majestic Industries

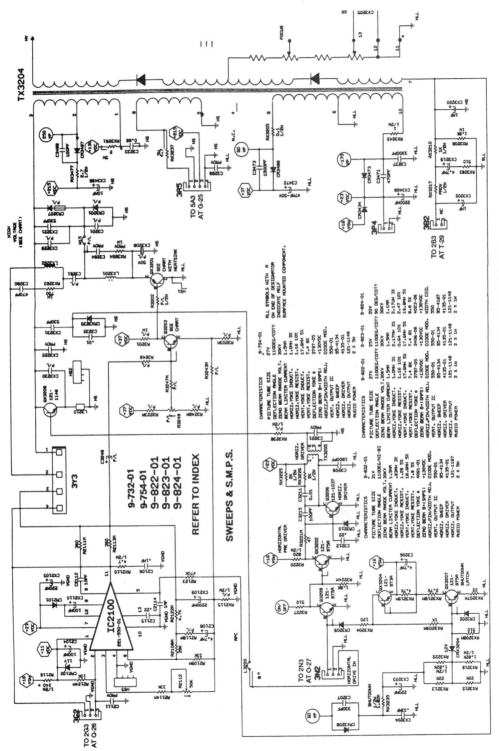

9-8 Sweep and horizontal/vertical driver circuits including TX3204 flyback transformer. Majestic Industries

shaping networks that will not be examined with three exceptions:

- Energy from the secondary of the flyback transformer through R2123 is shaped by C2114 for auto sync control by feedback into pin 5 of IC2100.

- Zener CR2102 supplies additional regulation and an 11 V operating voltage for IC2100.

- Output-drive pulse shaping for Q3203 results primarily from the series combination of R2110 and C2106 and other parallel- and series-connected components develop what will soon become a trapezoidal waveshape to produce a sawtooth of current for vertical deflection (Fig. 9-9).

This waveform is inverted and routed to the base of QX3201 to drive vertical output power transistor QX3201 and its compensated emitter output for the deflection yoke. Note, however, there is a W15 link in addition to several capacitors and two diodes that can effect horizontal drive at its extremities. Width potentiometer R3249 in the base circuit of Q3203 can vary the positive base of this transistor increasing or decreasing horizontal sweep width, a most interesting circuit indeed.

Once horizontal drive completes its sweep function, flyback current reverses developing primary and secondary voltages you see listed between coil terminals 1 and 10; the secondary high-voltage coil being approximately centertapped for focus potential, which in the 110 degree Coty 29 system is usually between 16 percent and 20 percent of the 28 kV rated high voltage. (Being completely enclosed in the crt socket and flyback, I was unable to measure it, but at 20 percent this would amount to approximately 5.6 kV.)

Horizontal triggering begins as a series of horizontal-rate pulses from chroma/luma/sync processor IC2301. It inputs into horizontal sweep

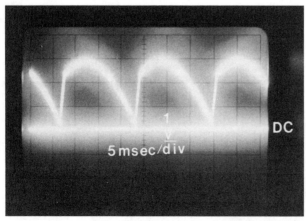

9-9 Trapezoidal-type voltage forming at the base of Q3203 vertical driver.

through pin 1 of 3N2 to the base of npn transistor Q3209, which is also connected to the shutdown latch through diode CR3209. Drive waveforms at 0.5 V and 20 μs/div are illustrated in the lower portion of Fig. 9-10 and flyback pulses from the HV transformer appear above at 20 V/div. Note that the peaks of the upper display and leading edges of the lower rectangular drive waveform are coincident in time. These flyback pulses serve as sync reference and excitation for the luma/chroma processor, microprocessor, and IC6001, the random access memory, arriving at terminal 3N2 via two capacitors and clamping diode CR3201.

Rectangular energy continues on through inverter QX3202 and from there to horizontal driver Q3206 with a negatively polarized shunt diode in its base. This transistor drives current through transformer TX3205 and provides sufficient power for horizontal output power transistor QX3208.

The shutdown circuit is an interesting circuit with a considerable number of passive components and only two transistors. If you look at the schematic there's a complementary npn/pnp stacked QX3204 and QX3207 pair of transistors that actually form a complex switch, with the emitter of QX3204 connected directly to the +16 V VSW source developed through the collector of QX3405 in the main power supply. The other extreme of this circuit on the left originates from terminal 9 in the primary of the TX3204 flyback transformer, which, of course is a pulse. This energy is rectified by CRX3206 as it passes the SD/VP terminal on the shutdown circuit, is filtered and divided by two capacitors and a 1.82 kΩ resistor acting as a choke in between, continuing on as filtered dc to the four half-voltage dividers and the cathode of Zener CRX3204. Observe that this is a 12 V zener, which will block all positive potential until it either zeners or avalanches.

Now in any stacked configuration, two conditions must occur: The zener has to conduct from overvoltage so that latch QX3207 furnishes a

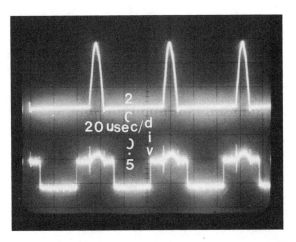

9-10 Flyback and horizontal drive waveforms at terminal 3N2.

base potential lower than the emitter potential for QX3204, permitting enabling of this upper transistor, whose emitter is directly tied to the + 16 VSW source. With both shutdown latch transistors conducting, voltage from the power supply immediately passes from QX3204's emitter to collector through RX3204 and diode CR3209, turning on Q3209 hard so that the ON/OFF system is triggered as well as the horizontal predriver and high voltage. And as long as this overvoltage condition continues, the system will automatically shut down until the cause has been removed. While 22 k and 1.82 kΩ resistors don't necessarily indicate precision components, any replacement here due to faults should be carefully measured before substitution, and transistor replacements should be exact, especially QX3204 where critical potentials mean the difference between safety and major system damage.

Digital stereo audio

A very worthwhile innovation for any and all television sound these days because it provides dramatic improvement over both analog stereo and monaural. Reducing FM modulation to simple 1s and 0s in a digital bitstream produces considerably cleaner response and this, coupled with additional volume and improved speakers, offers far greater music and even enjoyment over even what was available only a year or two past.

Essentially, this is more or less the same two ADC 2300 U and APU 2400 U ICs developed by ITT semiconductor GmbH in Freiburg, W. Germany with a few essential changes such as the addition of a phased-locked loop and dBx in the former and a 14 MHz stand-alone oscillator in the latter. Otherwise, the general theory of operation remains the same and the ICs have been redesignated as ADC 2320U and APU 2421U. An in-circuit schematic is illustrated in Fig. 9-11, and the description will be general but informative.

The IC1404 contains a 14/7 MHz clock divider, SAP and L–R demodulator (with control and synchronization), a muting circuit for L – R and SAP outputs, an IM bus, two pulse density modulators, and three analog switches for separate signal inputs. Composite audio input is through pin 5; auxiliary right input through pin 7; and auxiliary left input through pin 24, completing the various inputs as indicated through 9C4.

Incoming signals pass through four buffers, two switches, then into the pair of pulse density modulators. If such signals are second audio programs (SAP), they go through a filter, are detected, and continue. Outputs of the pulse-density modulations are 1-bit data streams at a rate of 7 MHz max. Analog switches are IM bus-controlled to select local audio or RF, depending on inputs. And the L – R demodulator operates with digitally-controlled detection and especially low harmonic distortion. The IM bus links this IC with the microprocessor and the stereo detection system which follows.

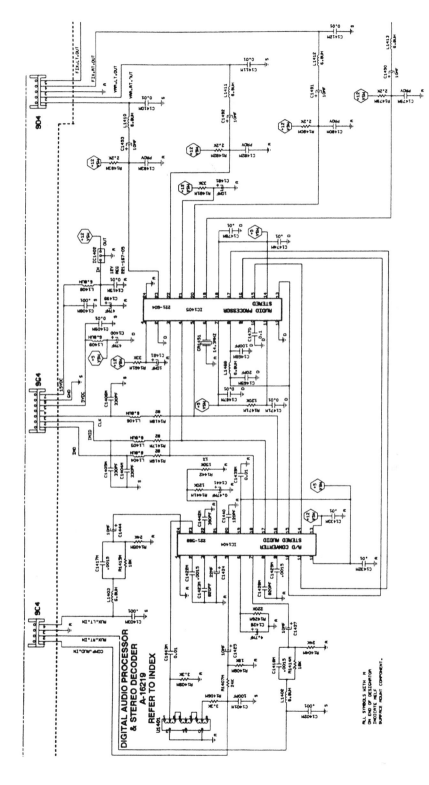

9-11 Majestic's digital stereo system, essentially flat to 14 kHz. Majestic Industries

IC1405 is the second and final 24-pin NMOS IC of the pair and receives L, R. MPX, and SAP information from IC1404. Here, pulse density modulation converts to parallel data at an audio sampling rate via decimation filters, there is gain, phase equalization, deemphasis for the L + R channel, and then a dematrix for both L + R and L − R with fixed preemphasis for both, while the pilot signal is detected. Outputs for the final amplifiers are at pins 19 and 20, with 14.3 MHz self-contained crystal-controlled oscillator.

Following L and R outputs, treble/bass and stereo controls issue from pins 22 and 23 also for the final amplifiers. Troubleshooting these ICs can be troublesome because of analog to coding changes and fast clock rates. So about all you can do is measure a few dc values and look at the outputs with an oscilloscope if you have a 1 or 3 kHz signal source. But do make sure of the inputs and that all IC pins are firmly soldered in. D istortions are easily recognized in the fixed and variable outputs with either a signal tracer or scope.

Troubleshooting

Since this is generally an analog receiver, general troubleshooting is still possible on either the main or sweep/power boards, and even the video output board, too, Once the back's off, a single screw and two plastic frame lifts allow either of the large boards to be withdrawn to some extent for servicing. We suggest pin extenders for the ICs and either probe hooks or pins for oscilloscope investigations. Many of the components are rather small and tightly stretched on the boards, so access isn't all that simple. Nonetheless, it can be done without pulling an entire board, so at least try before whole board substitution. It also might be a very profitable arrangement to have several different boards available so either shop or home servicing could become quite convenient. They're not too difficult to change as long as you pay attention to the various terminals and wire lead dress. And with this fairly complete service manual, ordinary faults shouldn't be at all difficult to solve.

Servicing suggestions

Power problems Fixing power problems can be the most puzzling in many breakdowns when and if they occur. Initially check line fuse, then the 150 V main output. If these are okay, confirm + 16 V at pin 3 of connector 3A6, + 12 V SB at pin 1 of 6H9, and + 5 V SB at pin 3 of IC6002. Then discover if there is a 60 Hz reference at pin 5 of 3A6. Also, + 5 V at pin 6 of 3A6 and at pin 41 IC 6000 are necessary for the power condition.

You must have + 16 V SW at pin 1 of 3A6 connector and pin 1 of 306 connector and + 12 V SW at pin 3 of IC4100, + 8 V SW at pin 3 of IC4101, + 5 V SW at pin 3 of IC4102. The high-voltage transformer-derived voltages also important if possible difficulties arise from these sources.

Adjustments Adjustments include the *130 Vdc*, which is conducted with the 5L jumper in setup plus picture and black level controls retarded to minimum. A digital VOM then should be connected across RX3407 and R3418 adjusted for proper voltage. *Width* should be adjusted for approximately 1/2-inch horizontal overscan, or 1/2 of a gated rainbow bar so that yellow orange on the left and bright green on the right are among the full 10 color bars apparent. Use R3249 or LX3201 on 20-inchers. On these receivers, high voltage and B+ regulations are so tight that once set, width remains constant even with beam current changes. The same is true for your *height* adjustment (1/2" overscan), done with R2112. *Purity* adjustments take place with a 470-ohm resistor shunting video outputs to common via 5C2, pin 1 for red, pin 2 for green, and pin 3 for blue—all on the video output module on the crt. If you have an NTSC generator with raster and the three RGB fields, shunting is unnecessary—just push buttons. Once correct rasters have been set, cathode-ray-tube temperature should measure 8100 degrees Kelvin, at least for the 27-inch group.

Signal adjustments Signal adjustments include RF, sound, and composite video. RF AGC has to be done with off-air signals and set so that R1222 eliminates noise (snow) on all channels within reasonable reception. *Composite video level* requires adjustment of R1226 for a signal of 1 V peak-to-peak at W14. Use a scope. And the *4.5 MHz detector coil L1213* needs only to be set for adequate sound and minimum buzz.

All these adjustments are carefully made when receivers leave the factory, so none should require a recheck before customer delivery unless there are noticeable problems. When replacing modules you should also check affected adjustments just to be sure!

Independently measured parameters

All the following characteristics of an M32 Majestic 27-inch chassis were established from measurements in my own laboratory during the spring/summer period of 1990. With equivalent equipment you should be able to duplicate all with similar results.

Tuner sensitivity: −60 dBm
Signal-to-noise at red gun of crt: 38 dB
Ac power range: 90 to 130 volts without noticeable power/audio/video/
    picture change
Low- and high-voltage regulation: essentially 100 percent over ac range
    and HV at 28.5 kV
AGC response: −57.5 to +8 dB, or 65.5 dB before pix. change
AFC (AFT) response centered on video carrier: ±1 MHz
Maximum bandpass via tuner and IFs: 4.2 MHz (on multiburst)
Gray scale: Excellent stepped staircase but with a few overshoots and pre-
    shoots measured at red gun of crt. (These could be designed in.)

Crt temperature: 8100 degrees K

Gated rainbow color vector response: essentially perfect with exact 30 degree petal separation.

Horizontal overscan: 5 percent or $1/2$ color bar at each end

Audio passband: 60 to 14 MHz, essentially flat

Stereo/channel separation: 12.6 dB

Visual: Linearity, convergence, gray scale, controls, multiburst, red, blue, green fields and purity: all excellent.

10

Many a mile left in the old jalopy

JUST A LITTLE AUTOMOTIVE INGENUITY PAYS OFF HANDSOMELY WHEN pocketbook or fond attachment saves the old bus from a junk heap. Ours had 85,000 miles, a history of intermittent pinging, a radiator fluid and slight oil leak, and sounds much akin to noisy valve lifters. If this sort of troubleshooting interests you, here's how to indulge your fancies and put a few hours of spare moments to money-saving uses. It all takes work, a little study, considerable determination, and the will to learn about such things as exhaust gas recirculation (EGR), vacuums and distribution, electronic ignition, and the cooling system. The strictly mechanical portions such as brakes, transmissions, and front wheel alignments will be left to the local garage or those who delight in obvious hardware. This type of work is primarily under the hood and not under the car because this is where instrument applications and somewhat more than average reasoning can make a difference.

True, I restrict my descriptions to an individual 10-year-old product, but the family considers it the "greatest," and therefore a thorough restoration should establish their trust one way or the other. It might also be added that most of these applications apply to other vehicles of contemporary age, too, and so should be of benefit to those who would tackle similar undertakings.

Problems that do require some cerebral dexterity are the various mechanical changes manufacturers undertake unannounced, leaving you to fend for yourself in a small world of discovery. Some of these are rather disconcerting, but most can be overcome either through outright tenacity or by reading some of the do-it-yourself publications available in the auto supply stores and also from test equipment manufacturers. Normally, most of the answers can be found via one of these readily available sources, or at least they should give you enough of a hint to guide you to some modest measure of success. When all else fails, there's always the trusty mechanic at your auto dealer or handy garage who will usually answer a simple question or two if you seem to have an idea of either what you're doing or want to do. Don't go in cold, though, or you'll probably pay through the nose for Silent Cal to do the whole job at his amiable convenience and $40 per hour labor charge. Part timers usually work for less and are often just as good and possibly more efficient, especially if they've been in the business for any length of time. The regulars are usually assigned piece work and are paid according to time charged and products (parts) sold.

The overall restoration job described, occupied all three labor categories and did, indeed, turn out remarkably well, so much so that my wife will expect identical results every time in the future for half the price and one-quarter the time.

Step by step

To be honest, what really caused this jalopy excursion wasn't just the relatively minor irritants but total power failure at intermittent intervals. Driving down the road, the vehicle would suddenly stop its engine, losing all steering and brake-assisted power and virtually dare you to keep it on the road. Maneuver the thing to a shoulder, kick the starter, and away you'd go without hesitation—for a little while, anyway. After some experimenting, I could actually pop the automatic gearshift lever in neutral, restart the engine on the roll, and continue on as though nothing had happened, slowing down only about 5 mph in the process. In these electronic ignition systems, just suspect the electronic module and be done with it! Coils, spark plugs, plug wires, batteries and distributors just don't act like that.

Since there are at least four transistors in the module, you either have an open or shorted condition, both of which can temporarily heal themselves, and both will operate for some finite time before giving you problems. Because the entire semiconductor assembly and its metal shield and housing are doubly secured internally with a hard filler of epoxy, any repairs are out of the question. So take your old part (or its exact numbers) to either some retailer or distributor ($72 versus $59) and pick up a new one.

Installation (on Ford products) is just a matter of four securing fender screws and 2 to 4 sometimes difficult operating voltage and signal connectors, and you're on your way once more, but this time without middle-of-the-road stops that can be downright scary.

If you have a dual-trace oscilloscope and would like to see the module's shenanigans, take a 6-foot piece of coaxial cable, wrap its center conductor around a 1- to 2-inch-wide copper clamp on one end and a BNC connector on the other, and you have a pickup probe that will easily show all cylinder firings when attached to the spark lead between the distributor and its high-voltage coil. If you want to look at each cylinder in its firing mode (Fig. 10-1), another similar probe can be attached to channel No. 2, and to each plug wire in turn. Sufficient sync should derive from the distributor-coil connection to make your traces stand relatively still—or it may take an external sync connection, depending on the quality of your oscilloscope. On some scopes, your time base will have to undergo some experimentation before sufficient sync can steady the trace(s).

Our Polaroid photo offers a good example of these waveforms that are common to all vehicles of this type. Here, you're looking at pure voltages, just as your local mechanic can do with his $10,000 large-screen scope that won't do a bit better than yours except produce a larger, dimmer trace. If you'd like to take this analysis a bit further, however, a couple of handy (but expensive) ac current probes calibrated in milliamperes/millivolts or volts, can furnish an exact display of what the module itself is doing. And that is really what you want to know in this instance Fig. 10-2. Otherwise, the initial voltage displays will tell you if the cylinders are "sparkin' plenty" and if their amplitudes and firing times are relatively equal or possibly defective.

Here, we'll have to show only good waveforms and describe the shorting symptoms because intermittent opens simply cause everything to fail at once and actually leave no troubleshooting traces. First we'll illustrate the out-of-phase input waveforms into the electronic module and its single output. The latter is the main concern because leakage and shorting failures show up usually only in the output due to internal transistor action.

In the lower trace, observe the single integrated output. This is the critical area if the module is operating at all. Otherwise, you'll have to substitute a replacement to see if it actually cures the problem. If not, then check the battery and voltage regulator output to see if 12 V is being delivered. Normally, however, with the stated symptoms, only the electronic

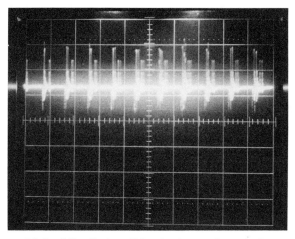

10-1   All cylinders firing in time and regularly.

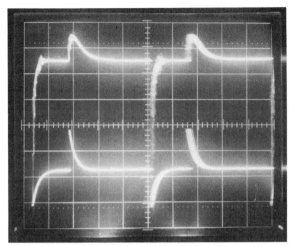

10-2 Input and output electronic module waveforms
as seen through a pair of ac current probes.

module is bad, and most everything else is reasonable. There are exceptions to peripheral conditions, and we'll get to them shortly.

In this instance, however, with engine gone and all power with it, an obvious open was indicated, and so it was. Had this been a short, peaks of the output display would have appeared to fold over or diminish gradually and then totally die. Nonetheless, both end results are virtually the same except that engine heat would allow the short a relatively specific time to develop, whereas the open could occur any time and the engine might be started immediately without waiting for cool down.

If you really value your auto, the next logical step would be setting both curb and fast idles, and checking the antidieseling (or carburetor) solenoid. But there's a job to do beforehand.

Leaky distributor shaft?

Here's where you can both learn a lesson and positively court disaster. The books don't talk much about a faulty distributor shaft because most of their writers probably never pulled one in their lives. If they did, and fouled up the car's timing, they'll probably never do it again. But by making mistakes, you often learn a great deal (I did)! (See Fig. 10-3.)

With an old bottle of nail polish, draw a bead between can-appearing vacuum advance and (in this instance) the air conditioner support housing. Next, mark the position of the rotor inside the distributor housing in the same place. You'll then have two marks to use to realign the shaft and not get into trouble. Removing the hold-down bolt frees the shaft.

However, upon replacing the single O ring about three-quarters of the way up the shaft and its set of crankshaft-meshing gears, you will find it

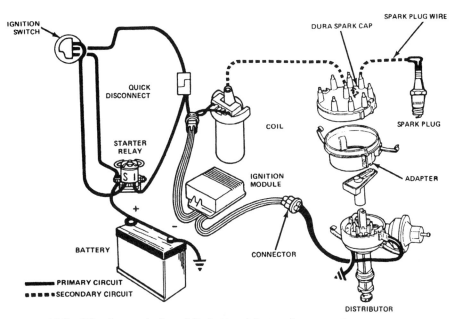

IGNITION SWITCH

QUICK DISCONNECT

STARTER RELAY

BATTERY

COIL

IGNITION MODULE

CONNECTOR

SPARK PLUG WIRE

DURA SPARK CAP

SPARK PLUG

ADAPTER

DISTRIBUTOR

▬▬▬ PRIMARY CIRCUIT
■ ■ ■ ■ SECONDARY CIRCUIT

10-3 Distributor shaft and its battery/electronic connections. Ford Motor Co.

necessary to back off on the rotor some *two* gear notches—about 1/4 of a turn (here counterclockwise since the distributor turns counterclockwise, too) before attempting to reseat the shaft. As the shaft and gears mesh with the crankshaft and its gears, the rotor will once again assume the correct position, as will the pointing direction of the vacuum advance enclosure.

What you're not told by writers of some of these instructions is that the crankshaft and distributor gears often don't want to mate freely because the shaft hangs up on a little oil-pump stub it must accommodate. After an hour or so of trying to back off two turns on the rotor while keeping the vacuum advance pointed properly, you suddenly find that one additional gear notch will allow the assemblies to mate. Just fall for that little gimmick and you'll be in a lot worse trouble. If the gears don't mesh properly, the engine won't start, backfiring through the carburetor will occur, and you'll be positive the old jitney has seen its last. But had you remained two positions counterclockwise with the rotor and "bumped" the engine with either its starter or an external, hand-held switch and applied a little pressure to the distributor's top, the shaft and its gears would have dropped right in.

Otherwise, pull out the No. 1 spark plug, locate the top dead center (Fig. 10-4) (TC or TDC) on the crankshaft pulley, and then "bump" the engine over until you hear and feed a rush of air, denoting high compression. Since this occurs before TDC, you can then continue to bump the engine further until it reaches the TDC mark, or a couple of degrees, one

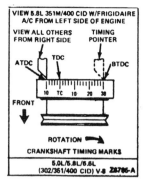

10-4 Timing marks on crankshaft for before top dead center, on, and after top dead center. Ford Motor Co.

way or the other. (Some mechanics stick their finger in the No. 1 plug hole, but this might not be necessary if there's plenty of compression.) You might (and probably will) have to repeat this procedure three or four times before compression and TDC are one; but afterwards, it's a simple matter to back off two gears and aim the distributor rotor so that it falls into place pointed at the No. 1 cylinder wire mark located on *top* the distributor. If the two gears are still stubborn, "bump" the engine again and all should seat comfortably. Should you still be out a single gear rotation, lift the shaft once more and compensate one gear turn in the appropriate direction. Replace the lockdown bolt, turn the vacuum advance to its original position, and the jalopy should once again become alive and kicking.

So with a new O ring installed, the oil leak should stop at once. But wait a couple of days to see. Mine, unfortunately did not, but for a very good reason.

Manifold gaskets

If your manifold gaskets leak, you're very likely to have puddles of oil and cooling fluid on either side of the distributor (at least this is what occurs on the Cougar XR-7). You add a few drops of oil now and then and extra coolant to the radiator where levels continue to fall as the problem increases. And when replaced, all leakage halts and the top of your engine stops accumulating the usual dirty grime associated with such fluid.

There are two manifolds: the intake and exhaust manifolds. Think of them as valved chambers. The first is active on a cylinder's downstroke (Fig. 10-5), and the second is operational on the up or exhaust stroke. Of the two, the intake manifold is by far the most important because it directly supplies the necessary vacuum for the entire engine. Lose or impair this vacuum and you have trouble with exhaust gas recirculation, the carburetor, vacuum advance, automatic choke, snorkel vacuum motor, temperature sensor, etc. (see Fig. 10-6). In short, without the necessary vacuum, this type of engine should measure between 16 and 22 Hg (inches of mercury) at sea level, but allow about one inch less for each 1,000 feet *above* sea level. A complete vacuum would measure 30 Hg. This "average"

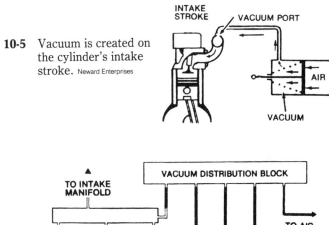

10-5 Vacuum is created on the cylinder's intake stroke. Neward Enterprises

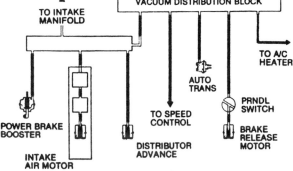

10-6 Typical vacuum distribution system. Neward Enterprises

reading for a gasoline engine, therefore, is just over half a perfect vacuum and is highly important to the proper operation of your vehicle. Furthermore, the Hg reading must be taken at some direct entrance to the manifold and not through ancillary hoses that may have vacuum motors or possible air leaks.

With new gaskets installed, the engine idled considerably better and very smoothly, indicating both circulatory and vacuum loss resulted from intake manifold leakage. So that portion of the "rebuilding" was seemingly complete.

Another sooty spark plug

Shortly after the gasket replacement, however, I noted the engine seemed to lose some power and began running a little roughly. By pulling a few plug wire connectors (no scope this time), I soon discovered plug No. 8 was fouled with a sooty, black mixture that was perfectly dry. In this instance, too rich a fuel mixture was indicated, and I backed off on the thermal choke spring so the shock plate would again open wide with a normally operating engine at full temperature (Fig. 10-7).

That seemed to cure the problem of rough running, and I was even able to save the plug by sand blasting with an air-driven unit that cleaned away the entire dark-coated surface from the center and ground electrodes

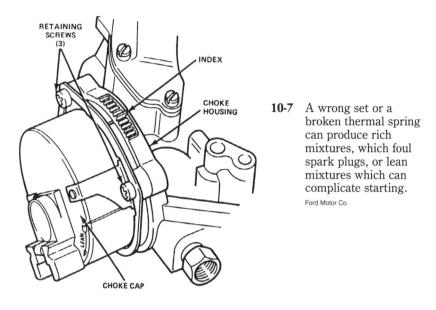

RETAINING
SCREWS
(3)

INDEX

CHOKE
HOUSING

CHOKE CAP

10-7 A wrong set or a broken thermal spring can produce rich mixtures, which foul spark plugs, or lean mixtures which can complicate starting. Ford Motor Co.

as well as the insulator. If this convenient equipment isn't available, a new plug is usually required. Also, anyone else afflicted with such a problem had best recheck the lean/rich choke plate settings before inviting a whole set of plug replacements. You might also have a look at the connecting tube between manifold and auto choke assembly. This can become carbon-clogged just like the EGR valve, rendering the sensitive choke spring largely ineffective. Simply disconnect and clean it out with forced air or a stiff brush.

And by all means, check the EGR valve (Fig. 10-8) while you're at it. Instead of improving these exhaust gas recirculation necessities, manufacturing seems to have even less quality control than before, along with higher prices. In checking the action of the diaphram and "valve," pulling the vacuum line on and off at advanced speed will give some indication, but the best method I've found is to apply a vacuum between 2 to 8.5 Hg (inches of mercury) and see if the valve opens. If not, you'll buy a new one—metal support frame, gasket and all at considerable loot. *Note*: Since backpressure from the manifold aids, vacuum alone won't do the job.

A Mityvac to the rescue

For some reason, many amateurs and some vocational automobile mechanics don't use vacuum pumps to diagnose a variety of ills in the highly important vacuum system (Fig. 10-9). It's a reliable way of discovering both good and bad component functions and saving a great deal of problematical guesswork, especially in sticky situations where "guesti-mates" could go either way. Yes, you do have to go by the book, but a users

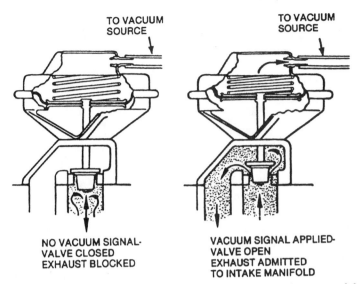

TO VACUUM
SOURCE

TO VACUUM
SOURCE

NO VACUUM SIGNAL-
VALVE CLOSED
EXHAUST BLOCKED

VACUUM SIGNAL APPLIED-
VALVE OPEN
EXHAUST ADMITTED
TO INTAKE MANIFOLD

10-8 Exhaust gas recirculation valves are tricky but essential. They help burn nitrogen oxides but can also produce pinging problems when diaphragms are either punctured or leaky.
Neward Enterprises

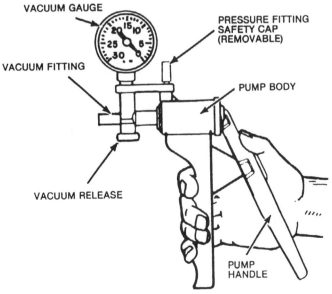

VACUUM GAUGE

PRESSURE FITTING
SAFETY CAP
(REMOVABLE)

VACUUM FITTING

PUMP BODY

VACUUM RELEASE

PUMP
HANDLE

10-9 The Mitivac pump is not expensive but is essential in evaluating all vacuum systems. Neward Enterprises manual with 96 numbered pages packs a remarkable amount of information. I'll give you some examples, after first explaining that at sea level, maximum expected vacuum ranges between 23 and 25 Hg, and in combustion engine vehicles, vacuum "motors," often compared to servos, supply controls to the EGR valve, brake boosters, air cleaner, automatic transmissions, cruise controls, carburetion, automatic chokes, timing advances, and so forth. Vacuum, therefore, and its tube or other passage ports and constrictor fittings to various parts of the engine, is a pretty important consideration in evaluating general engine performance. A clogged port or leaky hose can produce some highly undesirable effects that extend far beyond simple spark plugs and an occasional EGR valve.

Manifold examination   The manifold is the first check you'll want to make to be sure the "source" is producing what it should. Connect your instrument directly to a manifold port and, with the engine warm and idling, you should read from 16 to 21 inches of mercury. As Mityvac points out, if the intake vacuum motor isn't functional or leaking, carburetor air mix during warmup can be either too hot or cold and result in stalls (cold) or burned spark plugs, exhaust valves, and even pistons (hot).

Servo motors   Servo motors have either single or double diaphrams (Fig. 10-10), but both operate the same way: with no vacuum applied, they're spring loaded and block passage; when a vacuum is applied, the spring tension is overcome and the "motor" opens to allow conventional operation such as through passage of whatever's permitting to flow. Just connect your Mityvac and deliver the necessary vacuum. The servo either operates or it doesn't—as simple as that. Approximately 10 Hg should be sufficient.

Hoses   Hoses are always the main problem in any vacuum line. They might be old, brittle, oversized, poorly connected, or even severed. To check, simply use forced air at one end, hold the other, and judge or measure any air escape, preferably while bending or flexing. Here, a vacuum probably isn't a tough enough test. But with the hose blocked at one end and forced air from a pump at the other, you'll soon know its condition.

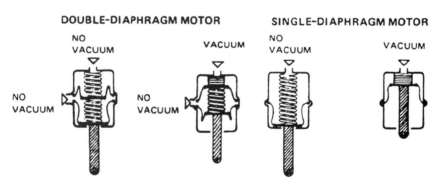

10-10   Single- and double-diaphragm vacuum motors. Neward Enterprises

With motor at idling speed vacuum pointer should hold steady between 15 and 21.

With motor at idling speed dropping back of vacuum pointer indicates sticky valves.

With motor at idling speed floating motion right and left of vacuum pointer indicates carburetor too rich or too lean.

With motor at idling speed low reading of vacuum pointer indicates late timing or intake manifold air leak

10-11 Vacuum gauge readings can indicate many engine faults. Neward Enterprises

Vacuum gauge signs When connected directly to the manifold (Fig. 10-11) vacuum gauges tell more than fairy tales. For instance, a floating gauge pointer indicates a too rich or too lean carburetor operation; lower-than-normal readings and pointer drop-backs can be sticky valves; lower-than-normal vacuum suggests manifold air leak or late timing; weak valve springs cause rapid pointer fluctuations between 10 and 21 Hg; leaky piston rings show little vacuum gain between idle and high engine rpm; similarly, exhaust problems won't show at idle but appear at greater engine speeds as the pointer drops toward zero; leaks in the intake manifold result in 3 to 9 Hg lower readings, but the pointer remains steady. If your vehicle has can or belt-driven vacuum pumps, all input and output hoses can be disconnected and plugged, the output port left open, and the Mitivac connected to the inlet. After a minute, with engine idling, the reading should remain a steady 20 Hg. Electric pumps, on the other hand, run for a time until vacuum is established and then shut down. Either intermittent operation at random or continuous running indicates a defect and the pump must be removed and tested outside the vehicle.

Vacuum advance The vacuum advance is maximum at engine idle, while at higher speeds there has to be a way for internal combustion to occur at approximately top dead center (TDC) as each piston reaches maximum thrust. At idle, distributor spark voltage is required immediately before TDC, but under load and higher rpms, spark needs to appear earlier since there is less time for cylinder mixtures to combust and burn.

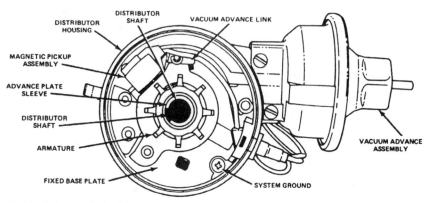

DISTRIBUTOR
HOUSING

DISTRIBUTOR
SHAFT

VACUUM ADVANCE LINK

MAGNETIC PICKUP
ASSEMBLY

ADVANCE PLATE
SLEEVE

DISTRIBUTOR
SHAFT

ARMATURE

FIXED BASE PLATE

SYSTEM GROUND

VACUUM ADVANCE
ASSEMBLY

10-12 Electronic ignition systems have produced many changes, especially in the distributor and spark advance. Ford Motor Co.

Consequently, there has to be less vacuum advance and quicker spark so the distributor can fire each cylinder more rapidly.

In electronic systems, the old centrifugal mechanical advance doesn't exist any more, and vacuum advance assumes spark advance responsibility (Fig. 10-12). Instead of breaker points and even mechanical centrifugal advance mechanisms, electronic ignitions have a toothed wheel that Ford identifies as an *armature*. A magnetic unit replaces the old breaker points.

In eight-cylinder automobiles, there are eight armature points that appear as "tooths," a permanent magnet, pickup, and an external electronic module. As each tooth passes, an electrical signal is introduced into the pickup coil delivering current to the system. But when an armature tooth and pickup are aligned, the electronic module is turned off, current flow ceases, and the secondary of the high-voltage inductor reverses current and generates high voltage for the various spark plugs that must fire as each piston reaches top dead center. And this is why the timing position of the distributor is so very important; these armatures and their mechanical distributor shaft and its gears must all coincide to produce a smoothly operating engine, and there must be no spark ping or knock with acceleration. If an accurate timing check (with loose vacuum hoses plugged) still produces those annoying pings and you're using proper fuel, then immediately check the EGR valve and you should find your trouble.

Yes, some of these problems are complex during initial attempts, but with a little practice and theory of operation understanding, solutions become considerably easier the second time around. As an example, when your engine is idling, pull off the vacuum advance hose and watch the engine slow down. And if you want to pass a state automobile inspection, be positive that all choke and timing adjustments meet manufacturer's specs, and be sure your air and breather element filters are clean and the positive crankcase ventilation valve (PCV) has been recently changed. A good tuneup just beforehand helps too, and could well save you a return trip to Tailpipe Village.

Knocks and pings

Knocks and pings are never a pleasant subject for even many mechanics, because problems beyond basic tuneups—timing, PVC, the various filters (including gas filter), and spark wires and plugs—are often very difficult to handle. This is particularly true for disturbances deep in the engine. An auto stethoscope and a good deal of experience are often required to distinguish between loose manifolds, main bearings, and even some cylinder slaps. Piston rings, fortunately or otherwise, wear thin and leak, or break and raise havoc, and the blue smoke out of a tailpipe is usually enough of a clue. Conversely, black smoke, upon startup or fast acceleration, often signifies nothing more than excess carbon buildup. Several tanks of high test gas or good gas additive normally dissolves this difficulty. But simple cures are far from appropriate when crankshafts, rods, and bearings are involved. For without these heavyweights properly lubricated and in non-wear conditions, the rest of the engine can be virtually perfect, but your vehicle is not long for the road.

Such noises often involve either the camshaft or crankshaft (Fig. 10-13), the former moving at half the speed of the latter. If the sound is erratic, it probably means trouble in one of the belt-driven "motors" such as the alternator, fan, or water pump. If you're in motion when this problem occurs, just switch off the engine and coast for a few seconds in neutral. Any remaining noise is not from the engine. Loose flywheels can also be detected by alternately switching the engine off and on while listening for a rather loud knock. A rattling knock that begins with some volume and then fades can result from a piece of carbon between piston and cylinder head.

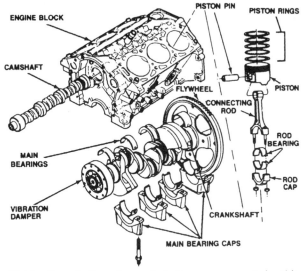

10-13 Camshaft and crankshaft are apparent in this illustration of engine-block components. Ford Motor Co.

But if your engine idles quietly and seems to " clatter" as the throttle is advanced to high rpms, look out! And if you've ignored this warning and continued to drive the vehicle for x miles thereafter, you've probably bought yourself either a new or rebuilt powerplant.

When does all this occur? It could happen any time, but more often when your trusty roadster is approaching 100,000 miles. If you're lucky, a bearing kit installed by the very experienced mechanic will save the day at a cost to you of a mere $500 to $600. But if the engine block is damaged, another engine could easily set you back $2,000 or more, depending on both labor charges and the rebuilder. Here, inquiries and estimates from 4 to 6 "good" sources, reinforced by well-intended recommendations, will steer you toward the most competent and frugal repair facility. When new engines or crankshaft repairs are needed, only those who handle such jobs regularly should be considered. Guarantees are usually 12 months or 12,000 miles, whichever comes first, for your new power plant. Shops with outstanding reputations that handle both trucks and automobiles are the more desirable because they're used to heavy, difficult work and have the necessary lifts and tools available. In Maryland, rebuilt (everything new except the block) engines cost $1,500 plus tax. Then add another few hundred for brakes, an EGR valve, brake pads, and a choke spring, and you're pretty close to $2,000 anyway. It all depends, thereafter, on vehicle body condition, springs, shocks, front end, etc., as to whether you really want to spend this much on an old jalopy.

Considering that many $20,000 automobiles don't even last 10 years, $2,000 might even put you ahead of the game. Certainly the insurance rates will be at least half, and anyone who can do simple maintenance should keep it running for well over 100,000 miles, possibly 200,000. Do, however, keep it in the garage, change oil and lube it every 3,000 miles, and backflush the cooling system every two years and then add new fluid. Your car and your pocketbook will be glad you did!

The new ones are different

In the 1990s, better everything seems to be taking over, at least among the more representative vehicles. There are more reliable and useful electronics, interiors are much quieter, fuel injection promotes higher efficiency and performance, tires deliver more mileage, seating and riding comforts have improved, and you are still obtaining good value for your money when shopping wisely and competitively at three or more dealers.

To stay in business, each auto or truck merchandiser has to make a profit, but take care you aren't victimized. In one recent instance, having the sales manager "review" his salesman's figures saved one buyer a cool $400. "Bait and switch" is another familiar tactic at some of the more aggressive dealers where fast tongues and diversionary tactics can often cost the unwary a real bundle. It's better to pay a little more to a reliable dealer if they know the product and can give you valuable advice rather than take "lowest bidder" from anyone. Service counts for considerably more after the sale than before because a slick sales pitch never yet repaired a slipping transmission or oil pressure problem. And the new 5- to 6-year warranties on engine and power trains avoids the necessity of extended warranties for a lot more money.

We have also found that paying cash with no trades helps the net dollar cause considerably, and those who can calmly wait for one or two months can usually save more by ordering only what they specifically want on their new auto or truck. Occasionally, however, that certain vehicle sits on their favorite dealer's lot, inventory floorplanning does become expensive, and he just might be willing to make you a real deal on the spot. Just keep your eyes peeled and billfold in a tight fist. In the end, you and the dealer may become fast friends, with considerable benefit to both.

Fuel injection

By far the greatest innovation in recent years has been the introduction and relative perfection of fuel injection (Fig. 10-14) and the elimination of carburetion. Engine performance has been vastly improved; automatic starting without accelerator mashing, a genuine relief; and even eight-cylinder idle smoothness has been restored without painstaking adjustments of old carburetor needle valves. Who says automobiles haven't been improved?

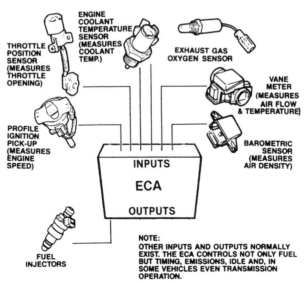

10-14 Components of a typical Ford electronic fuel-injection system. Monitors constantly meter air-flow, temperature, and other sensors.

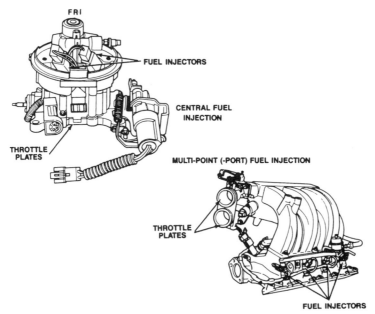

10-15 Two types of fuel injection in general use today: CFI and multipoint. Ford Motor Co.

Here, outside air mixes with fuel via engine vacuum and the combination is injected under pressure into the various cylinders under rigid electronic control. Systems may be either multipoint or central fuel injectors, with each actually doing the same thing (Fig. 10-15). In CFI, one or two fuel injectors are mounted in the fuel assembly on top the intake manifold. In EFI multipoint (or multiport), injectors are on the bottom of the intake manifold and direct fuel into each intake valve.

Each injector has a solenoid and valve assembly, electrical connectors, filter (Fig. 10-16), coil, armature, and a valve at the bottom called a pintle. Injector open time determines fuel feed, and this, in turn, depends on engine idle, load, speed, etc. Electrical sensors monitor engine operations and include air entry and its temperature, throttle, coolant status, air density, engine speed, exhaust gas oxygen content, all of which is collected and processed by the electronic control assembly (ECA).

The electronic control assembly then reacts to these inputs, telling the injectors when and how long to remain open, while maintaining the proper air/fuel ratio throughout. Should fuel pressure become high, resulting in an overrich mixture, the ECA can channel excess petrol away from the injectors and back to the main tank. If pressure becomes too low, a lean mixture will be strengthened by additional fuel flow.

Turbo and superchargers

Both are used for higher power output rather than merely increasing

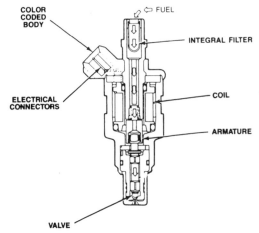

10-16 A fuel injector and its various parts. The coil (or *solenoid*) opens and closes the pintle valve to regulate fuel flow. Ford Motor Co.

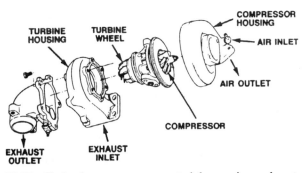

10-17 Turbochargers are operated by engine exhaust gases. Ford Motor Co.

engine displacement, which requires additional fuel and larger engines. They are different as night and day, but both do deliver greater engine efficiency by straightforward mechanical additions. The turbocharger (Fig. 10-17) consists of exhaust outlet and inlet, a turbine wheel, compressor and air inlet and outlet. The engine's exhaust gases spin a turbine, then a compressor, to move additional air into the combustion chambers. As speeds increase, air and fuel mixtures are further compressed so that cylinders derive greater power upon combustion. Called "turbo boost," it is not as effective as one might want at low speeds because of low exhaust gases, but at higher speeds, the system is quite effective.

The supercharger, conversely (Fig. 10-18), is driven by an engine's crankshaft, usually via belts or pulleys. Its charge remains constant regardless of speed, so that effectiveness is uniform whenever in use. But there is engine power loss due to the air compressor's being driven by the crankshaft. Some systems cool the hot, compressed air with an intercooler

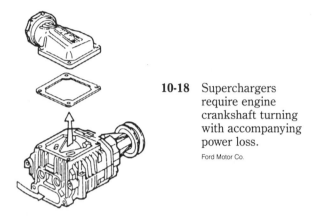

10-18   Superchargers require engine crankshaft turning with accompanying power loss.

Ford Motor Co.

before it enters the combustion cycle, thereby making it denser for additional fuel mix and efficiency. Intercoolers may be thought of as heat exchangers or even simple radiators.

Service precautions

While the newer automobiles and trucks are designed to operate on regular 87-octane unleaded gas, fuels without the necessary cleaning additives will eventually clog fuel injectors. Usually, such additives adequately dissolve "varnish" found on standard carburetor throttle plates, often called "butterflies." If not, Ford and also Wynn have available liquid cleaners that can do the job. A higher octane gasoline such as 89 or 91 will deliver better mileage and engine efficiency than the usual 87.

While today's engine displacements are usually measured in liter metric systems, some of you still may remember the English cubic inch terminology common to the U.S. for so many years. Table 10-1 provides a few conversions. Using simple arithmetic division, 1 liter equals approximately 61 cubic inches.

You might also like to know that compression ratio is simply the volume of air-gas compressed in a single cylinder between a piston's top and bottom dead centers. The greater the compression, the more power an engine develops. Gas engines usually have compression ratios of 9:1, according to Ford.

Table 10-1. Cubic-inch/liter equivalents

In^3	Liters
114	1.9
182	3.0
300	4.9
302	5.0
350	5.7
460	7.5

Troubleshooting probe

For those who can't or won't use an oscilloscope and standard logic equipment, the best and simplest electronics tester for trucks and automobiles seems to be the logic probe (Fig. 10-19). Available in input impedances ranging from 100 kilohms to 1 megohm, accompanying literature says it operates as a level and pulse detector, pulse stretcher, single-shot detector with memory, all indicated by red/green high/low fast LEDs, accompanied by a level switch for DTL/TTL and CMOS. These logic symbols stand for diode-transistor logic, transistor-transistor logic, and complementary metal oxide (gate) semiconductor. Similarly to bipolar logic, MOSFETS are p and n doped, according to positive or negative inputs and battery requirements. My particular logic probe from E&L Instruments/Global Specialties (New Haven, CT) can operate at 30 mA and 5 V, 40 mA and 15 V, and up to 30 V maximum (with power lead reverse protection). For logic swings to 2.25 V for DTL/TTL and 70 percent of V_{DD} for HTL/CMOS, a logic 1 (high) is represented; and for a 0.80 V, a logic 0 is registered for the bipolars and 30 percent for HTL/CMOS. The unit should never monitor signals in excess of 16 volts or contact secondary ignition emissions. Comprehensive 1,000-page student manuals are available with slide-together circuit modules for realistic testing of many automotive functions in addition to ordinary logic. Some of these are fuse and switch panels, power connections, cables, lamps, dc motors, solenoid, relays, turn signals, and so forth. Board power originates from an ac-to-dc supply that delivers both 12.6 and 14.5 volts simulating engine on and off conditions. Wire jumpers on each board are designed to replicate breakdowns, helping students to learn.

To avoid confusion, I might add that a logic 1 condition in positive logic is when the n-type semiconductor is not conducting and voltage rises to the "rails." A logic 0 occurs during hard conduction, just above common "ground." In negative logic (with p-type devices), the reverse is true because conduction or otherwise takes place between some negative potential and ground. Logic, unfortunately, is precisely the converse of analog ac and dc measurements that term maximum amplitudes "highs" rather than "lows." Unfortunately, you must master both concepts to work in today's electromechanics. Shifty analogs and rigid digits are everywhere.

In the LP-1 probe, pulse widths are detectable up to 50 nanoseconds, but LP-3 can see 15 nanoseconds widths and frequencies of 35 MHz as opposed to 10 MHz for the slower unit. In the LP-3, impedance inputs are

10-19 Convenient and useful logic probe for auto and allied electronics troubleshooting. Global Specialties (Interplex Electronics)

1 MHz rather than 100 kHz as in the LP-1, and E & L claims such impedances are constant across the frequency range. Operating temperatures are 0 to 50° C.

The LP-1 probe tip connects to a dual threshold "window" of operation comparator and a bipolar rising and falling edge detector. The comparator bias circuits logic threshold levels, while the bipolar edge detector measures positive and negative logic transitions and energizes a pulse stretcher. This circuit converts level changes and sharp pulses to $1/3$ of a second displays to drive one of the three high/low/pulse light-emitting diodes (LEDs). In the memory mode, such an output reaches a latching flip-flop and is stored so that low repetition rate or single-shot pulses and transients can be retained for future display. Operating dc power energizes the device through red ($+$) and black ($-$) leads attached to a cable and then to the LP-1. As long as there are high/low state changes, logic is operating. Its accompanying manual describes these conditions and others in between.

The real information, however, comes from E & L's Automatic Electronics Program, which covers the automotive parking lot. Otherwise, the probe can be used on any medium-speed logic setup as long as it doesn't load the output. The LP-3 would seem to be a better choice than the LP-1 for that reason, but it probably costs more. However, if you think 100 kilohms impedance will work, go for it!

The probe can be used in comparable electronics in other systems, including some television and possibly satellite positioner and skew control pulse circuits. Digital TV should be a natural for go/no-go applications in T^2L and ECL. For CMOS, however, you need at least 1-megohm input impedance to prevent FET loading. Just keep a 12 V power supply handy for source voltage. Max current drain should only be about 50 mA, so almost any little auxiliary plug-in-the-wall should satisfy.

Auto radios

Even automobile radios have made considerable progress from the straight FM/AM units of a few years back. The better ones today are both AM stereo and FM stereo, as well as full-frequency units with excellent front/rear speakers that make music listening on the road a real companion and a pleasure. Many of these radios also have a station seeking feature that permits lock-tuning to the stronger broadcast stations, and even further improvement in FM stereo sound.

This latter sound subject is of considerable importance because noise is further reduced, stereo effects maintained over wider frequency ranges, while improving adjacent channel rejection.

Most stereo FM systems usually "blend" toward monophonic when noise is evident in the intermediate frequency amplifiers (IFs) following the tuner. This immediately reduces stereophonic outputs and permits largely mono information to reach the speakers.

The SPRAGUE Semiconductor Group has recently developed a pair of ULN3800A and ULN3800 FM/FMX stereo decoders that actually extend the FM range and offer up to a 14 dB advantage in signal-to-noise (S/N) ratio, providing a considerable 45 dB mid-range stereo separation "even under low signal-level conditions." (See Fig. 10-20.)

Quieter FM stereo by Sprague develops from a very different approach. Normally there's a quiet zone about the 19 kHz stereo pilot. This frequency area is monitored and detected with the appearance of noise, and a dual bandwidth phase-locked loop switches to a narrow bandwidth for best phase stability. Stereo separation is then adjusted according to the S/N ratio, reducing low signal background noise and smoothly blending the necessary crossover point between mono and stereo where required. Consequently, pilot and 38 kHz carriers are not affected by 3rd and 5th harmonics as they would be if detection occurred in the higher kilohertz regions.

The FMX companding noise reduction system (Fig. 10-21) does not disturb the usual right L + R and left L − R (stereo) information but also adds a second L − R signal in quadrature that's not detected by standard FM receivers. This is a 10 Hz quadrature pilot used for switching and spe-

ULN3800A

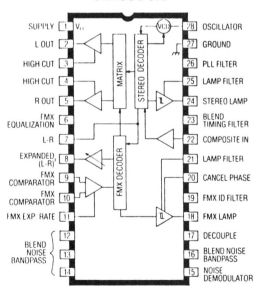

10-20 Pinout of the integrated circuit that produces excellent stereo separation and reduces noise. <small>Allegro Microsystems (formerly Sprague)</small>

FUNCTIONAL BLOCK DIAGRAM

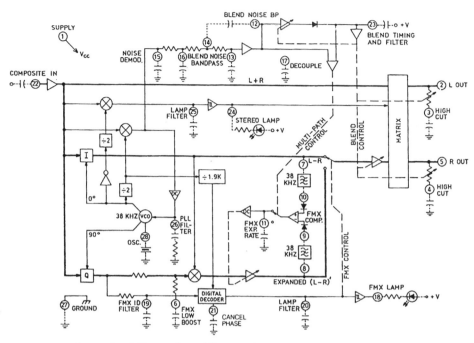

10-21 Operational illustration of Sprague's super stereo system. Allegro Microsystems

cial identification needs. As you can see from both the functional block
and the IC pinout diagrams, there's considerably more to this noise reducing system than I can report here. But if a demonstration of the system (or
its inclusion in a good radio) should be handy, you'll recognize the very
considerable difference at once.

AM stereo

Before ending the chapter, I'd like to invite further attention to AM stereo
radio that's now offered primarily as an option in many of the deluxe automobile receivers. In another several years, this AM companion will probably be just as standard as FM stereo because the number of stations
throughout the U.S. and foreign countries has grown considerably since
the Federal Communications Commission weaseled its way out of approv-
ing a single AM stereo system in its ambivalent "open market" decision of
March 4, 1982.

The result has been almost a ruinous contest between several AM pro-
ponents for a number of years, with Motorola's C-QUAM finally emerging
as the winner both here and abroad. I feel it was truly a bad decision with
disastrous consequences that delayed an important broadcast medium from

reaching worthwhile market coverage for almost a decade. And although there are still a number of automobiles not initially blessed, General Motors, Ford, Lincoln, Chrysler, Saab, Toyota, Volvo, Acura, Jeep, Mitsubishi, and Nissan purchasers can be so equipped if required. Now that FCC Commissioner James Quello has endorsed C-QUAM, the FCC may eventually approve this one system also. Home radios should be similarly available shortly now that the National Association of Broadcasters has endorsed it, too.

Having listened to "rolling" AM stereo for the past two years in trips around and across the country, there's usually at least one broadcaster per city that offers this added luxury. Not that it will supplant the wider-band FM stereo, but for distance and snap/fade avoidance, AM stereo does have its advantages. Table 10-2 is a list of the AM stereo broadcast stations as supplied by Motorola.

**Table 10-2. Motorola
C-QUAM AM stereo listing**

USA	514	Australia	73
Canada	66	Other	34
Total stations on the air			687

UNITED STATES

ALABAMA			ALASKA			CALIFORNIA		
			Anchorage	KHAR	590	Anaheim	KPZE	1190
Athens	WVNN	770	Juno	KINY	800	Bakersfield	KUZZ	550
Atmore	WASG	1140				Catalina	KBRT	740
Decatur	WAVD	1400	ARIZONA			Chico	KHSL	1290
Flomation	WRBK	1090				Fresno	KFRE	940
Florence	WSBM	1340	Phoenix	KMEO	740	Folsom	KKSA	1030
Fort Payne	WFPA	1400	Phoenix	KOOL	960	Hesperia	KSHO	540
Gadsden	WJBY	930	Sedona	KAZM	780	Los Angeles	KFI	640
Huntsville	WBHP	1230	Tempe	KNIX	1580	Los Angeles	KFWB	980
Jacksonville	WJXL	810	Tucson	KAIR	1490	Los Angeles	KIIS	1150
Jasper	WARF	1240	Tucson	KTZR	1450	Los Angeles	KMPC	710
Jasper	WWWB	1360	Tucson	KTKT	990	Los Angeles	KNX	1070
Mobile	WGOK	900				Los Angeles	KSKQ	1540
Muscle Shoals	WLAY	1450				Los Angeles	KLAC	570
Phenix City	WPNX	1460	ARKANSAS			Los Angeles	KWKW	1300
Russelville	WJRD	1150				Los Banos	KLBS	1330
Mobile	WGRR	960	Dermott	KXSA	1110	Modesto	KHYV	970
Tuscaloosa	WACT	1420	Farmington	KFAY	1030	Oxnard	KOXR	910
Valley Head	WQRX	870	Forth Smith	KFSA	950	Palmdale	KUTY	1470

Table 10-2 Continued

CALIFORNIA(continued)

City	Call	Freq
Palm Springs	KPSL	1010
Palm Springs	KDES	920
Pasadena	KRLA	1110
Redding	KRDG	1330
Redlands	KCAL	1410
Sacramento	KGNR	1320
Sacramento	KRAK	1140
San Diego	KCBQ	1170
San Diego	KFMB	760
San Francisco	KKHI	1550
San Francisco	KSFO	560
San Francisco	KABL	960
San Mateo	KOFY	1050
Santa Barbara	KESP	1290
Santa Barbara	KIST	1340
Santa Barbara	KKSB	990
Santa Maria	KGDP	660
Santa Maria	KSMA	1240
Santa Rosa	KRRS	1460
Santa Rosa	KPLS	1150
Stockton	KJOY	1280

COLORADO

City	Call	Freq
Denver	KEZW	1430
Denver	KLZ	560
Denver	KLSC	1090
Denver	KIMN	950
Manitou	KRYN	1490
Monument	KKRE	1040
Pueblo	KIDN	1350

CONNECTICUT

City	Call	Freq
Danbury	WLAD	800
Greenwich	WGCH	1490
Hartford	WDRC	1360
Hartford	WTIC	1080
New Haven	WNNR	1220
Sharon	WKZE	1020
Waterbury	WQQW	1590

DELAWARE

City	Call	Freq
Wilmington	WDEL	1150

FLORIDA

City	Call	Freq
Bradenton	WBRD	1420
Chiefland	WLQH	940
Ft. Myers	WDCQ	1200
Jacksonville	WRXJ	930
Jacksonville	WFYV	1460
Key West	WKIZ	1500
Melborne	WMEL	920
Miami	WCMQ	1210
Miami	WIOD	610
Miami	WWFE	670
Miami	WQAM	560
Milton	WEBY	1330
Ocala	WMOP	900
Ocala	WOCA	1370
Orlando	WHOO	990
Panama City	WGNE	590
Plant City	WPLA	910
Pompano Beach	WWHR	980
Sarasota	WSGX	1280
Seffner	WQYK	1010
St. Petersburg	WPLP	570
St. Petersburg	WSUN	620
Tampa	WQHK	1010
Wildwood	WHOF	640

GEORGIA

City	Call	Freq
Albany	WGPC	1450
Albany	WJAZ	960
Athens	WRFC	960
Athens	WGAU	1340
Atlanta	WSB	750
Atlanta	WKHX	590
Atlanta	WQXI	790
Atlanta	WGKA	1190
Augusta	WRDW	1480
Columbus	WDAK	540

GEORGIA(continued)

City	Call	Freq
Dalton	WLSQ	1430
Gainsville	WGGA	1240
Macon	WMAZ	940
Perry	WPGA	980
Savannah	WCHY	1290
Smyrna	WYNX	1550
Thomasville	WPAX	1240
Valdosta	WFVR	910
Vidalia	WVOP	970
Waycross	WAYX	1230
Rome	WIYN	1360

HAWAII

City	Call	Freq
Honolulu	KIKI	830
Honolulu	KQMQ	690

IDAHO

City	Call	Freq
Boise	KBOI	670
Boise	KGEM	1140
Idaho Falls	KUPI	980
Pocatello	KWIK	1240

ILLINOIS

City	Call	Freq
Aurora	WKKD	1580
Chicago	WGN	720
Chicago	WXEZ	820
Chicago	WGCI	1390
Chicago	WIND	560
Chicago	WBBM	780
Chicago	WMAQ	670
East St. Louis	WESL	1490
Elmhurst	WKDC	1530
LaGrange	WTAQ	1300
Marion	WDDD	810
Metropolis	WMOK	920
Paris	WPRS	1440
Peoria	WMBD	1470
Rockford	WROK	1440
Sterling	WSDR	1240

INDIANA

Bloomington	WGCL	1370
Columbus	WCSI	1010
Evansville	WGBF	1280
Ft. Wayne	WEZR	1450
Ft. Wayne	WQHK	1380
Indianapolis	WIRE	1430
Indianapolis	WNDE	1260
Indianapolis	WIBC	1070
Marion	WGOM	860
North Vernon	WNVI	1460
South Bend	WSBT	960

IOWA

Cedar Rapids	WMT	600
Clinton	KROS	1340
Des Moines	KSO	1460
Mason City	KGLO	1300
Mason City	KRIB	1490
Sioux City	KWSL	1470

KANSAS

Hays	KAYS	1400
Wichita	KFDI	1070

KENTUCKY

Danville	WHIR	1230
Gray	WKYZ	1590
Hazard	WKIC	1390
Hazard	WYZQ	1560
Henderson	WSON	860
Lexington	WLXG	1300
Lexington	WVLK	590
Louisville	WHAS	840
Madisonville	WFMW	730
Madisonville	WTTL	1310
Middlesboro	WFXY	1490
Newport	WNOP	740
Nicholasville	WCQW	770
Owensboro	WVJS	1420
Paducah	WKYX	570

KENTUCKY (continued)

Paintsville	WKLW	600
Pikeville	WPKE	1240
Richmond	WEKY	1340
Somerset	WSFC	1240

LOUISIANA

Alexandria	KSYL	970
Crowley	KSIG	1450
Denham Springs	WBIU	1220
Garyville	WCKW	1010
Hammond	WFPR	1400
Jennings	KJEF	1290
Lafayette	KXKW	1520
Lake Charles	KXZZ	1580
Leesville	KLLA	1570
Monroe	KNOE	540
New Orleans	WNOE	1060
New Iberia	KANE	1240
Pineville	KKLC	1110
Rayville	KXLA	990
Shreveport	KEEL	710
Shreveport	KOKA	1550
Shreveport	KRMD	1340
Sulphur	KEZM	1310
Thibodaux	KTIB	630
West Monroe	KMBS	1310

MAINE

Gardiner	WABK	1280
Gorham	WJBQ	1590
Lewiston	WLAM	1470
Rockland	WRKD	1450

MARYLAND

Annapolis	WANN	1190
Baltimore	WWIN	1400
Brunswick	WTRI	1520
Cumberland	WTBO	1450
Frederick	WFMD	930
Indian Head	WBZE	1030

MASSACHUSETTS

Boston	WBZ	1030
Boston	WMEX	1150
Marlboro	WSRO	1470
Springfield	WHYN	560
Westfield	WNNZ	640
West Yarmouth	WOCB	1240
Worcester	WORC	1310
Worcester	WTAG	580

MICHIGAN

Ann Arbor	WAAM	1600
Big Rapids	WBRN	1460
Benton Harbor	WHFB	1060
Detroit	WJR	760
Detroit	WCXI	1130
Grand Rapids	WCUZ	1230
Grand Rapids	WOOD	1300
Jackson	WJCO	1510
Kalamazoo	WQSN	1470
Lansing	WITL	1010
Monroe	WHND	560
Mt. Pleasant	WMMI	830
Saginaw	WSAM	1400
Ypsilanti	WWCM	990

MINNESOTA

Aitkin	KKIN	930
Hibbing	WKKQ	650
Minneapolis	WCCO	830
Pipestone	KLOH	1050
Richfield	WAYL	980
St. Cloud	KNSI	1450
St. Cloud	WJON	1240
Waite Park	KRAR	1390

MISSISSIPPI

Biloxi	WVMI	570
Columbia	WCJU	1450
Jackson	WJDX	620
Jackson	WJNT	1180
Jackson	WZRX	1590

Table 10-2 Continued

MISSISSIPPI (continued)			NEVADA (continued)			NORTH CAROLINA (continued)		
Greenville	WDDT	900	Las Vegas	KVEG	840	Asheville	WWNC	570
Gulfport	WROA	1390	Reno	KONE	1450	Belmont	WCGC	1270
Laurel	WQIS	1260				Boone	WATA	1450
Meridian	WALT	910	NEW HAMPSHIRE			Burnsville	WKYK	940
Pascagoula	WGLD	1460				Chapel Hill	WCHL	1360
Tupelo	WTUP	1490	Lebanon	WTSL	1400	Charlotte	WSOC	930
Vicksburg	WQBC	1420	Portsmouth	WHEB	750	Charlotte	WAES	610
						Cherryville	WCSL	1590
			NEW JERSEY			Goldsboro	WGBR	1150
MISSOURI						Kings Mountain	WKMT	1220
			Asbury Park	WJLK	1310	Lenoir	WKGX	1080
Cape Girardeau	KAPE	1550	Morristown	WMTR	1250	Morganstown	WCIS	760
Joplin	WMBH	1450	Newark	WSKQ	620	Newton	WNNC	1230
Kansas City	WDAF	610	Paterson	WPAT	930	Raleigh	WPTF	680
Kansas City	KMBZ	980	Princeton	WHWH	1350	Raleigh	WAUG	750
Kansas City	WHB	710				Raleigh	WPJL	1240
Kennet	KBOA	830				Shelby	WADA	1390
Sedalia	KSIS	1050	NEW MEXICO			Shelby	WOHS	730
Springfield	KGBX	1260				Winston Salem	WSJS	600
Springfield	KTTS	1400	Albuquerque	KRZY	1450			
St. Louis	KUSA	550	Albuquerque	KXKS	1190	NORTH DAKOTA		
St. Louis	KMOX	1120	Aztec	KCEM	1340			
						Bismarck	KBMR	1130
MONTANA			NEW YORK			Bismarck	KFYR	550
						Bismarck	KLXX	1270
Billings	KGHL	790	Albany	WPTR	1540	Fargo	KQWB	1550
Billings	KBIT	970	Albany	WOKO	1460	Grand Forks	KXXL	1440
Great Falls	KMON	560	Beacon	WBNR	1260			
Kalispell	KOFI	1180	Buffalo	WWKB	1520	OHIO		
			Elmira	WELM	1410			
NEBRASKA			Endicott	WENE	1430			
			Glens Falls	WSTL	1410	Akron	WAKR	1590
Lincoln	KLMS	1480	New York	WINS	1010	Akron	WHLO	640
Omaha	KFAB	1110	New York	WFAN	660	Bucyrus	WBCO	1540
Omaha	KKAR	1180	Patchogue	WLIM	1580	Canton	WTOF	900
Omaha	KOIL	1290	Rochester	WHAM	1180	Canton	WHBC	1480
Omaha	WOW	590	Rochester	WPXY	1280	Cleveland	WHK	1420
			Syracuse	WHEN	620	Cleveland	WRMR	850
NEVADA			Syracuse	WSEN	1050	Cleveland	WRDZ	1260
						Columbus	WTVN	610
Las Vegas	KENO	1460	NORTH CAROLINA			Dayton	WHIO	1290
Las Vegas	KRSR	1140				Dayton	WING	1410
Las Vegas	KFMS	1410	Albemarle	WZKY	1580	Dayton	WONE	980

OHIO (continued)			PENNSYLVANIA(continued)			TENNESSEE (continued)		
Elyria	WEOL	930	Harrisburg	WHP	580	Kingsport	WKPT	1400
Findlay	WFIN	1330	Homer City	WCCS	1160	Knoxville	WIVK	990
Hamilton	WMOH	1250	Lancaster	WLAN	1390	Knoxville	WTNN	670
Lima	WCIT	940	Lancaster	WLPA	1490	Lawrenceburg	WLLK	590
Piqua	WPTW	1570	Lebanon	WADV	940	Memphis	WRVR	680
Toledo	WSPD	1370	Lehighton	WYNS	1150	Maryville	WCGM	1120
Wooster	WWST	960	Mount Carmel	WMIM	1590	Murfreesboro	WGNS	1450
			Philadelphia	KYW	1060	Nashville	WSM	650
OKLAHOMA			Philadelphia	WFIL	560	Nashville	WENO	760
			Pittsburgh	KDKA	1020	Sevierville	WSEV	930
Ardmore	KVSO	1240	Reading	WRAW	1340	Sparta	WTZX	860
Bartlesville	KWON	1400	Reading	WEEU	850			
Broken Arrow	KXTD	1530	Roaring Spring	WKMC	1370	TEXAS		
Guymon	KGYN	1210	Scranton	WICK	1400			
Oklahoma City	KOMA	1520	Wilks-Barre	WILK	980	Amarillo	KPUR	1440
Oklahoma City	WKY	930	York	WXKU	1250	Amarillo	KQTY	1490
Oklahoma City	KXXY	1340				Austin	KOKE	1370
Owasso	KELI	1430	RHODE ISLAND			Austin	KVET	1300
Ponca City	WBBZ	1230				Beaumont	KLVI	560
Tulsa	KRMG	740	Cumberland	WICE	550	Big Spring	KBST	1490
Tulsa	KVOO	1170	Providence	WWAZ	790	Brownsville	KBOR	1600
			Woonsocket	WNRI	1380	Corpus Christi	KDAE	1590
OREGON						Corpus Christi	KSIX	1230
			SOUTH CAROLINA			Corpus Christi	KUNO	1400
Dallas-Salem	KWIP	880				Dallas	KMEZ	1480
Eugene	KDUK	1280	Columbia	WVOC	560	Dallas	KLDD	570
Gresham	KKGR	1230	Conway	WJXY	1050	Dallas	KPBC	1040
Hillsboro	KUIK	1360	Florence	WJMX	970	Dallas	KVIL	1150
Lake Oswego	KZRC	1010	Greenville	WESC	660	El Paso	KHEY	690
Medford	KYJC	610	Greenville	WFBC	1330	Fort Worth	WBAP	820
Oregon City	KSGO	1520	Greenwood	WGSW	1350	Fort Worth	KESS	1270
Pendleton	KTIX	1240	Greenwood	WMTY	1090	Harlingen	KGBT	1530
Portland	KGW	620	Hilton Head	WHHQ	1130	Houston	KLAT	1010
Portland	KEX	1190	Lancaster	WAGL	1560	Houston	KRBE	1070
						Houston	KKBQ	790
			SOUTH DAKOTA			Longview	KFRO	1370
PENNSYLVANIA						Lubbock	KFYO	790
			Rapid City	KKLS	920	McAllen	KIKN	840
Allentown	WXKW	1470	Sioux Falls	KELO	1320	Midland	KCRS	550
Altoona	WFBG	1290				Nacogdoches	KSFA	860
Canonsburg	WWCS	540				Palastine	KNET	1450
Chester	WCZN	1590	TENNESSEE			Paris	KPRE	1250
Easton	WEST	1400				San Angelo	KAYJ	1260
Erie	WJET	1400	Arlington	WGSF	1210	San Antonio	KKYX	680
Euphrata	WGSA	1310	Athens	WLAR	1450	San Antonio	KCOR	1350
Everett	WSKE	1040						

Table 10-2 Continued

TEXAS(continued)		
San Antonio	KSJL	760
San Antonio	KXET	1250
San Antonio	KSAH	720
Tomball	KTBT	700
Victoria	KAMG	1340
Wichita Falls	KGTM	990

UTAH		
Price	KRPX	1080
Salt Lake City	KALL	910
Salt Lake City	KBUG	1320
Salt Lake City	KFAM	700
Salt Lake City	KMGR	1230
Salt Lake City	KUTR	860

VERMONT		
Burlington	WDOT	1390
Burlington	WMMT	620
Mountpelier	WSKI	1240
Waterbury	WDEV	550

VIRGINIA		
Alexandria	WCPT	730
Arlington	WMZQ	1390
Charlottesville	WCHV	1260
Danville	WBTM	1330
Danville	WDVA	1250
Harrisonburg	WHBG	1360
Harrisonburg	WKCY	1300
Norfolk	WTAR	790
Radford	WRAD	1460
Woodstock	WAMM	1230
Wytheville	WYVE	1280

WASHINGTON		
Kennewick	KONA	610
Lacey	KTOL	1280
Olympia	KQEU	920
Seattle	KING	1090
Seattle	KMPS	1300
Seattle	KOMO	1000
Spokane	KJRB	790
Tocoma	KTAC	850

WEST VIRGINIA		
Beckley	WWNR	620
Bluefield	WHIS	1440
Buckhannon	WBUC	1460
Fairmont	WTCS	1490
Huntington	WKEE	800
Morgantown	WCLG	1300

WISCONSIN		
Appleton	WHBY	1230
Appleton	WYNE	1150
Baraboo	WRPQ	740
Chippewa Falls	WOGO	680
Fond Du Lac	KFIZ	1450
Green Bay	WDUZ	1400
Green Bay	WGEE	1360
La Crosse	WLXR	1490
Madison	WTDY	1480
Madison	WIBA	1310
Milwaukee	WOKY	920
Milwaukee	WISN	1130
Neenah	WNAM	1280
Wausau	WRIG	1390

WYOMING		
Laramie	KLDI	1210

##################################

CANADA		
ALBERTA		
Calgary	CHQR	770
Calgary	CFAC	960
Calgary	CFFR	660
Calgary	CISS	1140
Camrose	CFCW	790
Drumheller	CKDQ	910
Edmonton	CHQT	880
Edmonton	CJCA	930
Grand Prarie	CFGP	1050
Lethbridge	CHEC	1090

BRITISH COLUMBIA		
Kelowna	CKOV	630
New Westminster	CKNW	980
Prince George	CJCI	620
Richmond	CISL	940
Vancouver	CKXY	1040
Vancouver	CKLG	730
Vancouver	CFUN	1410
Vancouver	CJVB	1470
Vancouver	CKWX	1130
Vancouver	CHRX	600
Victoria	CFAX	1070
Victoria	CJVI	900

MANITOBA		
Winnipeg	CJOB	680
Winnipeg	CKRC	630
Winnipeg	CKY	580

NEW BRUNSWICK		
Saint John	CFBC	930
Saint John	CHSJ	700
Fredericton	CIHI	1260
Moncton	CKCW	1220

NEWFOUNDLAND

St. Johns	VOCM	590

NOVA SCOTIA

Bridgewater	CKBW	1000
Dartmouth	CFDR	680
Halifax	CHNS	960
Halifax	CJCH	920
Sydney	CJCB	1270

ONTARIO

Belleville	CJBQ	800
Fort Erie	CJFT	530
Guelf	CJOY	1460
Hamilton	CHML	900
Hamilton	CKOC	1150
Hamilton	CHAM	820
Kitchener	CKKW	1090
Kingston	CKLC	1380
Kingston	CFFX	960
London	CFPL	980
London	CKSL	1410
Newmarket	CKAN	1480
North Bay	CHUR	1110
Ottawa	CJSB	540
Ottawa	CFGO	1200
Richmond Hill	CFGM	640
Thunder Bay	CJLB	1230
Toronto	CFRB	1010
Toronto	CFTR	680
Toronto	CHIN	1540
Welland	CHOW	1470

PRINCE EDWARD ISLAND

Charlottetown	CFCY	630

QUEBEC

Montreal	CJAD	800
St. Georges	CKRB	1460

SASKATCHEWAN

Moose Jaw	CHAB	800
Regina	CJME	1300
Regina	CKCK	620
Saskatoon	CKOM	1250
Saskatoon	CFQC	600

#############################

AUSTRALIA

NEW SOUTH WALES

Albury	2AY	1494
Bathurst	2BS	1503
Byrock	2BY	657
Canberra	2CA	1053
Canberra	2CC	1206
Canberra	2CN	666
Canberra	2XX	
Coffs Harbour	2CS	639
Gofford	2GO	801
Goulburn	2GN	1386
Kempsey	2MC	531
Lismore	2LM	900
Murwillumbah	2MW	972
Newcastle	2HD	1143
New Castle	2NC	1233
Newcastle	2KO	1413
Newcastle West	2NX	1341
Norfolk Island	2NI	1566
North Sydney	2SM	1269
Sydney	2BL	702
Sydney	2CH	1170
Sydney	2GB	873
Sydney	2KY	1017
Sydney	2UE	954
Sydney	2UW	1107
Sydney	2WS	1224
Wagga Wagga	2WG	1152
Wollongong	2OO	1575
Wollongong	2WL	1314

NORTHWEST TERRITORY

Darwin	8DN	1242
Darwin	8DR	657

QUEENSLAND

Ayr	4AY	936
Brisbane	4BC	1116
Brisbane	4IO	1008
Brisbane	4KQ	693
Brisbane	4BH	882
Brisbane	4BK	1296
Brisbane	4QR	612
Cairns	4CA	846
Gladstone	4CC	927
Gympie	4GY	558
Nambour	4SS	828
Oakey	4AK	1242
Rockhampton	4RO	990
Southport	4GG	1197
Toowoomba	4GR	864
Townsville	4TO	774

SOUTH AUSTRALIA

Adelaide	5AD	1323
Adelaide	5AN	891
Adelaide	5DN	972
Adelaide	5KA	1197

TASMANIA

Hobart	7HO	864
Hobart	7HT	1080
Hobart	7ZR	936
Launceston	7LA	1098

VICTORIA

Ballart	3BA	1314
Bendigo	3BO	945
Melbourne	3AK	1503
Melbourne	3AW	1278
Melbourne	3DB	1026
Melbourne	3KZ	1179
Melbourne	3LO	774
Melbourne	3UZ	927
Melbourne	3XY	1422
Mornington	3MP	1377
Sale	3TR	1242

Table 10-2 Continued

VICTORIA (continued)		
Shepparton	3SR	1260
Warrnambool	3UL	531

WEST AUSTRALIA		
Perth	6IX	1080
Perth	6KY	1206
Perth	6PM	990
Perth	6PR	882
Perth	6WF	720

##

SOUTH AFRICA	
Radio 702 Johannesburg	702
Radio 5 Johannesburg-2	576
Radio CMCK	1098

VENEZUELA		
Radio Capital-Caracas		710
Radio Metropolitana	YVMM	1550
Exitos	YUSZ	1090
Merida Radio Exito		1560

VENEZUELA (continued)		
Tumero	YVWP	1320
Radio Barnes	0000	1190

BRAZIL		
Belem Para	Radio Guajara	1270
Fort Aleza	Radio Joral	1010
Jauziero	ZYH459	1190
Lins	ZYK607	1080
Manaus	ZYH286	1290
	Radio Alverado	1080
Marechal Deodore	Radio Cicade Imperial	610
Ponta Grossa	Radio Clube	1080
Rio Dejaneiro	Radio Manudial	860
Rio Dejaneiro	Radio Manchete	760
Rio Dejaneiro	Radio Jornal	940
	Radio Inconfidencia	980
Sao Louiz	ZYH886	1340
Sao Paulo		1150
	Radio Gaucha	1120

CHINA		
Hangzhou	Radio Zhejiang	1530

SPAIN		
Madrid	Radio Popular	999

CHILE		
Santiago	Radio Diego Portales	1180

R.O.C.		
Kaohsiung		720
Taipei	BCC	657
Taipei	ICRT	567
Taichung		720

PUERTO RICO		
Mayaguez		710

THAILAND	MCOT	1143
		1494

Index

311

Quantum antenna, Channel Master brand, 120-122

R

R.L. Drake Model 2450 signal analyzer, satellite signals, 188-190
radiation fields, antenna, 110
radio (*see* audio signals)
ratio detectors, FM, 20
reactances, 3, 7-8
real-time spectrum analyzers, 29-31
receivers, satellite signals, 175-178
receiving antenna, 111-114
rectifiers, 8, 13
reflection, 65, 68
reflectors, antenna, 112-113
resistor-capacitor-transistor logic (RCTL), 15
resistor-transistor logic (RTL), 15
resistors and resistance, 2-6
resonance, LC circuits, 4
return loss/VSWR listing, 253
RF signals, video, 99-103
RLC circuits, parallel configurations, 5

S

SAP
  BTSC-dbx, 217-224
  master antenna systems (MAT), 232
satellite master antenna systems (SMATV), 229
satellite master antenna systems (SMATV), 229, 244-245
satellite signals, 27, 147-189
  actuators, 173
  antenna installation, 165-168, 187-188
  antenna selection, 155-156, 162-164, 171
  attenuation, 159
  azimuth location, 150
  C band, 147, 154
  cabling, 172
  California Amplifier Co. feedhorns, 161-162
  carrier-to-noise ratio, 158-159
  CHC feedhorns, 160
  compass variation corrections, 152-153
  cost analysis, 147-148

declination, 150-152
downlinks, 154-156
effective isotropic radiated power (EIRP), 154
elevation location, 150
feedhorns, 160-162, 171-172
"footprints," 154, 169, 171
interference, 171, 180-182
Ku-band, 147, 154, 156-159, 186
location, 148-153
M/A-Com T-6 receiver/positioner, 177-178
mounts, 168-169
polarities, 181-182
positioners, motor-driven, 172-175
R.L. Drake Model 2450 signal analyzer, 188-189
receivers, 175-178
satellite life spans, 147-148
satellite master antenna systems (SMATV), 229, 244-245
SBX Corporation feedhorns, 160
signal faults, 181-182
signal-to-noise ratios, 179
slant range, 148-153
threshold calculation, 158-159
tracking, 171, 172
transponder signals, 178-180
SBX Corporation feedhorns, satellite signals, 160
scalar equations, series problems, 3
Schottky devices, 22
secondary images, master antenna systems (MAT), 234, 250
semiconductors, 8-14
separation, stereo, BTSC-dbx, 219, 221
series configurations, 2-6
servo motors, automotive troubleshooting, 290
signal analyzers, 188-189
signal faults, satellite signals, 181-182
signal generators, 42-46
signal-to-noise ratio
  antenna, 126
  audio signals, 202
  BTSC-dbx, 219, 221
  fiberoptics, 59-60
  master antenna systems (MAT), 229-230, 232-234, 246, 248
  satellite signals, 179

signature analyzers, 36-40
silicon-controlled rectifiers (SCR), 8, 13
sine waves, 194
slant range, satellite signals, 148-153
solid-state modulator circuit, 85
sound (*see* audio signals; radio)
spark plugs, automotive troubleshooting, 287-288
spectrum analyzers, 28-31, 199-201
  antenna testing, 128-131
  MAT checkout, 240-241
standard logic, 22
stereophonic sound, 204-227
  AM, 205, 211-212, 302-303
  auto radio, 300-302
  C-QUAM, 208-211, 215, 216
  channel separation, 206, 207
  digital stereo, 276-278
  digital, 224-227
  FM, 205, 206
  integrated circuits, Motorola brand, 212-215
  multichannel (BTSC-dbx), 205, 217-224
  TV generator, B&K Precision, 220
storage factor (Q), antenna, 114
superchargers, automotive troubleshooting, 296, 297
surface-wave acoustical (SAW) filters, 18-19
sweep circuits, television, 271-276
sweep generators, 42-46
sweep mode receiver module, television, 258
sweep-checking copper cable, 69-71
swept-tuned spectrum analyzers, 29-31
synchronization, video, 95-99
synchronous detection, 18-20

T

television
  adjustments, 279
  antennas, 109-146
  audio output module, 259
  big-screen cathode-ray tubes, 105-106
  cathode-ray tubes, 103-108, 269-272

Other Bestsellers of Related Interest

TROUBLESHOOTING AND REPAIRING COMPACT DISC PLAYERS
—Homer L. Davidson

Here's all the expert guidance you need to maintain and repair your CD player! Repairs can be a very costly proposition. With this book, you can learn to troubleshoot and repair this complicated electronic unit yourself, saving money and time. Davidson guides you through CD players, showing each section, circuit, and component and explaining how they all work together. 350 pages, 429 illustrations. **Book No. 3107, $18.95 paperback, $26.96 hardcover**

TROUBLESHOOTING AND REPAIRING AUDIO EQUIPMENT—*Homer L. Davidson*

When your telephone answering machine quits . . . when your cassette player grinds to a stop . . . when your TV remote control loses control . . . or when your compact disc player goes berserk . . . you don't need a degree in electronics or even any experience. Everything you need to troubleshoot and repair most common problems in almost any consumer audio equipment is here in a servicing guide that's guaranteed to save you time and money! 336 pages, 354 illustrations. **Book No. 2867, $18.95 paperback, $25.95 hardcover**

TROUBLESHOOTING AND REPAIRING CAMCORDERS—*Homer L. Davidson*

This superb troubleshooting guide shows you how to repair any brand of VHS, VHS-C, Beta, or 8-millimeter video camera on the market today. Davidson provides clear instructions along with diagrams and service literature from a wide variety of manufacturers, plus hundreds of schematics to speed diagnostics and repair. Some of the many topics covered include cleaning and lubricating camcorders, system control circuits, audio circuits and microphones, and the various motors in a camcorder. 544 pages, 606 illustrations. **Book No. 3337, $22.95 paperback, $35.95 hardcover**

TROUBLESHOOTING AND REPAIRING SOLID-STATE TVs—*Homer L. Davidson*

Packed with case study examples, photos of solid-state circuits, and circuit diagrams. You'll learn how to troubleshoot and repair all the most recent solid-state TV circuitry used by the major manufacturers of all brands and models of TVs. This workbench reference is filled with tips and practical information that will get you right to the problem! 448 pages, 516 illustrations. **Book No. 2707, $17.95 paperback, $26.95 hardcover**

TROUBLESHOOTING AND REPAIRING ELECTRONIC CIRCUITS
—2nd Edition—Robert L. Goodman

Here are easy-to-follow, step-by-step instructions for troubleshooting and repairing all major brands of the latest electronic equipment, with hundreds of block diagrams, specs, and schematics to help you do the job right the first time. You will find expert advice and techniques for working with both old and new circuitry, including tube-type, transistor, IC, microprocessor and analog and digital logic circuits. 320 pages, 236 illustrations. **Book No. 3258, $18.95 paperback, $27.95 hardcover**

THE TAB SERVICE MANUAL FOR CCTV AND MATV—*Robert L. Goodman*

Written especially for technicians, this guide explains the installation, repair, and adjustment of all popular brands of closed-circuit and master antenna TV systems complete with operational block diagrams and layouts. The CCTV section covers video monitors, TV camera and remote camera control, theory of operation, repair techniques, required adjustments, case histories, camera pickup tubes, vidicons, and lighting information. The second half of this manual is devoted to MATV systems and how to install and adjust MATV antennas. 256 pages, 191 illustrations. **Book No. 3343, $18.95 paperback, $29.95 hardcover**

VIDEO, STEREO AND OPTOELECTRONICS: 18 Advanced Electronic Projects—*Rudolf F. Graf and William Sheets*

With the challenging projects included here, you can produce devices that are both modern in design and genuinely useful. You'll find projects for wireless headphones, FM stereo and TV transmitters, receivers for longwave and FM broadcast bands, and more. Each project includes step-by-step construction plans, parts lists, and working diagrams. None of these plans calls for expensive or hard-to-get components. 368 pages, 216 illustrations. **Book No. 3358, $18.95 paperback, $29.95 hardcover**

500 ELECTRONIC IC CIRCUITS WITH PRACTICAL APPLICATIONS —*James A. Whitson*

More than just an electronics book that provides circuit schematics or step-by-step projects, this complete sourcebook provides both practical electronics circuits AND the additional information you need about specific components. You will be able to use this guide to improve your IC circuit-building skills as well as become more familiar with some of the popular ICs. 336 pages, 600 illustrations. **Book No. 2920, $24.95 paperback, $29.95 hardcover**